Current Topics in Bioenergetics

Volume 6

Current Topics in Bioenergetics

Edited by
D. RAO SANADI

Boston Biomedical Research Institute
Boston, Massachusetts

VOLUME 6

1977

ACADEMIC PRESS
NEW YORK SAN FRANCISCO LONDON

A Subsidiary of Harcourt Brace Jovanovich, Publishers

ACADEMIC PRESS, INC.
111 Fifth Avenue, New York, New York 10003

United Kingdom Edition published by
ACADEMIC PRESS, INC. (LONDON) LTD.
24/28 Oval Road, London NW1

LIBRARY OF CONGRESS CATALOG CARD NUMBER: 66–28678

ISBN 0–12–152506–6

PRINTED IN THE UNITED STATES OF AMERICA

Contents

Energy Balance in Muscle Contraction: A Biochemical Approach

MARTIN J. KUSHMERICK

Transport in Membrane Vesicles Isolated from the Mammalian Kidney and Intestine

BERTRAM SACKTOR

Membranes and Energy Transduction in Bacteria

FRANKLIN M. HAROLD

Proton Translocation in Chloroplasts

G. Hauska and A. Trebst

The Use of Ionophores and Channel Formers
in the Study of the Function of
Biological Membranes

A. Gómez-Puyou and C. Gómez-Lojero

Mitochondrial Calcium Transport

FYFE L. BYGRAVE

List of Contributors

Numbers in parentheses indicate the pages on which the authors' contributions begin.

FYFE L. BYGRAVE (259), *Department of Biochemistry, Faculty of Science, The Australian National University, Canberra, Australia*

C. GÓMEZ-LOJERO (221), *Departamento de Bioquímica, Centro de Investigaciones y Estudios Avanzados, Instituto Politécnico Nacional, México, D.F., México*

A. GÓMEZ-PUYOU (221), *Departamento de Biología Experimental, Instituto de Biología, Universidad de México, México, D.F., México*

FRANKLIN M. HAROLD (83), *Division of Molecular and Cellular Biology, National Jewish Hospital and Research Center, and Department of Microbiology and Immunology, University of Colorado Medical School, Denver, Colorado*

G. HAUSKA (151), *Lehrstuhl für Biochemie der Pflanzen, Ruhr Universität Bochum, West Germany*

MARTIN J. KUSHMERICK (1), *Department of Physiology, Harvard Medical School, Boston, Massachusetts*

BERTRAM SACKTOR (39), *Laboratory of Molecular Aging, National Institute on Aging, National Institutes of Health, Baltimore City Hospitals, Baltimore, Maryland*

A. TREBST (151), *Lehrstuhl für Biochemie der Pflanzen, Ruhr Universität Bochum, West Germany*

Preface

The main objective in initiating this serial publication was to provide a forum for communication between workers in the different areas of bioenergetics. By bringing together in one publication articles on such closely related subjects as photosynthesis, oxidative phosphorylation, transport across membranes, and muscle contraction, it was hoped that more rapid progress in the field would result. Topics were selected that dealt directly with the phenomenon of energy transduction, intentionally omitting aspects on regulation, biosynthesis, and utilization of energy in the more classical type of reactions (e.g., CO_2 fixation using ATP energy).

Indeed, progress in the field of membranes and bioenergetics has been phenomenally rapid, and it is hoped that this serial publication has been a part of this growth. Subsequent to the appearance of the last volume in 1973, an evaluation was carried out to determine the usefulness and effectiveness of the publication. We are convinced that a distinct need is being met, and are encouraged by the response. We are planning to enlarge and broaden the scope of the topics. For example, the next volume will be exclusively on photosynthesis, and it is hoped that every other volume will focus on a specific area.

In this volume the solute transport functions of membrane vesicles from kidney and intestine and the specialized calcium transport system of mitochondria are discussed from both biological and mechanistic viewpoints. The article describing ionophores and channel formers and their use in the study of transport mechanisms maintains the emphasis of this volume on transport phenomena. From the standpoint of mechanism, the articles on energy-transducing mechanisms in bacteria and chromoplast are timely and of particular interest. The review of newer sophistication in measuring and interpreting overall muscle energetics should generate renewed interest in this long-standing question.

D. RAO SANADI

Contents of Previous Volumes

Energy Balance in Muscle Contraction:
A Biochemical Approach

MARTIN J. KUSHMERICK
Department of Physiology,
Harvard Medical School,
Boston, Massachusetts

I. Introduction

Living animal cells constantly take up molecules into their interior, where an array of oxidations and other enzymic reactions occur. Chemical energy is released in these oxidative processes, catabolism in the classical sense, and transformed into a variety of forms of stored energy: macromolecular synthesis, chemical potential gradients (e.g., membrane potentials, osmotic gradients), and pools of "high energy phosphate" compounds, such as ATP and phosphorylcreatine. Under a given set of physiological conditions there is a steady dissipation of these stored forms of chemical energy (macromolecular degradation and sodium transport for maintenance of osmotic balance, to name two obvious examples) and a steady rate of synthesis of chemical energy. This must be so since cells have a composition different from their environment and have a finite membrane permeability to molecules inside and outside themselves. Thus, under normal conditions, the cell is an open system in a steady state where its internal composition is maintained by a steady flow through the cell of substrates and their oxidation products. There is a classical principle in physiology, homeostasis as W. B. Cannon termed it, that the whole organism responds to different sets of conditions with minimal disturbances to its internal environment, and this principle is useful on the cellular level as well, as we shall see.

A study of energetics concerned itself with these transformations of energy both on the level of the molecular mechanisms involved and on the level of overall energy conservation as a complete description of the whole cell or tissue. In skeletal muscle cells the student of muscle energetics has a rich opportunity for both approaches. In this essay we will be concerned with the question of overall energy conservation: the details of the necessary equivalency between the energy input to the muscle, the energy transduced, and the energy put out by the muscle. Although muscle cells, as are all cells, are complex chemical machines, there are two good reasons for studying energy balance in some detail. First, an unambiguous demonstration that known chemical reactions are sufficient to explain energy transformations in the whole cell is a prerequisite to the partition of the extents of these reactions among the various specific transformations (mechanical work, ion transport, etc.) and the related questions of their kinetics, control, stoichiometry, and efficiency. Second, no one has yet a method to study actomyosin ATPase and its regulation while the system develops tension, shortens, and performs useful mechanical work that will replace the quite imperfect technique of studying mechanochemistry in whole muscles. Skeletal muscle cells are unique in that there is a very large (about 10^2-10^3) increase in the rate of energy utilization by contracting muscle compared to the relaxed, so-called "resting," muscle and this transition can be achieved in a matter of tens of milliseconds by direct electrical stimulation. A practical consequence for experimental design is that these very large changes are quickly superimposed onto the steady-state metabolite concentration, reaction rates, etc., characteristic of the resting state.

Over the past dozen years or so, renewed interest in problems concerning overall energy balance in the sense just described was developed and significant problems have emerged. For example, are the known chemical reactions (turnover of ATP and concomitant breakdown of PCr) sufficient to account for the energy released by a whole contraction–relaxation cycle of skeletal muscle? The interesting alternative is that important energy-yielding reactions remain unidentified. Are the known reactions sufficient to account for the energy released during various portions of the contraction? Finally, there is the related, and logically antecedent, question which may require reanalysis: When, precisely, during the contraction–relaxation–recovery is chemical energy transformed by muscle cells? Although considerable conceptual and experimental effort has gone into these questions, important aspects of the topic of energy balance remain poorly understood. The study of energetics of muscle now has entered an era of great sophistication and complexity, where much remains to be learned concerning the thermodynamic, physiological, and biochemical aspects of muscle contraction as viewed from the muscle cell. When this overall energetic picture and the details of energy balance are sorted out, we will have a greater insight not only into the control coupling and integration of cellular energy metabolism, but also into aspects of the contractile mechanism during chemomechanical transduction. This essay will describe a biochemically based approach to questions involving energy balance.

II.   Energy Stores and ~P Pools

The concept of homeostasis applied to cells means that at some time after the contraction is finished there is reversal of chemical reactions which had occurred during the contraction so that the initial steady-state conditions are restored. It is useful to catalog the various biochemical reactions that are known to occur during and after muscle contraction. We rely on the concept that there are "high energy" compounds in the cell (the ~P pool) which serve as the "energy coinage" of the cellular realm (Lipmann, 1941). As pointed out by George and Rutman (1960), the term "high energy bond" is formally incorrect. Actual bond energies effect the detailed chemical mechanisms, but not the utility of the concept, of energy-transferring molecules. ATP and phosphorylcreatine comprise most of the ~P pool. The most direct source of chemical energy to power actomyosin is net splitting of ATP to ADP and inorganic phosphate (Englehart and Ljubimova, 1939), and this reaction was finally shown by Cain and Davies (1962) to occur during the muscle contraction. There are other modes of ATP utilization that occur as a consequence of muscle activation: sarcoplasmic reticulum ATPase coupled to calcium transport, Na-K stimulated ATPase coupled to maintenance and restoration of transmembrane ionic gradients, and phosphorylation of the enzymes phosphorylase and glycogen synthetase, to name several documented mechanisms. In all these the direction of flow of chemical energy is from ATP to other "high energy" compounds, to electrical, chemical, or mechanical work, to other forms of chemical potential energy, and finally to heat. The only known biochemical routes to ATP synthesis are metabolic oxidations [although intercellular conditions might be appropriate for transformation of electrochemical potential energy into chemical energy, for example, by the reversal

of the calcium pump of the sarcoplasmic reticulum (Makinose, 1973)].
While a process such as the last-mentioned represents a pool of potential
chemical energy in the cell, it is obvious that this energy was initially
derived from ATP; its capacity is limited by a limited store of calcium
and the relative unavailability of ADP.

The size of the ATP pool itself is small, 3–5 μmoles per gram muscle
wet weight. The size of readily available "high energy phosphate"
compounds is expanded considerably by the content of PCr, which is
present in the range of 20–30 μmoles per gram in skeletal muscle. There
is considerable evidence that PCr is at or very near equilibrium with the
ATP pool (Carlson and Siger, 1959; Vincent and Blair, 1970; Canfield
and Maréchal, 1973) via the Lohmann reaction (reaction 2) and maintains steady ATP concentrations by mass action:

$$ATP \rightarrow ADP + P_i \qquad \text{(Reaction 1)}$$

$$PCr + ADP \rightleftharpoons ATP + Cr \qquad \text{(Reaction 2)}$$

$$PCr \rightarrow Cr + P_i \qquad \text{(Reaction 3)}$$

The adenylate kinase reaction:

$$2ADP \rightleftharpoons ATP + AMP \qquad \text{(Reaction 4)}$$

and adenylate deaminase reaction:

$$AMP \rightarrow IMP + NH_4 \qquad \text{(Reaction 5)}$$

must also be considered. Reaction (4) is thought to be an equilibrium
with reactions (1) and (2) (Carlson and Siger, 1959; Vincent and Blair,
1970; Canfield and Maréchal, 1973). When reaction (2) is blocked by
fluorodinitrobenzene (FDNB) (Cain and Davies, 1962), ADP accumulates and the extent of the adenylate kinase reaction is significant
(Dydynska and Wilkie, 1966; Kushmerick and Davies, 1969). Normally,
however, free ADP levels are very low (Chance and Connolly, 1957).
The extents of Reactions (4) and (5) are very large in FDNB-poisoned
muscles, in prolonged tetani of unpoisoned muscles (Canfield et al.,
1973), and in fatigued muscles (Fleckenstein et al., 1954). In summary,
there is reasonable evidence that there is equilibration among the "high
energy phosphate" compounds in muscle, mainly ATP and PCr, which
comprise virtually all the ~P pool and are thus available to provide
chemical energy for cellular processes (see also Atkinson, 1971). Some
details require further experimental analysis since, for example, Hill's
data (1962) indicate that a fraction of PCr is bound in muscle, whereas

data from nuclear magnetic resonance of the phosphorus in PCr indicates that PCr exists in only one compartment (Bushby *et al.*, 1975).

The available evidence suggests that almost all, if not all, of the ATP turnover is measured as net PCr splitting and occurs during contraction and mechanical relaxation, as might be expected from the large content of myosin (Infante and Davies, 1962; Mommaerts and Wallner, 1967; Kushmerick *et al.*, 1969; Curtin and Woledge, 1974). The durations of contractions used for measurements of ATP turnover were on the order of seconds to a few tens of seconds whereas resynthesis reactions as measured by oxygen consumption (Hill, 1940; Kushmerick and Paul, 1976a, b) and by NADH fluorescence (Jöbsis and Duffield, 1967) occur afterward and more slowly. These observations give rise to a model of muscle energetics based on the underlying biochemical reactions, where the energy-consuming processes are separable in time from metabolic oxidations that give rise to ~P resynthesis. The latter are given the name recovery reactions, recovery metabolism, or simply recovery. It is implicit in the model that ~P pools are indeed restored to precontraction levels; that is, the net change in chemical potential of the muscle (an open system) is zero over a complete contraction–relaxation–recovery cycle. In this view, muscle contraction is considered as a rapid or step depletion of the ~P pool relative to the steady state characteristic of resting muscle; during recovery this depleted ~P pool is restored. This model is developed further in Sections V and VI.

Muscle stimulation also dissipates energy in the forms of ionic, osmotic, and potential gradients. The restoration of these forms of electrochemical energy by ~P splitting may be slow compared to the contraction–relaxation time course. Thus some degree of separation of energy dissipation and ATP turnover is expected in the nonsteady state type of experiments used to study muscle energetics (i.e., brief tetanic stimulation compared to an unstimulated control state). This energy dissipation will not be detected by measurements of ATP turnover during contraction, but may be by heat measurements (Sections III and IV) or by net ~P splitting after contraction. Based on estimates from nonmuscle excitable tissues, the magnitude of the energy liberated by such processes is quite small (Abbott and Howarth, 1973), possibly as small as 0.1% of the total energy released during a brief tetanus.

III. Myothermic Methods and Energy Balance

The classical approach to the problem of energy balance is to consider heat and work production and chemical change in muscle in the light of the first law of thermodynamics, and this approach has been extensively reviewed and discussed by Wilkie (1960), Mommaerts (1969), Woledge

(1971), and Caplan (1971). A simplified outline will be satisfactory for our purposes. In general, for a closed system one writes the conservation equation for the difference of internal energy between two equilibrium states:

$$\Delta U = Q + W \tag{1}$$

ΔU is the increase in internal energy of the system between the two states; Q is the heat gained by the system, ideally equal to $T\Delta S$, and W is the work done on the system by the surroundings. Since the muscle is studied at atmospheric pressure and contains within itself no rigid walls to withstand significant pressure gradients, and one can write:

$$\Delta U = \Delta H \tag{2}$$

where ΔH is the change in enthalpy of the system because pressure-volume work is negligible. In the case of a muscle, the W term is negative, as it represents all work done by the muscle on the surroundings. The most obvious example is mechanical work when the muscle moves an external load some distance, as in an isotonic contraction. Chemical work on the surroundings by flow of matter out of the muscle is excluded since the system is considered to be closed. Creation of electrochemical gradients within the muscle is a form of work implicit in the W term.

The next step of the classical approach energy balance is to consider that the total enthalpy change is due to the individual chemical reactions since the muscle is a chemical machine:

$$\Delta H_t = \sum n_i \Delta H_i \tag{3}$$

that is, the total enthalpy difference, ΔH_t, is equal to the sum of the product of the molar enthalpy changes for each reaction, ΔH_i, times the molar extent of that reaction, n_i. The experimental observations to be compared are the total enthalpy change (ΔH_t), the extents of the reactions (n_{PCr}, etc.), and the molar enthalpy of the reactions obtained from calorimetry (ΔH_{PCr}, etc.). Because experimental observations (discussed in Section IV) do not satisfy Eq. (3) for the known reactions (described in Section II) it is important to state explicitly the conditions required for this application of the first law to be valid: (A) the various states of the muscle under study are equilibrium states or other thermodynamically defined states; (B) the muscle is a closed system; (C) the molar enthalpy of the reactions are constant and determinable. Also the reactions that need to be considered should be few in number to minimize the total analytical error.

There is no question that living cells are not at thermodynamic equilibrium. However, in principle, one can define the states of muscle adequately. Living systems are characteristically open systems, exchanging matter as well as energy with the surrounding. However, by suitable experimental design, a muscle *in vitro* can be made to be a closed thermodynamic system, either by making the surroundings part of the systems under study or by studying short intervals of time such that the molar amounts exchanged (for example, O_2 uptake and CO_2 release) are quantitatively insignificant compared to molar amount of phosphorylcreatine broken down.

The molar enthalpy of a reaction, defined under constant conditions, must be constant during muscle contraction. But reactions, well-defined *in vitro*, may not be well-defined *in vivo*. Consider a side reaction occurring such as:

$$AL \rightarrow B + L$$

where L is some ligand, perhaps a charged species (H^+ or metal cation). The apparent enthalpy of the main reaction

$$A \rightarrow B$$

depends on the concentration of L. In other words, the enthalpy, which is a parameter of the state of the system, could appear to depend on changes in the composition since the enthalpies of the buffer or cation binding reactions would also need to be considered (as is the case of Mg^{2+} binding and net hydrolysis of phosphorylcreatine and splitting of ATP, major reactions occurring during muscle contraction). Some of these side reactions are known, and Woledge (1971, 1973) has carefully reviewed current information on this point. However in muscle cells the knowledge of the intracellular buffer capacity, pH, and actual buffering species and free divalent ion concentrations are incompletely known. That is the enthalpy values determined from calorimetry and adjusted to be applicable to intracellular conditions may not yet be the appropriate ones to use in Eq. (3). Moreover these quantities may change with conditions, perhaps even during the course of a contraction. In this sense, the actual values to be used in Eq. (3) might be variable or at least may be inaccurately known. Ideally, this problem is circumvented by including the side reactions explicitly in the summation, such as Eq. (3), and certainly Woledge (1971, 1973) has made considerable progress in this direction. The reader who is unfamiliar with this literature should note that these side reactions contribute very significantly to the predicted enthalpy of net ATP splitting or PCr splitting in the muscle cell.

It is thought possible to design experiments such that ATP turnover and net PCr breakdown occurs without significant advancement of reactions of glycolysis and oxidative phosphorylation. That is, the experimenter can achieve pure chemical energy utilization in the absence of chemical energy synthesis by studying single tetani of short duration. The evidence for this view is based on direct measurements of the metabolites of interest is poisoned and unpoisoned muscles (see Section II), the time course of oxygen consumption, which is much slower (about 10^{-2} times) than reactions occurring during the tetanus, and the fluorometric measurements (Jöbsis and Duffield, 1967), which show that NADH oxidation occurs after a single isometric twitch. Even so, under certain circumstances the experimenter must deal with several reactions involving adenine nucleotides (reactions 1 to 5, Section II) as well as portions of the Embden–Meyerhof pathway (for example, Dydynska and Wilkie, 1966; Kushmerick and Davies, 1969; Canfield *et al.*, 1973; Curtin and Woledge, 1975).

IV. Myothermal Observations Concerning Energy Balance

For the experimental analysis of energy balance by myothermic methods, measurements are made of muscle heat, work, and concurrent chemical changes. Then the ratio is constructed, from Eqs. (1) to (3),

$$Q + W/\sum n_i \, \Delta H_i$$

and its value is compared to 1. Testing this equality is the basis of myothermic methods. An observed value of 1 for the above quantity allows the conclusion that the measured reactions account for the total energy output of the muscle tissue. In principle this equality can be tested for repeated contraction–relaxation cycles, a single contraction and portions thereof. If net PCr splitting (Reaction 3) is thought to be the only chemical reaction occurring, then matters are simpler since

$$Q + W = \Delta\text{PCr}\Delta H_{\text{PCr}} \tag{4}$$

is the relevant form (ΔPCr is the usual way of expressing the extent of PCr splitting, n_{PCr}, in the literature).

A detailed study of tetani and series of twitches were made in which measurements of heat, work, and breakdown of phosphorylcreatine were made in the same muscles. Wilkie (1968) found a consistent result (Fig. 1): the output of heat + work by the contracting muscle was found to be strictly proportional to the extent of PCr breakdown, and, using Eq. (4) as a working hypothesis, the slope of the relationship (ΔH_{PCr}) was −11.1 kcal/mole. This value agreed very well with the data of Meyerhof and Schultz (1935) for the enthalpy of PCr splitting. Thus on thermodynamic grounds there was no reason to doubt that the overall energetic description of muscle contraction was correct and complete.

Several observations since then have weakened and shed considerable doubt on this important conclusion: (A) The relationship between Q + W and ΔPCr was observed to vary during an isometric tetanus. (B) The relationship between Q + W and ΔPCr for single isometric contractions was different in muscles obtained from *Rana temporaria* and *Rana pipiens*, the common leopard frog in Europe and in Northern America, respectively, and may differ among various batches of frogs used by several investigators. (C) The enthalpy of PCr breakdown has been overestimated and in muscle is probably no higher than −8 kcal/mole (Woledge, 1973). Altogether these several experimental observations are difficult to reconcile with the results of Wilkie (1968) and the prior results of Carlson *et al.* (1963, 1967) and show that an unknown exothermic reaction occurs during a muscular contraction. Alternatively, these results support the contention (Caplan, 1968a,b) that heat is not uniquely defined in muscle, in terms of the extent of reactions, n_i. We now consider some details of the experiments and arguments.

(A) Wilkie studied repeated twitches and tetani and, as he cautioned, his results did not necessarily indicate energy balance at each moment during a contraction. Single isometric tetani of frog sartorius at 0°C were used by Gilbert *et al.* (1971) to study the relationship between heat and work and phosphorylcreatine splitting during the course of a single contraction. Two striking observations were made (Fig. 1): (1) The rate (actually amount ÷ time interval) of heat + work released at 0.5 seconds of stimulation was much greater than later in the tetanus compared to the rate (actually amount ÷ time interval) of PCr broken down. In fact ΔPCr was not significantly different from zero at 0.5 second. From 2 to 15 seconds the slope of the line of heat + work and of ΔPCr versus tetanus duration were superimposable using −11 kcal/mole. (2) This initial discrepancy, or unexplained heat + work, persisted throughout relaxation, but there was some indication of PCr splitting without net heat production during the minute after relaxation. The latter was studied in detail by Curtin and Woledge (1974) and found not to occur. These results indicated the existence of an unknown and net exothermic process during the first part of a tetanus. One difference between the experiments of Gilbert *et al.* (1971) and of Wilkie (1968) was that Gilbert

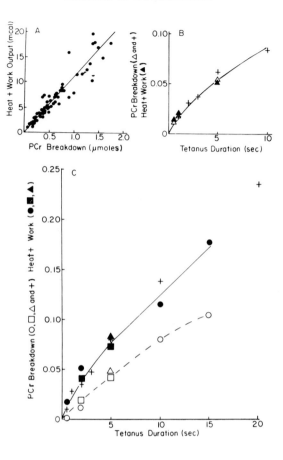

FIG. 1. Relation between the output of muscle heat + work (Q + W) and creatine phosphate breakdown. (A) The data of Wilkie (1968) show that heat + work is linearly related to PCr breakdown with the slope of -11.1 kcal/mole for a series of twitches and tetani, sartorius, *Rana temporaria*, 0°C; the data are redrawn without distinguishing the differing types of contraction and conditions that Wilkie studied. (B) Graphs of heat + work and PCr breakdown during a single isometric tetanus of *Rana pipiens* are each plotted as a function of duration of stimulation. Data for PCr ($\triangle$, +) splitting are normalized (μmoles/μmole creatine) to total muscle creatine (PCr + Cr), which is a useful measure of cytoplasmic mass. The data for heat + work ($\blacktriangle$) are similarly normalized and are then divided by -11 kcal/mole to scale them into comparable chemical units. $\triangle$, $\blacktriangle$ from Homsher *et al.* (1975); + from Kushmerick and Paul (1976b). (C) Graphs of heat + work and PCr breakdown during a single isometric tetanus of *R. temporaria* are each plotted as a function of duration of stimulation. PCr breakdown ($\bigcirc$, $\square$, $\triangle$, and +) and heat + work output ($\bullet$, $\blacksquare$, $\blacktriangle$) are expressed as in (B). A smooth curve is drawn free hand through the filled symbols, and a dashed line through the open symbols. $\bigcirc$, $\bullet$ data of Gilbert *et al.* (1971); $\square$, $\blacksquare$ Curtin and Woledge (1975); $\triangle$, $\blacktriangle$, Homsher *et al.* (1975); + M. J. Kushmerick, previously unpublished data (1974).

et al. used oxygenated muscles and Wilkie used muscles poisoned to block glycolysis and oxidative phosphorylation (muscles were anaerobic and treated with iodoacetate). But control experiments show that poisoning did not alter the results (Table 6 of Gilbert *et al.*, 1971).

(B) In similar experiments where PCr splitting was expected to be the only reaction, but using *Rana pipiens,* Homsher *et al.* (1975) observed $(Q + W)/\Delta$PCr was constant for tetanic durations of 0.5–5 seconds, actually between -9 and -13 kcal/mole. They found no evidence of the early unexplained enthalpy (Fig. 1). Chaplain and Frommelt (1972) also made energy balance studies in isometric and isotonic contractions in *Rana temporaria* and concluded that the $(Q + W)/\Delta$PCr is about -12 kcal/mole. Canfield *et al.* (1973) observed $(Q + W)/\Delta$PCr was about -11 kcal/mole at 20°C for short-duration tetani of sartorii from *Rana temporaria*, but for long-duration tetani, when reactions in addition to net PCr splitting also occurred, the quantity

$$(Q + W)/\sum n_i \, \Delta H_i$$

was significantly greater than 1. Finally Kretzschmar (1975) reported that for a brief tetanus of anaerobic rat soleus muscles only two-thirds of the measured heat + work could be explained by known reactions.

(C) Woledge (1971, 1973) carefully reexamined the calorimetric data used to predict the enthalpy of PCr breakdown via the Lohmann reaction in muscle and the associated side reactions (especially Mg^{2+} binding and proton buffer heat). He concluded the enthalpy of PCr splitting in muscle is -8 kcal/mole, significantly lower than the old value (-12 kcal/mole) of Meyerhof and Schultz (1935). Thus the new and presumably more accurate value is significantly lower than *any observed value* for the ratio of $(Q + W)/\Delta$PCr. He was forced to conclude that in every observation of muscle, heat, work, and chemistry there was a significant amount of unexplained heat + work, i.e. $[(Q + W)/\sum n_i \, \Delta H_i] > 1$.

Thus if the enthalpy of PCr splitting in frog skeletal muscle is -8 kcal/mole, then there are two discrepancies, which have been interpreted as missing reactions. The first occurs only early during a tetanus and is required to explain the differences in slopes of heat + work and PCr splitting as a function of tetanus duration in the work of Gilbert *et al.* (1971) (Fig. 1). The second reaction continues throughout contraction and is required to explain the steady difference between the value of the observed quantity

$$(Q + W)/\Delta\text{PCr}$$

(which in the various experiments is reported to be -10 to -18 kcal/mole) and the calorimeter-determined enthalpy of net PCr splitting, -8 kcal/mole.

These experimental results summarize the quantitative difficulties in achieving the predicted relations between muscle heat + work and net PCr splitting. It may be overly simplistic to assume systematic errors in some of the data in order to reconcile opposing observations. Rather more fruitful is the possibility that quantitative aspects of energetics depend on hitherto unrecognized features of the major chemical reactions concerned and associated side reactions, or on unknown reactions.

To define further the properties of the hypothetical missing reaction, balance experiments were made using contractions where a large fraction of the heat + work released is mechanical work. In the isometric contractions already discussed the fraction of total energy released appearing as mechanical work was 10% or less and was due to shortening of the series elastic elements. With an ergometer to constrain the muscle to shorten at constant velocity, the fraction work/heat + work can approach 0.5 (Hill, 1964). This fact allows a test of the hypothesis that the chemical energy supplied by the "missing reaction" might be converted into useful work; in that case it would be an integral part of the overall cross-bridge mechanism. The criteria to test that hypothesis is to calculate the quantity (see Fig. 2):

$$W/\Delta PCr$$

under experimental conditions where PCr splitting is thought to be the only (or major) reaction. This quantity is compared to the calculated free energy change (ΔF) expected for net PCr breakdown. The latter is not known with high accuracy nor is ΔF for net ATP breakdown. A reasonable calculation for the latter has been made (Kushmerick, 1969; Curtin et al., 1974) and is -10 to -12 kcal/mole. The value for net PCr splitting must be similar if ATP-creatine phosphoryltransferase reactions is in equilibrium (Carlson and Siger, 1959). If the quantity

$$W/\Delta PCr$$

were very much greater than -10 to -12 kcal/mole then serious consideration could be given to the idea that the chemical energy obtained from the hypothetical missing reaction could be converted into useful work. Several sets of experiments studied this aspect of the unexplained heat (Gilbert and Kushmerick, 1970; K. M. Kretzschmar and M. J. Kushmerick, unpublished experiments, 1970; Gilbert et al.,

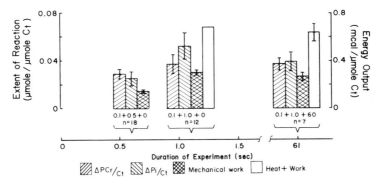

FIG. 2. The relation between muscle heat + work output ($\Delta Q + W$), mechanical work (W) and chemical change (PCr breakdown and P_i production) for muscles contracting at constant velocity such that a large amount of mechanical work is performed. The data are normalized and expressed as explained in Fig. 1. Error bars represent one standard error of the mean; n is the number of experiments. The numbers under each set of vertical bars ($X + Y + Z$) represent: X, duration of isometric stimulation in seconds; Y, duration of shortening in seconds; and Z, interval after the last stimulus in seconds before freezing. The experiments at 0.6 and 1.1 seconds were frozen while contracting by rapid freezing apparatus. Experiments at 61 seconds were frozen after relaxation and after the total heat production was measured with a thermopile. This measured heat was used to extrapolate the total energy output of the middle set of experiments; this quantity is illustrated by the open vertical bar. The sartorius muscles at 0°C from *Rana temporaria* were made anaerobic and treated with 0.5 mM iodoacetate to inhibit respiration and glycolysis. Data were taken from Gilbert and Kushmerick (1970) and previously unpublished experiments (1970) of K. M. Kretzschmar and M. J. Kushmerick.

1973; Curtin *et al.*, 1974). The quantity

$$(Q + W)/\Delta PCr$$

ranged from -11 kcal/mole to -17 kcal/mole, but the quantity

$$W/\Delta PCr$$

was between -6 and -9 kcal/mole. Also for the same total amount of heat + work, PCr splitting was significantly greater when greater amounts of external work were done (Gilbert *et al.*, 1973; Curtin *et al.*, 1974), an observation consistent with the results of Kushmerick and Davies (1969). Since $W/\Delta PCr$ is less than 100% of the predicted free energy of phosphorylcreatine splitting, there is no direct evidence that chemical energy released by the hypothetical missing reaction can be converted into useful mechanical work, although the observed ratio

$$W/\Delta PCr$$

can be a large fraction of the calculated free-energy change (Kushmerick and Davies, 1969).

Another perplexing feature of the available data is illustrated in Fig. 1 and this paragraph. There is very good agreement in the published results of Homsher *et al.* (1975) and of Kushmerick and Paul (1976b) for comparable tetani in *R. pipiens* (Fig. 1B), and those results are consistent with $\Delta H_{PCr} \simeq -11$ kcal/mole. In similar 5-second isometric tetani, T. Butler and R. E. Davies (personal communication, 1973) measured virtually identical chemical changes. In contrast, recent observations of J. Dawson, D. Gower, K. M. Kretzschmar, and D. R. Wilkie (1976) observed somewhat lower chemical changes so that $Q + W/\Delta PCR \simeq -16.5$ kcal/mole for 5-second isometric tetani of *R. pipiens*, i.e., a great amount of heat + work remained unaccounted for by known chemical reactions. Moreover, in *R. temporaria* the chemical changes observed in Kushmerick's laboratory (Fig. 1C) are substantially higher than the values reported by others and are consistent with $\Delta H_{PCr} \simeq -11$ kcal/mole. It is possible, and it was not tested in the experiments I made (Fig. 1C), that the heat + work output were also proportionally greater (almost 2-fold) than values reported by others.

In summary, one observes more (sometimes a great deal more) heat + work than can be accounted for by measured chemical changes and predicted heats of reaction, that is:

$$[(Q + W)/\sum n_i \, \Delta H_i] > 1$$

when Woledge's (1973) calorimetric data ($\Delta H_{PCr} \simeq 8$ kcal/mole) are used. For reasons outlined in Section III it must be kept in mind that it is not firmly settled whether this conclusion results from an underestimate of the appropriate values for ΔH_i *in vivo*, or systematic errors in muscle heat, work, and chemical changes or from unidentified exothermic reaction(s). Given this state of affairs my laboratory began quantitative biochemical studies of $\sim$P splitting and its resynthesis. The remainder of this essay is devoted to this topic.

V.   Restoration of Chemical Energy Pools

Depletion of $\sim$P pools (directly or indirectly) provides signals that regulate metabolic reactions coupled to resynthesis of $\sim$P and restoration of $\sim$P pools to the precontraction steady state. Well-defined biochemical pathways and physiological mechanisms are involved in the oxidation of substrates, release of products, and coupling of these to $\sim$P resynthesis. The favored muscle used for studies of energy balance has been the frog sartorius. Our discussion of metabolism can be somewhat limited because that muscle is a fast glycolytic type of muscle. The oxidizable substrate in relaxed and contracting muscle *in vitro* appears to be carbohydrate (glucose added to the bathing solution or endogenous glycogen) since (1) respiratory quotient is very near unity (Fenn, 1927); (2) the content of metabolizable triglyceride is small, in contrast to mammalian muscle, where it can be substantial (Issekutz, 1970; Fritz, 1960); (3) glycogen stores are large in amphibian muscle, ranging about 60 μmoles of glucose units per gram wet weight and depending on the nutritional states of the animal; and (4) glycogen can be shown to decrease as a consequence of contractile activity (see Section VI). However, amino acid oxidation, which occurs in rat skeletal muscle and may account for about 15% of energy production (Odessey and Goldberg, 1972), has not been measured in amphibian muscle.

Glucose units are metabolized via the Embden–Meyerhof pathway (Fig. 3). The overall stoichiometry is:

$$1 \text{ glucose (from glycogen)} + 3 \text{ ADP} \rightarrow 2 \text{ pyruvate} + 3 \text{ ATP}$$

The net operation of the Embden–Meyerhof pathway depends on a source of cytoplasmic NAD (glyceraldehyde phosphate dehydrogenase step, Fig. 3), which in anaerobic muscles can be accomplished by stoichiometric reduction of pyruvate to lactate:

$$\text{pyruvate} + \text{NADH} \rightarrow \text{lactate} + \text{NAD}^+$$

In aerobic muscles in which oxygen supply to mitochondria is not limited, pyruvate is oxidized to CO_2 plus water by the tricarboxylic acid cycle. The net reaction then is (starting with glycogen):

$$1 \text{ glucose unit} + 6 \text{ O}_2 + 37 \text{ (or 39) ADP} \rightarrow 6 \text{ CO}_2 + 6\text{H}_2\text{O} + 37 \text{ (or 39) ATP}$$

The reason for the uncertainty of the stoichiometry of $\sim$P resynthesis concerns the mechanism of oxidation of cytoplasmic NADH produced by the glyceraldehyde phosphate dehydrogenase step. If the reducing equivalents are carried to the mitochondria by the α-glycerol phosphate-dihydroxyacetone phosphate cycle, 37 ATP molecules are produced per mole of glycosyl units oxidized. The reason for this is the mitochondrial glycerol-phosphate dehydrogenase transfers its electrons to flavoproteins and thereby bypasses one of the phosphorylation steps of oxidative phosphorylation. The overall stoichiometric coupling factor is 39 if malate-oxaloacetate cycle carries the reducing equivalents; then three phosphorylations occur per electron because mitochondrial malate dehydrogenase is linked via NADH. The mechanism of mitochondrial

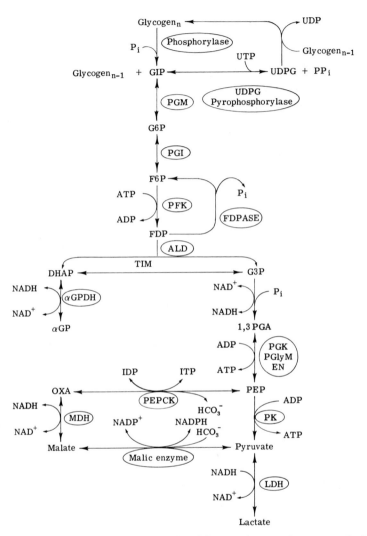

FIG. 3. Metabolic pathway for glycogen breakdown to lactate, glycogen synthesis, and related reactions. Three possible loci for futile substrate cycles are shown. Standard abbreviations for substrates are shown in boldface, and abbreviations for enzymes are circled.

oxidation of cytoplasmic NADH is not the same in all types of muscles (Crabtree and Newsholme, 1972; Newsholme and Start, 1973) and remains a fruitful area of investigation.

Thus, on the basis of studies in individual reactions and of the identification of the required enzymic activities in frog skeletal muscle, a fairly precise relationship between ~P resynthesis and metabolic oxidations may be predicted. For anaerobic muscles with glycogen as the substrate the ratio between the number of moles of $\sim P$ resynthesized and lactate produced by Embden–Meyerhof pathway (we shall call this the $\sim P$/lactate ratio) is 1.5. For aerobic muscles with glycogen as a substrate the ratio between the number of moles of $\sim P$ resynthesized and the moles of O_2 consumed a quantity (which we shall call $\sim P/O_2$ ratio) by the combined operation of the Embden–Meyerhof pathway, the tricarboxylic acid cycle and oxidative phosphorylation is 6.5 (or 6.17, an uncertainty discussed above).

Scopes (1973, 1974) mixed purified enzymes of the Embden-Meyerhof pathway *in vitro* and observed the predicted $\sim P$/lactate ratio of 1.5. These stoichiometric factors were also inferred from a variety of indirect measurements of whole muscle. For example, during a series of twitches of frog gastrocnemius muscles, the rate of decrease of PCr during stimulation were greater in iodoacetate-poisoned muscles than in anaerobic muscles. This difference was attributed to the glycolytic resynthesis in the unpoisoned muscles. From measurements of the differences in the rates of PCr decrease between poisoned and unpoisoned muscles and the rate of lactate production in the unpoisoned muscles, $\sim P$/lactate ratios were obtained and averaged 1.3 (Cerretelli *et al.*, 1972). By different and more complex technique, the calculated $\sim P$/lactate ratio varied between 1.5 and 1.8 (Ambrosoli and Cerretelli, 1973). These measurements are thus very much closer to the predicted $\sim P$/lactate ratio than that which was observed originally by Lundsgaard (1931), who reported values ranging from 2 to 5, and the value of 2 which is consistent with the interpretation of anaerobic heat data in terms of $\sim P$ and lactate synthesis (Woledge, 1971). $\sim P/O_2$ ratios have been inferred from studies of the gastrocnemius muscle of the anesthetized dog by measuring alactic acid oxygen debt and PCr levels during exercise of various intensities (Piiper and Spiller, 1970). Unfortunately, different values were obtained depending on whether part ($\sim P/O_2 = 5.4$) or the whole ($\sim P/O_2 = 3.4$) of the repayment of oxygen debt was used for the calculation. Thus estimates of the stoichiometric factors, $\sim P$/lactate and $\sim P/O_2$, from measurements on whole muscles isolated *in vitro* or on cannulated preparations *in situ* leave room for doubt that the predicted stoichiometries actually occur. That is, the experimental design of the studies described are sufficiently indirect so that the hypothesis that the stoichiometric factors predicted from biochemical pathways actually are observed in whole cells has not been adequately tested. It is clear, however, that some available measurements are consistent with the hypothesis.

The danger of accepting the predicted coupling factors is that alternative metabolic pathways or futile substrate cycles (Scrutton and Utter,

1968; Newsholme and Start, 1973) may occur to a significant extent. In addition, there is a possibility that mitochondrial oxidative phosphorylation may be partly uncoupled by conditions found in the cytoplasm [as certainly occurs in brown adipose tissue (Flatmark and Pedersen, 1975) and as occurs at ADP levels well below saturation of isolated mitochondria (Ernster *et al.*, 1963)]. Nonetheless, measurements of O_2 consumption and lactate production by contracting muscle and by exercising whole animals continues to be a very valuable tool to monitor chemical energy utilization (see Jöbsis, 1969, for a review of this topic). O_2 consumption is a highly quantitative and relatively easily performed measure, and it may bear a fixed relationship to $\sim$P utilization. Certainly a fixed $\Delta \sim P/\Delta O_2$ ratio of about 6 is usually assumed.

In mammalian skeletal muscles flow of carbohydrate carbons through the pentose phosphate pathway is of no quantitative importance (Jolley *et al.*, 1958; Green and Landau, 1965). There is a definite possibility of energetically significant futile substrate cycling since red and, especially, white skeletal muscle contain fructose-1-6-diphosphatase activity (Krebs and Woodford, 1965; Opie and Newsholme, 1967) (see Fig. 3). Based on maximal activity in tissue extracts of frog muscle, the ratio of enzyme activity of phosphofructokinase to fructose-1,6-diphosphatase is about 10 or 20 to 1. The actual operation of this futile substrate cycle has been demonstrated in liver slices (Clark *et al.*, 1975) and in insect flight muscle (Clark *et al.*, 1973). Two other possibilities of futile metabolic cycling are also given in Fig. 3 (involving glycogen phosphorylase–synthetase, and malic enzyme–PEP carboxykinase). The net effect of such a reaction is to reduce the apparent stoichiometry of $\sim$P synthesis to a net pyruvate or lactate synthesis and to generate heat, which serves an important physiological function in flight muscles of insects.

To summarize this section, well-defined energetic pathways of carbohydrate utilization occur in skeletal muscle and a definite prediction of a stoichiometry of $\sim$P synthesis can be made. Not all published evidence is consistent with the predicted stoichiometry, and adequate tests of the hypothesis that the stoichiometry predicted from individual enzymic reactions actually occurs in whole cells is not available. Moreover, futile substrate cycling and true metabolic uncoupling might occur to energetically significant extents and thus represent an interesting class of energy-consuming processes that occur as a consequence of muscle activation, and consume some chemical energy in the process of restoring $\sim$P pools to precontractile levels.

VI. A Biochemical Model of Energy Balance

Several years ago Dr. Richard J. Paul and I set out to study energy metabolism in frog skeletal muscle by a biochemical approach to see whether an energy balance could be obtained. This section is a progress report of our published and ongoing work.

The biochemical model being tested is that the stoichiometric relations in whole muscle cells between net creatine phosphate and ATP hydrolysis during contraction and their resynthesis during subsequent recovery period are those predicted by the isolated pathways of metabolic oxidation as discussed in Section V. We first studied the apparent ~P/O_2 ratio in aerobic muscles, and more recently Robert DeFuria has been studying the apparent ~P/lactate ratio anaerobic muscles of *R. pipiens*.

A. EXPERIMENTAL METHODS

Oxygen consumption of single frog sartorius muscles at 0°C were measured polarographically in a closed chamber made of glass and stainless steel (see Kushmerick and Paul, 1976a, for technical details). The rate and extent of oxygen depletion from the chambers were actually measured (Fig. 4). Periodically oxygenated Ringer's solution was added to the chambers to keep the pO_2 between 100 and 200 mm Hg; the oxygen consumption within that range did not depend on pO_2. Recovery oxygen consumption is the amount of O_2 consumed above a steady base line during the recovery period. The recovery period is the

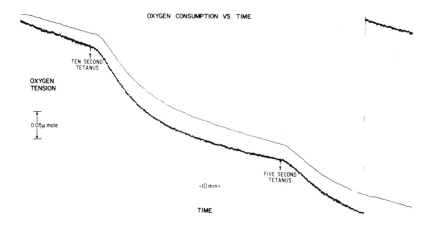

FIG. 4. Photograph of an experimental record of O_2 consumption following a single tetanus. Upper and lower traces are from one member of a pair of sartorii, each in a separate chamber. The abscissa is time and runs from left to right. The ordinate is the output of the O_2 electrode scaled to the amount of O_2 in the closed chambers. A downward deflection indicates O_2 uptake by the muscle. The rapid vertical rise in the lower trace is an artifact due to a shift in bias voltage. The O_2 tension during the experiment was kept at that of air ± 20%. The muscle of the upper trace was stimulated 1 minute after the lower. Reproduced from Paul and Kushmerick (1974a) by permission of the publisher, Elsevier Scientific Publishing Company, Amsterdam.

interval between stimulation of the muscle to the time when the oxygen consumption rate returns to the basal rate. Since the measurements are nondestructive, observations were made repeatably and reliably in the same preparation, in some cases over the course of 2 days.

Measurements of net PCr breakdown requires a more complex experimental design. The technique destroys the muscle so only one measurement can be made per muscle. At the required time, during or after a tetanic stimulation, one member of a pair of sartorii is rapidly frozen to stop chemical reactions. The other member of the pair is a suitable treated control muscle and is also frozen. The technology of rapid freezing was greatly advanced by the introduction of a hammer apparatus by Kretzschmar and Wilkie (1969). This apparatus consists of flat and polished aluminum or brass plates chilled in liquid nitrogen which will flatten and freeze a sartorius muscle completely in less than 100 msec. The metabolites of interest are extracted from the frozen muscles and analyzed by standard techniques. We use a buffered aqueous methanol solution at $-35°$ to achieve extraction (see Kushmerick and Paul, 1976a); others pulverize the frozen muscle and extract with cold perchloric acid. The extent of chemical reaction during the contraction is measured by the difference in chemical content of the experimental and control muscles.

Animals are selected without bias from a common pool either for measurements of oxygen consumption or for PCr breakdown. Muscles from each group are tetanized for identical durations and develop the same, or near so, tension per unit cross-sectional area. Mean values of PCr breakdown and recovery oxygen consumption can be used to form the ratios $\sim P/O_2$. In another experimental design, measurements of recovery oxygen consumption are made first, then the pair of muscles are rapidly frozen after appropriate stimulation of the experimental member of the pair. This procedure allows one measurement of the $\sim P/O_2$ ratio to be made in the same muscle. The results for both types of experimental design were similar (Paul and Kushmerick, 1974a).

B. Testable Assumptions

1. Since the reaction occurring during contraction is thought to be the Lohmann reaction (reaction 2, Section II), the net reaction is

$$PCr \rightarrow Cr + P_i$$

We measured the decrease in substrate PCr and the appearance of both products creatine and P_i. ATP levels were also measured because the Lohmann reaction might not maintain the ATP pool and because Gilbert *et al.* (1971) reported a small ATP increase during brief tetani. Analysis of substrates and products provides a more accurate and precise measure of the extent of the Lohmann reaction than analysis of any single component. We calculated for each experimental and control muscle pair the mean change in PCr, P_i, and creatine. We defined this mean as $\Delta\sim P$, and it is the best estimate of the change in the "high energy phosphate" compounds during contraction (Paul and Kushmerick, 1974a). These analyses also allow a check of the stoichiometry of the phosphate-containing compounds. If there are no changes in ATP levels, then the Lohmann reaction predicts the following equalities:

$$-\Delta PCr = \Delta P_i = \Delta Cr$$

These relations can be tested statistically by calculating the quantity:

$$- \left[\frac{(\Delta Cr) - (\Delta PCr)}{2}\right] + \Delta ATP + \Delta P_i$$

which should not be significantly different from 0. Our results on this point (Table I) show that the stoichiometry of the Lohmann reaction is observed in aerobic unpoisoned muscles; at most PCr splitting exceeds P_i production by about 10%. P_i production is much less than PCr splitting when the muscles are anaerobic and poisoned with 0.5 m*M* iodoacetate (last row of Table I) indicating that additional reactions involving P_i occur under these conditions.

2. Although tetani give highly repeatable contractions for many hours in isolated frog muscles at 0° and PCr synthesis has been shown to occur following contraction (in frog sartorius, see Dydynska and Wilkie, 1966; Ambrosoli and Cerretelli, 1973; in dog gastrocnemius, see Piiper and Spiller, 1970), it is necessary to test whether the steady-state content of metabolites is restored after a tetanus. Our data on this point are given in Fig. 5. Kinetics of recovery was first order. Time constants for PCr synthesis and P_i and creatine disappearance were quite similar. Restoration of the initial metabolite levels, i.e., levels before tetanization, was complete.

3. The energetic model being studied requires that the initial PCr splitting be separated in time from its resynthesis. A good deal of evidence validates this assumption. D. K. Hill (1940) concluded that suprabasal recovery oxygen consumption at 0°C begins after the tetanus is completed. If there were resynthesis of PCr during a tetanus then the observed PCr splitting for identical tetani should be lower in unpoisoned and oxygenated muscles than in iodoacetate-poisoned anaerobic muscles [or dinitrofluorobenzene-poisoned anaerobic muscles, which inhibits

TABLE I

Observed Chemical Changes during Single Isometric Tetani of Unpoisoned Frog Muscles at 0°C[a]

Duration of tetanus (sec)	n	$\Delta PCr/gm$		$\Delta P_i/gm$		$\dfrac{-[\Delta Cr/gm - \Delta PCr/gm]}{2}$ $-\Delta ATP/gm - \Delta P_i/gm$		
		$\bar{x}$	SE of the mean	$\bar{x}$	SE of the mean	$\bar{x}$	SE of the mean	n^c
1	19	−0.64	0.09	0.72	0.14	0.30	0.11	19
2	15	−1.16	0.12	1.21	0.11	−0.15	0.25	15
3	8	−1.28	0.13	1.13	0.12	−0.13	0.29	8
5	30	−2.44	0.15	2.07	0.13	0.46	0.18	19
10	22	−2.99	0.21	3.01	0.14	0.88	0.15	6
20	20	−5.83	0.17	4.70	0.17	0.85	0.18	9
40	6	−8.23	0.77	7.62	0.39	0.37	0.85	6
60	6	−9.61	1.19	9.25	0.46	0.31	0.99	6
60[b]	6	−12.50	0.51	8.09	0.51	4.40	0.93	6

[a] Paired muscles were used (see text). Chemical changes are the pairwise differences in chemical content per wet tissue weight between unstimulated control muscles and their mates frozen after the indicated duration of tetanic stimulation. Data in last column and bottom row have not previously been published; the other data are taken from Kushmerick and Paul (1976b).

[b] These muscles only were incubated in 0.5 mM iodoacetate in Ringer solution equilibrated with 100% N_2 for 45 minutes at 0°C before stimulation of the experimental member of the pair; these muscles on average had 10% higher tensions than the unpoisoned muscles in the second to last row.

[c] These numbers when different from the second column indicate that ATP analyses were not made for every muscle pair.

creatine phosphokinase in addition to glycolysis and oxidative phosphorylation (Infante and Davies, 1965)]. No such differences have been observed (Kushmerick and Davies, 1969; Gilbert et al., 1971; Paul and Kushmerick, 1974a). Last, the time course of suprabasal recovery oxygen consumption was strictly exponential after allowing for a lag due to diffusion within the muscle (Kushmerick and Paul, 1976a). Thus the extent of recovery during the tetanus could be calculated with the (worst case) assumption that recovery oxygen consumption began at its maximal rate with the tetanus. This calculation shows that negligible oxidative phosphorylation could have occurred even during a moderately long tetanus (for example, 20 seconds) because the time constant for recovery oxygen consumption is on the order of 15 minutes.

4. Basal and recovery oxygen consumption is due to oxidative phos-

phorylation in the mitochondria because 1 mM KCN completely blocks both basal and recovery muscle oxygen consumptions.

5. Oxidative phosphorylation is causally related to resynthesis of $\sim$P (Fig. 5) because the time course for each is exponential and their time constants (τ) are very nearly the same. For PCr synthesis, τ is 13.5 minutes; for P_i and creatine decrease τ is 12 min. The mean value for recovery oxygen consumption following a 20-second tetanus is 17 ± 3 minutes (SE of the mean; $n = 5$).

Oxidative phosphorylation is virtually the only resynthesis pathway, because $\sim$P resynthesis by substrate level phosphorylation in glycolysis was measurable and found to be small. Lactate production by aerobic muscles in the chambers used for oxygen measurements and in aerobic

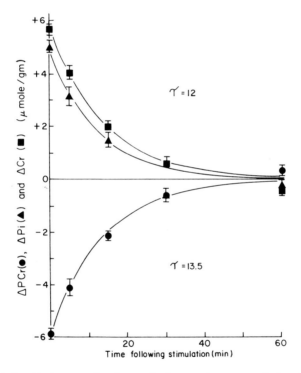

FIG. 5. Relationship between the changes in the muscle content of phosphorylcreatine (ΔPCr/gm), free creatine (ΔCr/gm) and inorganic phosphate (ΔP_i/gm) vs the time following a 20-second tetanus. ▲, ■, and ● represent the mean ΔP_i/gm, ΔCr/gm, and ΔPCr, respectively, in eight muscle pairs; bars indicate one standard error of the mean. Smooth curves are exponential curves fitted to these values of time constants, τ: 12 minutes for ΔP_i/gm and 13.5 min for ΔPCr/gm and ΔCr/gm. Reproduced from Kushmerick and Paul (1976a) with permission of the publisher.

TABLE II

LACTATE PRODUCTION BY ISOMETRICALLY CONTRACTING AEROBIC FROG SARTORIUS
MUSCLES AT 0°C

A. Total recovery lactate production and recovery O_2 consumption

Conditions	Lactate production ÷ O_2 consumption (mole/mole)	Fraction[a] of total ~P resynthesis due to glycolysis
Unstimulated basal	0.29	0.068
10-Sec tetanus	0.24	0.057
20-Sec tetanus	0.27	0.063
40-Sec tetanus	0.27	0.063
60-Sec tetanus	0.74	0.156

B. Lactate content of muscles suspended in moist air and frozen at the times indicated in the left columns

Duration of tetanus (sec)	+	Duration of aerobic recovery (min)	Lactate content: stimulated—control (μmole/gm)
10	+	0	0.05
10	+	3	0.08
10	+	60	0.02
20	+	0	0.08
20	+	5	0.51
20	+	15	0.53
20	+	30	0.49
20	+	60	0.17
40	+	0	0.13
60	+	0	0.33

[a] This calculation assumes that glycogen is the predominant substrate for metabolism with 1.5 and 6 moles of ATP produced per mole of lactate and O_2 consumed. Data are taken from Kushmerick and Paul (1976a).

muscles suspended in a gas phase so no lactate diffuse away provided a measure of net glycolysis (Table II). A steady rate of lactate production occurred in unstimulated frog sartorii at 0°, averaging 2.1 ± 0.5 nanomole per gram per minute (SE of the mean; $n = 6$). Suprabasal lactate production occurred only following a tetanus for the tetanic durations studied (obviously lactate accumulation could be demonstrated during very long tetani). An important result of these studies for our purposes is given in Table II: except for very long tetanic durations of 60 seconds, lactate production and recovery oxygen consumption occur in constant molar ratios. Based on predicted stoichiometry of the relevant metabolic pathways (Section V), the fraction of ~P resynthesized by glycolysis was about 6%. The remainder was due to oxidative phosphorylation.

6. Skoog and Stephens (1973) reported $\sim P/O_2$ ratios near 6 for frog muscle mitochondria in the temperature range of 17°–35°C; nevertheless it was necessary to study these mitochondria at the temperature of our experiments. Mitochondria were isolated from thigh muscles and sedimented at 10,000 g using standard techniques. Suspensions of these mitochondria were studied (Estabrook, 1967) in the presence of glutamate and malate as substrates and in an excess of inorganic phosphate in the polarographic muscle chambers at 0°C. Control of respiration by ADP (state 4 to 3 to 4 transitions) and ADP/O_2 ratios were measured (Fig. 6). The average ADP/O_2 ratio for the three preparations of mitochondria studied was 6.2 ± 0.6 (standard deviation). This result shows that oxidative phosphorylation in frog muscle mitochondria at 0°C is not different from standard mitochondrial preparations at saturating substrate and P_i levels.

C. High Energy Phosphate Splitting during Contraction and the Extent of Recovery Oxygen Consumption

The first experimental plan was a study of frog muscles at 0°C tetanized isometrically for 10 seconds (Paul and Kushmerick, 1974a).

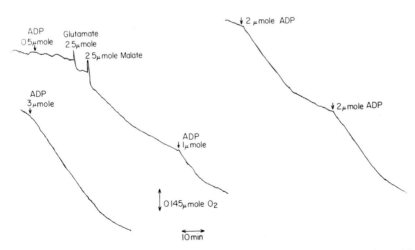

FIG. 6. Stimulation of respiration by successive additions of ADP in mitochondria isolated from thigh muscles from *Rana pipiens*. The continuous record was interrupted for photographic purposes. Incubation conditions were: 0°C, 7.2 mg of mitochondrial protein, 0.4 mg of bovine albumin, 910 μmoles of sucrose, 10 μmoles of KCl, 70 μmoles of TES buffer, pH 7.4, 15 μmoles of P_i, 0.16 μmoles of EDTA in a total volume of 4 ml of a solution previously equilibrated with air.

The level of phosphocreatine decreases about 10% during such a contraction. The muscles were frozen during the tetanus ($n = 16$). In other experiments ($n = 20$) total recovery oxygen consumption (ΔO_2) was measured following similar 10-second tetani. The observed ratio, $\Delta \sim P/\Delta O_2$, was 3.78 and is significantly lower than the expected value of 6 (rounded off for convenience from the predicted value of 6.17 or 6.5 discussed in Section V). In five other experiments, ΔO_2 was first measured in duplicate and then the muscles were frozen for measurement for $\Delta \sim P$. The observed $\Delta \sim P/\Delta O_2$ ratio for this experiment was 3.40 ± 0.14 (SE of the mean).

We added to these observations in more extensive experiments (Kushmerick and Paul, 1976b) which studied tetanic durations ranging from 1 to 60 seconds; most observations were made for 5, 10, or 20 seconds stimulus durations. The relevant results for our purposes of these studies is given in Table III. In part A of Table III the ratios, $\Delta \sim P/\Delta O_2$, were constructed directly from the averaged values and the standard deviation of the ratios were estimated. Since there were some differences in tetanic tension and areas under the isometric myograms between the muscles frozen and those used for oxygen measurements, the chemical changes were normalized to the average tension per cross-sectional area times the duration of tetanus (which we call tension–time

TABLE III

RATIOS OF $\Delta \sim P/\Delta O_2$ FOR 5, 10, AND 20-SECOND TETANI STIMULATIONS[a]

Duration of stimulation (sec)	A. Ratio obtained from observed chemical changes							
	$\Delta \sim P/gm$ (μmole/gm)			$\Delta O_2/gm$ (μmole/gm)			$\dfrac{\Delta \sim P}{\Delta O_2}$	
	Mean	SD	n	Mean	SD	n		SD
5	2.26	0.75	30	0.555	0.062	8	4.1	1.4
10	2.94	0.52	22	0.849	0.148	14	3.5	0.9
20	5.39	0.85	20	1.23	0.26	11	4.4	1.2

Duration of stimulation (sec)	B. Ratio obtained from chemical changes normalized to the tension-time integral							
	$\Delta \sim P/L_0 \int P \, dt$ (μmole/kgwt·sec·cm)			$\Delta O_2/L_0 \int P \, dt$ (μmole/kgwt·sec·cm)			$\dfrac{\Delta \sim P}{\Delta O_2}$	
	Mean	SD	n	Mean	SD	n		SD
5	0.209	0.060	30	0.043	0.006	8	4.9	1.6
10	0.130	0.029	22	0.034	0.007	14	3.8	1.2
20	0.124	0.016	20	0.028	0.003	11	4.5	0.7

[a] Data are taken from Kushmerick and Paul (1976b).

integral, $\int P dt$). The justification for this normalization is given in the original paper (Kushmerick and Paul, 1976b). Part B of Table III gives $\Delta \sim P/\Delta O_2$ ratios calculated from normalized data, and this calculation confirms the original result. There was no significant difference for shorter (5 seconds) and longer (20 seconds) tetanic durations. It must be concluded that the apparent $\Delta \sim P/\Delta O_2$ ratio is different from the value of 6 predicted from well-defined biochemical pathways and their stoichiometric relations (Section V) since the averaged observed value is 4.2.

Initial $\sim P$ utilization and extent of recovery oxygen consumption were each studied as functions of tetanic duration and of the tension–time integral. Graphs of chemical energy utilization ($\Delta \sim P$ and ΔO_2) as a function of tetanus duration were curvilinear (Fig. 1; see also Figs. 2 and 3 of Kushmerick and Paul, 1976b). In contrast when the tension–time integral was used as the independent variable (Fig. 2 and 3 of Kushmerick and Paul, 1976b), the curve was linear with a statistically significant positive intercept on the ordinate. For tetani longer than 5 seconds a small decline in isometric tension averaging about 1% per second of stimulation was discernible; the decline was substantial for 60-second tetani. Normalization of the data to the tension–time integral takes into account this decrease in tension and thus for tetanic stimulations 5 seconds and longer the graphs of chemical energy utilization as a function of tension–time integral are linear (Fig. 7). This is an important point for the $\sim P$ splitting per unit tension maintained is observed to be a constant value while the PCr levels are being depleted to 60–70% of the original levels. ATP levels remain constant in all these muscles, a result not in keeping with equilibration of the Lohmann reaction and which merits further investigation.

A second feature of the results is the curvilinearity for short tetanic durations (less than 5 seconds) of graph of $\Delta \sim P$ vs tension–time integral (Fig. 7). The isometric tension normally reaches a plateau by 1 second. These results show the steady state rate of net PCr splitting is not achieved until about 5 seconds of maintained stimulation in contrast to the data of Gilbert et al. (1971) (Fig. 1). This greater initial rate of PCr splitting is quite interesting per se because it reflects an amount of chemical energy utilization which is independent of tension development, maintenance, and relaxation. Its magnitude decreases if the muscle was previously stimulated within 3 minutes (Paul and Kushmerick, 1974b). These observations are under continued study and may be related to a myothermic observation by Aubert (1956) called "labile heat." The question for the purpose of this essay is whether recovery O_2 consumption is also curvilinear for short tetanus durations with respect to tension–time integral as the independent variable. Unfortunately measurements for such brief tetani (1–3 seconds) are almost always very

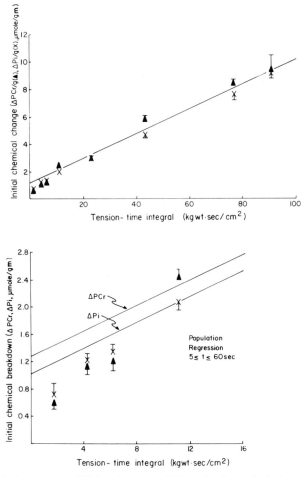

Fig. 7. Relation between PCr breakdown and P_i production and tension–time integral. Single sartorii of *Rana pipiens* were tetanically stimulated at 0°C under isometric conditions for various durations from 1 to 60 seconds. The line in the upper panel is the least squares regression line for the best estimate of high energy phosphate breakdown, taken from Kushmerick and Paul (1976b). Bars indicate one standard error of the mean; no bars are visible in some points because the symbol is larger than the error. In the lower panel the data nearer the origin are replotted on an expanded scale to show the initial curvilinearity. Regression lines for ΔPCr and ΔP_i as the dependent variables are not significantly different from each other or from the regression line in the upper panel.

near the resolution of our method. It can only be concluded that the recovery oxygen consumption curve is probably also superimposable in the region of interest (see Kushmerick and Paul, 1976b), but at the moment too few observations ($n = 4$) are available to make this conclusion with great certainty.

Since $\Delta \sim P$ and ΔO_2 as functions of tetanus duration and tension–time integral have the same form (linear functions with a positive and statistically significant intercept on the ordinate) and since both measures probably show the same initial curvilinearity, both curves can be superimposed by a constant scaling factor relating $\Delta \sim P$ to ΔO_2. This factor is most easily obtained from the ratios of the slopes and intercepts, and these calculations are given in Table IV. $\Delta \sim P/\Delta O_2$ ratios obtained by this method are clearly similar to those obtained previously (Table III) and again are clearly lower than the predicted value of 6. This superposition of both measures of chemical energy utilization means that the ratio of $\Delta \sim P$ and ΔO_2 is constant at least for tetanic stimulations of 5–20-second durations and very likely also for shorter durations of stimulation and for longer tetani (up to 60 seconds for measurement of $\Delta \sim P$ and up to 30 seconds for measurement of ΔO_2).

Since the results of Homsher *et al.* (1975) suggest the unexplained heat was much more prominent in *R. temporaria* than in *R. pipiens,* we made experiments similar to those just described in Section VI,C (M. J. Kushmerick, unpublished experiments, 1974) using *R. temporaria* obtained from England. Qualitatively the relations of $\Delta \sim P$ and ΔO_2 to isometric tetanus duration and tension–time integral were similar to what was observed in *R. pipiens*. The actual values of $\Delta \sim P$ and ΔO_2 for

TABLE IV

RATIOS OF $\Delta \sim P/\Delta O_2$ OBTAINED FROM LINEAR REGRESSION ANALYSES OF CHEMICAL CHANGE AS A FUNCTION OF THE TENSION–TIME INTEGRAL[a]

	$\Delta \sim P$	ΔO_2	$\dfrac{\Delta \sim P}{\Delta O_2}$	SD
A.				
Slopes (μmoles/gm $\div$ kgwt·sec·cm/gm $\pm$ SD)	0.104 ± 0.008	0.0263 ± 0.0019	4.0	0.4
Intercepts (μmoles/gm $\pm$ SD)	0.69 ± 0.23	0.138 ± 0.058	5.0	2.7
N[b]	36	15		
B.				
Slopes (μmoles/gm $\div$ kgwt·sec·cm/gm $\pm$ SD)	0.094 ± 0.006	0.0212 ± 0.0058	4.4	1.2
Intercepts (μmoles/gm $\pm$ SD)	1.10 ± 0.17	0.289 ± 0.129	3.8	1.8
N	72	(mean value of regression parameters for 11 muscles)		

[a] Data are taken from Kushmerick and Paul (1976b).

[b] N = number of data used to calculate the regressions.

similar tetani averaged 40% higher than those for *R. pipiens,* a result consistent with the higher maintenance heat rate in *R. temporaria* (see Fig. 1). The important quantitative result for our present purposes is that the ratio, $\Delta \sim P/\Delta O_2$, was lower than the predicted value (6) and was similar to that obtained in *R. pipiens*.

There are three classes of explanations for the lower observed $\Delta \sim P$ to ΔO_2 ratio: (1) Oxidative phosphorylation in intact mitochondria in their cytoplasmic environment is partially uncoupled. The uncoupling could be a direct, or true, uncoupling whereby the protomotive force (or alternatively the high energy intermediate) is dissipated without phosphorylation. Or the uncoupling could be only apparent whereby the energy of electron transport through the respiratory chain is coupled not to $\sim$P synthesis but to size and shape changes, ionic accumulations within the mitochondria, etc. (2) There is a significant amount of PCr splitting during the recovery period itself (i.e., after relaxation of tension) simultaneous with recovery $\sim$P resynthesis. Experiments discussed above have attempted, always with negative results, to demonstrate directly any significant delayed $\sim$P utilization. (3) There exists an unknown source of chemical energy, a hypothesis put forward by Gilbert *et al.* (1971) and suggested by Kushmerick and Davies (1969). This hypothetical reaction would be of the general form:

$$X \sim Y \rightarrow X + Y + \text{energy}$$

which occur spontaneously to the right during contraction in order to fit simply the myothermal data of Gilbert *et al.* (1971) or afterward as allowed by our data, and which is reversed during recovery.

Significant alterations in the current views in muscle energetics will be required, whichever of these possible mechanisms turn out to be the correct explanation. At the moment none of these hypotheses can be excluded experimentally.

D.   HIGH ENERGY PHOSPHATE SPLITTING DURING CONTRACTION AND THE EXTENT OF LACTATE PRODUCTION DURING RECOVERY OF ANAEROBIC MUSCLES

Anaerobic glycolysis consists of fewer reactions than does aerobic oxidation, and it occurs entirely in the cytoplasm. Thus it may prove easier to study than the aerobic pathway just described. The next experimental design therefore was a study of the relationship between anaerobic recovery and initial $\sim$P utilization. The hypothesis to be tested is that the quantitative prediction of the Embden–Meyerhof pathway (from glycogen to lactate the $\sim$P/lactate ratio is 1.5) is obtained in whole muscle during anaerobic recovery. Preliminary experiments show that the time course for anaerobic recovery at 0°C was many hours. In order to make several observations on a single preparation Robert DeFuria in my laboratory set up a method to measure the lactate production during recovery of a single frog sartorius at 20°C. $\Delta \sim P/\Delta O_2$ ratios at this temperature were 3.6 so there was no logical problem in changing the temperature of the experiment. The overall experimental design was similar to that described above for oxygen measurements. The muscle chamber was modified to allow continuous bubbling with nitrogen gas and to allow a pump to provide a steady flow of Ringer's solution into and out of the chamber. The effluent was collected at regular time intervals and the lactate content of each fraction was measured. An example of the experimental data so obtained is given in Fig. 8. The total amount of lactate produced above the base line is the recovery lactate production. The time interval from the stimulation to the return of the lactate production to base line values is the duration of recovery. These experiments are in progress, but the data obtained will be described because conclusions relevant to this essay are already clearly established.

To interpret lactate production quantitatively it is necessary to test whether restoration of the initial $\sim P$ pools occurs during anaerobic recovery and whether the restoration is complete. Previous studies of

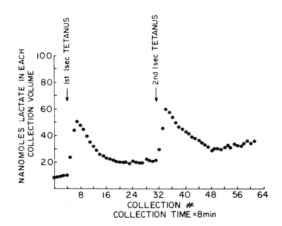

FIG. 8. Total lactate efflux from a single anaerobic sartorius muscle (*Rana pipiens*) at 20°C during and following 1-second isometric tetani. The flow of Ringer's solution was constant, the basal rate can be extrapolated and no intercellular lactate accumulated after recovery (see text), so total muscle lactate production during recovery from each tetanus can be calculated. Suprabasal recovery of lactate (μmoles/gm dry weight): 1st 1-second tetanus, 11.5; 2nd 1-second tetanus, 10.8.

anaerobic frog skeletal muscles suggested that complete recovery of ~P pools does not occur (Cerretelli *et al.*, 1972; Ambrosoli and Cerretelli, 1973). A few measurements have been made; an example is given in Table V. Clearly the ~P pool can be completely restored. Also notice that the intracellular lactate content is constant before and after recovery, a result which shows that the method of measuring lactate production from base line to base line provides a valid measure of the total lactate produced during recovery, but not necessarily of the true rate of lactate production.

The next question was whether lactate was the sole end product of anaerobic recovery metabolism. Other biochemical end products are theoretically possible, and various animals have been shown to have a variety of anaerobic metabolic end products (see Hochachka and Somero, 1973). To test this hypothesis an experiment similar to the previous one was made; this time the glycogen depletion was compared to the total lactate produced. In control muscles the average glycogen content was 57.2 ± 1.8 μmoles of glucose units per gram wet tissue weight (SE of the mean; $n = 10$). The glycogen content of individual pairs of muscles differed by less than 3%. The lactate production in one member of a pair was measured before, during, and after recovery (20.7 μmoles/gm), and then its glycogen content was measured (45.9 μmoles/gm) and compared to the glycogen content of the control muscle (55.5 μmoles/gm). Clearly the glycogen depleted (9.6 μmoles/gm) quantitatively accounts for the total lactate produced (20.7 μmoles/gm). The amount of lactate predicted for the glycogen depletion is $2 \times 9.6 = 19.2$ μmoles/gm which is very close to the observed lactate production.

No oxidative phosphorylation occurred because the amount of lactate

TABLE V

RECOVERY OF METABOLITE CONTENT TO INITIAL LEVELS AFTER ANAEROBIC RECOVERY OF FROG SARTORIUS AT 20°C[a]

	Unstimulated	Stimulated	% Change
	(μmoles/gm)		
Free creatine	13.36	13.66	+2.2
Inorganic phosphate	8.74	8.90	+1.8
Creatine phosphate	25.58	25.06	−2.0
ATP	3.54	3.59	+1.4
Lactate	0.73	0.73	0

[a] Stimulated muscle was observed to produce lactate during recovery as illustrated in Fig. 7 and was frozen when lactate products returned to the base line. The unstimulated muscle was similarly treated except for the stimulation.

produced following a 1-second tetanus was not detectably different in muscles gassed with nitrogen or with carbon monoxide. Had aerobic resynthesis occurred, the amount of lactate produced would have been drastically increased with CO inhibition because of the markedly higher efficacy of $\sim$P production per mole of glucose oxidized aerobically (Section V).

The first experiments to measure the $\Delta \sim P/\Delta$lactate ratio was similar in design to our method for measuring the $\Delta \sim P/\Delta O_2$ ratio described above. A total of 18 frogs was divided in half without bias. In one group the experimental member of a pair of muscles were tetanized anaerobically and isometrically at 20°C for 1 second and frozen just as the tension returned to zero. The control muscle was not stimulated. The observed ΔPCr/gm was 2.84 ± 0.16 μmoles/gm wet weight. In the other group, one muscle was similarly tetanized and used for lactate measurements. Lactate production was 2.36 ± 0.08 μmoles/gm wet weight. The apparent $\Delta \sim P/\Delta$lactate ratio calculated from preceding quantities is 1.2. The ratio decreases to 0.9 if the data were normalized to the tension time integral to take into account differences in the isometric tension and areas under the myogram (Kushmerick and DeFuria, 1976). Thus the observed $\Delta \sim P/\Delta$lactate ratio is significantly lower than the predicted stoichiometric factor of the Embden–Meyerhof pathway in which the true $\Delta \sim P/\Delta$lactate ratio equals 1.5. These experiments were repeated in a larger series of frogs and the apparent $\Delta \sim P/\Delta$lactate ratios were similarly obtained for tetanic durations of 0.5, 1.0, and 3.0 seconds at 20°C and were, respectively, 1.1, 1.1, and 1.2. Although additional experiments and controls must be made, the conclusion seems inescapable that the predicted $\Delta \sim P/\Delta$lactate ratio (1.5) is not observed during anaerobic recovery of whole muscles.

Interpretation of the lower $\Delta \sim P/\Delta$lactate ratios are similar to the three classes of explanations for the observed $\Delta \sim P/\Delta O_2$ ratios discussed above with the exception that true uncoupling of oxidative phosphorylation seems to be excluded. The argument here is that uncoupling of oxidative phosphorylation cannot be the sole cause of the reduction in $\Delta \sim P/\Delta O_2$ ratios and $\Delta \sim P/\Delta$lactate ratios because oxidative phosphorylation does not occur in anaerobic muscles. Dissipation of chemical energy by anaerobic mitochondria cannot be excluded. Moreover, mitochondrial ion accumulation is possible in anaerobic muscles because ATP in the cytoplasm can be coupled to mitochondrial ion transport and volume changes (see Cockrell et al., 1966; Packer and Gooch, 1973). The significance of the fact that both the observed $\Delta \sim P/\Delta$lactate and $\Delta \sim P/\Delta O_2$ ratios are about two-thirds their respective predicted values is not clear at this time, and the underlying biochemical mechanism of each is unknown.

VII. Epilogue

Experiments relating to energy balance are essentially quantitative analyses and descriptions of the necessary equivalency between the energy inputs and outputs during and following muscular contractions. The important problem therefore is not to prove that an equivalency exists. The interest in energy balance is the study of muscle contraction and energy metabolism by means of quantitative balance measurements as a tool. The available data fit neither a thermodynamic model of energy balance based on total energy conservation (Sections III and IV) nor a biochemical model based on defined metabolic pathways (Sections V and VI). We have studied the beginning (PCr splitting) and end points (recovery metabolism) of cellular energy metabolism because of the intrinsic metabolic interest of such measurements and because the interpretation of myothermal measurements requires, inter alia, detailed knowledge of quantitative aspects of the operation of metabolic pathways in the muscle cell.

The observed $\Delta \sim P/\Delta O_2$ and $\Delta \sim P/\Delta$lactate ratios are each lower than the predicted quantities. The lower $\Delta \sim P/\Delta$lactate ratio shows that splitting of high energy phosphates occurs after relaxation, that is during recovery. This conclusion can be easily understood by writing the following identity for a whole contraction-relaxation-recovery cycle in anaerobic muscles:

$$\text{Total} \sim P \text{ used} = 1.5 \text{ lactate} = \Delta \sim P_{\text{during tetanus}} + \Delta \sim P_{\text{recovery}}$$

This conclusion is not contradictory to the negative results obtained previously from experiments designed to measure directly postcontractile PCr splitting; only short postcontraction intervals had been studied (Section II). This qualitative result is contrary to the view that all the chemical energy used by contracting muscle occurs during the contraction. This finding may provide a rational biochemical explanation for the "missing reaction" hypothesis: The observed values for the ratios $\Delta \sim P/\Delta O_2$ and $\Delta \sim P/\Delta$lactate are consistent with high energy phosphate splitting during recovery which could reverse the unknown and spontaneous exothermic process during the contraction. An important corollary is that rapid freezing techniques do not measure the total net "high energy" phosphate splitting associated with the contraction–relaxation cycle.

However, the interpretation of those observed ratios do not depend on the outcome of myothermic energy balance studies. The measured $\Delta \sim P/\Delta O_2$ and $\Delta \sim P/\Delta$lactate ratios are related to many aspects of cellular energy metabolism, such as the degree of coupling of oxidative phosphorylation, the control of respiration, and the possibility of futile metabolic cycling *in vivo*. Experiments of the type described in Figs. 4 and 5 are proving to be useful tools for studying rates and control of cellular energy metabolism because kinetic data are readily derived from such measurements. For example, kinetics of respiration in whole muscle (Fig. 4) are apparently first order during recovery, whereas respiration in isolated mitochondria is zeroth order with respect to ADP during most of the state 4-3-4 transition (Fig. 6). In addition, the time course of recovery in whole muscle (Fig. 4) is slower than in isolated mitochondria (Fig. 6). These observations suggest the hypothesis that oxidizable substrate may be rate limiting to cellular respiration and so be an important regulator in addition to ADP levels.

Students of energy balance have followed Whitehead's aphorism "Seek simplicity and then distrust it." That strategy is now yielding fruit as new insights into energy metabolism in skeletal muscles are emerging.

REFERENCES

Abbot, B. C., and Howarth, J. V. (1973). *Physiol. Rev.* **53**, 120–158.
Ambrosoli, G., and Cerretelli, P. (1973). *Pflüegers Arch.* **345**, 131–143.
Atkinson, D. E. (1971). *Adv. Enzyme Regul.* **9**, 207–233.
Aubert, A. (1956). "Le couplage energetique de la contraction musculaire." Editions Arscia, Brussels.
Bushby, S. J. W., Gadian, D. G., Rada, G. K., and Seeley, P. J. (1975). *Abstr., Int. Biophys. Congr., 5th, 1975*, p. 153.
Cain, D. F., and Davies, R. E. (1962). *Biochem. Biophys. Res. Commun.* **8**, 361–366.
Canfield, P., and Maréchal, G. (1973). *J. Physiol. (London)* **232**, 453–466.
Canfield, P., Lebacq, J., and Maréchal, G. (1973). *J. Physiol. (London)* **232**, 467–483.
Caplan, S. R. (1968a). *Biophys. J.* **8**, 1146–1166.
Caplan, S. R. (1968b). *Biophys. J.* **8**, 1167–1193.
Caplan, S. R. (1971). *Curr. Top. Bioenerg.* **4**, 1–79.
Carlson, F. D., and Siger, A. (1959). *J. Gen. Physiol.* **43**, 301–313.
Carlson, F. D., Hardy, D. J., and Wilkie, D. R. (1963). *J. Gen. Physiol.* **46**, 851–882.
Carlson, F. D., Hardy, D. J., and Wilkie, D. R. (1967). *J. Physiol. (London)* **189**, 209–235.
Cerretelli, P., di Prampero, P. E., and Ambrosoli, G. (1972). *Am. J. Physiol.* **222**, 1021–1026.
Chance, B., and Connolly, C. M. (1957). *Nature (London)* **179**, 1235–1237.
Chaplain, R. A., and Frommelt, B. (1972). *Pflüegers Arch.* **334**, 167–180.
Clark, D., Lee, D., Rognstad, R., and Katz, J. (1975). *Biochem. Biophys. Res. Commun.* **67**, 212–219.
Clark, M. C., Bloxham, D. P., Holland, P. C., and Lardy, H. A. (1973). *Biochem. J.* **134**, 589–597.
Cockrell, R. S., Harris, E. J., and Pressman, B. C. (1966). *Biochemistry* **5**, 2326–2335.
Crabtree, B., and Newsholme, E. A. (1972). *Biochem. J.* **126**, 49–58.
Curtin, N. A., and Woledge, R. C. (1974). *J. Physiol. (London)* **238**, 437–466.
Curtin, N. A., and Woledge, R. C. (1975). *J. Physiol. (London)* **246**, 737–752.

Curtin, N. A., Gilbert, C., Kretzschmar, K. M., and Wilkie, D. R. (1974). *J. Physiol. (London)* **238,** 455–472.

Dydynska, M., and Wilkie, D. R. (1966). *J. Physiol. (London)* **184,** 751–769.

Englehart, W. A., and Ljubimova, M. N. (1939). *Nature (London)* **144,** 668–669.

Ernster, L., Azzone, G. F., Danielson, L., and Weinbach, E. C. (1963). *J. Biol. Chem.* **238,** 1834–1840.

Estabrook, R. W. (1967). *In* "Methods in Enzymology" (R. W. Estabrook and M. E. Pullman, eds.), Vol. 10, pp. 41–47. Academic Press, New York.

Fenn, W. O. (1927). *Am. J. Physiol.* **83,** 309–322.

Flatmark, T., and Pedersen, J. I. (1975). *Biochem. Biophys. Acta* **416,** 53–103.

Fleckenstein, A., Janke, J., Davies, R. E., and Krebs, H. A. (1954). *Nature (London)* **174,** 1081–1084.

Fritz, I. B. (1960). *Am. J. Physiol.* **198,** 807–810.

George, P., and Rutman, R. J. (1960). *Prog. Biophys. Biophys. Chem.* **10,** 1–53.

Gilbert, C., and Kushmerick, M. J. (1970). *J. Physiol. (London)* **210,** 146P–147P.

Gilbert, C., Kretzschmar, K. M., Wilkie, D. R., and Woledge, R. C. (1971). *J. Physiol. (London)* **218,** 163–193.

Gilbert, C., Kretzschmar, K. M., and Wilkie, D. R. (1973). *Cold Spring Harbor Symp. Quant. Biol.* **37,** 613–618.

Green, M. R., and Landau, B. R. (1965). *Arch. Biochem. Biophys.* **111,** 569–575.

Hill, A. V. (1964). *Proc. R. Soc. London, Ser. B* **159,** 319–324.

Hill, D. K. (1940). *J. Physiol. (London)* **98,** 207–227.

Hill, D. K. (1962). *J. Physiol. (London)* **164,** 31–50.

Hochachka, P. W., and Somero, G. N. (1973). "Strategies of Biochemical Adaptation." Saunders, Philadelphia, Pennsylvania.

Homsher, E., Rall, J. E., Wallner, A., and Ricchiuti, N. V. (1975). *J. Gen. Physiol.* **65,** 1–21.

Infante, A. A., and Davies, R. E. (1962) *Biochem. Biophys. Res. Commun.* **9,** 410–415.

Infante, A. A., and Davies, R. E. (1965). *J. Biol. Chem.* **240,** 3996–4001.

Issekutz, B. (1970). *In* "The Physiology and Biochemistry of Muscle as a Food" (E. J. Briskey, R. G. Cassens, and B. B. Marsh, eds.), pp. 623–643. University of Wisconsin Press, Madison.

Jöbsis, F. F. (1969). *Curr. Top. Bioenerg.* **3,** 279–349.

Jöbsis, F. F., and Duffield, J. C. (1967). *J. Gen. Physiol.* **50,** 1009–1047.

Jolley, R. L., Cheldelin, V. H., and Newburgh, R. W. (1958). *J. Biol. Chem.* **233,** 1289–1294.

Krebs, H. A., and Woodford, M. (1965). *Biochem. J.* **94,** 436–445.

Kretzschmar, K. M. (1975). *J. Supramol. Struct.* **3,** 175–180.

Kretzschmar, K. M., and Wilkie, D. R. (1969). *J. Physiol. (London)* **202,** 66P–67P.

Kushmerick, M. J. (1969). *Proc. R. Soc. London, Ser. B* **174,** 348–352.

Kushmerick, M. J., and Davies, R. E. (1969). *Proc. R. Soc. London, Ser. B* **174,** 315–353.

Kushmerick, M. J., and DeFuria, R. (1976). *Fed. Proc., Fed. Am. Soc. Exp. Biol.* **35,** 300, abstr. 525.

Kushmerick, M. J., and Paul, R. J. (1976a). *J. Physiol. (London)* **254** 693–709.

Kushmerick, M. J., and Paul, R. J. (1976b). *J. Physiol. (London)* **254** 711–727.

Kushmerick, M. J., Larson, R. E., and Davies, R. E. (1969). *Proc. R. Soc. London, Ser. B* **174,** 293–313.

Lundsgaard, E. (1931). *Biochem. Z.* **233,** 322–341.

Makinose, M. (1973). *Cold Spring Harbor Symp. Quant. Biol.* **37,** 681–683.

Meyerhof, O., and Schultz, W. (1935). *Biochem. Z.* **281,** 292–305.

Mommaerts, W. F. H. M. (1969). *Physiol. Rev.* **49,** 427–508.

Mommaerts, W. F. H. M., and Wallner, A. (1967). *J. Physiol. (London)* **170**, 343–357.

Newsholme, E. A., and Start, C. (1973). "Regulation in Metabolism." Wiley, New York.

Odessey, R., and Goldberg, A. L. (1972). *Am. J. Physiol.* **223**, 1376–1383.

Opie, L. H., and Newsholme, E. A. (1967). *Biochem. J.* **103**, 391–399.

Packer, L., and Gooch, V. D. (1973). *In* "Organization of Energy-Transducing Membranes" (M. Nakao and L. Packer, eds.), pp. 279–290. Univ. Park Press, Baltimore, Maryland.

Paul, R. J., and Kushmerick, M. J. (1974a). *Biochim. Biophys. Acta* **347**, 483–490.

Paul, R. J., and Kushmerick, M. J. (1974b). *Fed. Proc., Fed. Am. Soc. Exp. Biol.* **33**, 1401.

Piiper, J., and Spiller, P. (1970). *J. Appl. Physiol.* **28**, 657–662.

Scopes, R. (1973). *Biochem. J.* **134**, 197–208.

Scopes, R. (1974). *Biochem. J.* **138**, 119–123.

Scrutton, M. C., and Utter, M. F. (1968). *Annu. Rev. Biochem.* **37**, 249–302.

Skoog, C. M., and Stephens, N. L. (1973). *Proc. Can. Fed. Biol. Soc.* **16**, 34 (abstr. 136).

Vincent, A., and Blair, J. Mc D. (1970). *FEBS Lett.* **7**, 239–244.

Wilkie, D. R. (1960). *Prog. Biophys. Biophys. Chem.* **10**, 260–298.

Wilkie, D. R. (1968). *J. Physiol. (London)* **195**, 157–183.

Woledge, R. C. (1971). *Prog. Biophys. Mol. Biol.* **22**, 37–73.

Woledge, R. C. (1973). *Cold Spring Harbor Symp. Quant. Biol.* **37**, 629–634.

Transport in Membrane Vesicles Isolated from the Mammalian Kidney and Intestine

BERTRAM SACKTOR

Laboratory of Molecular Aging,
National Institute on Aging,
National Institutes of Health,
Baltimore City Hospitals,
Baltimore, Maryland

I. Introduction

The epithelium of the renal proximal tubule and the small intestine, which mediates vectorial net transport of solutes and fluid, is characterized by cells with determined polarity. This asymmetry is evident ultrastructurally by the differentiation of the plasma membrane into two distinct components, the apical brush border and the pertibular basal-lateral membranes, and functionally by differences in the enzyme composition of the two membranes and in the mechanisms by which substances enter and exit the cell. The net movement of solutes, e.g., sugars, amino acids, and electrolytes, that cross these cells against existing electrochemical gradients has been demonstrated in a variety of physiological studies, both *in vivo* and with relatively intact intestinal and renal preparations. However, the relative contributions of the brush border and the basal-lateral membranes to the transepithelial transport systems have been difficult to assess. More important, the precise mechanisms of the membrane transport have become only marginally manifest. This prompted, first with the intestine and lately with the kidney, the development of techniques for the isolation of the brush border and basal-lateral membranes and for the use of these membranes as model systems to examine how solutes are translocated. In this review, selected recent findings with these isolated membrane preparations will be discussed.

II.   Ultrastructure and Biochemical Composition of the Membranes

A.   MORPHOLOGICAL ASPECTS

The epithelium of the renal tubule or intestine is comprised of a single layer of cells surrounding the lumen. At the luminal pole of the cell, the plasma membrane is modified into a brush border consisting of numerous fingerlike processes, the microvilli, that project into the lumen. There are approximately 60 microvilli per 1 μm^2 of luminal surface area in the rat proximal tubule (Maunsbach, 1973). The length of the microvilli varies along the proximal tubule, being 2.5 μm in the segment adjacent to the glomerulus and 1.5–3.0 μm in the more distal segments. The microvilli of the intestine are considerably shorter, averaging 1.0 μm in length with a range of 0.75 to 1.5 μm (Trier, 1968). The width of the microvilli varies from 0.08 to 0.1 μm in both tissues. It has been estimated that the microvilli increase the luminal cell surface approximately 40 times (kidney) and 14 to 39 times (intestine) over that which would be presented by the cell with a flat apical plasma membrane.

The brush border has characteristic ultrastructural features (Fig. 1). The plasma membrane of the microvillus is a triple-layered structure comprising two electron-dense layers separated by an electron-translucent space. The total thickness of the trilamellate membrane is approximately 90 Å, which is thicker than the membrane of the basal-lateral region of the plasma membrane. In cross section, thin filaments are seen

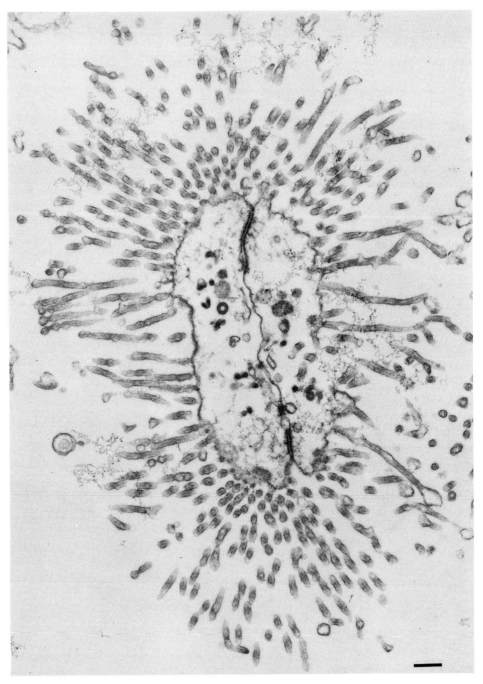

FIG. 1. Electron micrograph of isolated brush border membranes from rabbit renal cortex. Bar indicates 1 μm.

within the microvillus. The filaments are approximately 60 Å in diameter and run parallel to the long axis of the microvillus. Thuneberg and Rostgaard (1969) have shown that the filament resembles actin, and Rostgaard *et al.* (1972) have proposed that this contractile mechanism with movement of the microvilli suggests a role for the filaments in transport. Upon disruption and fractionation of intestinal brush border preparations the filaments appear to cosediment with the "core" fraction (Eichholz and Crane, 1965). Faust and Shearin (1974) have reported the isolation of a protein from the "core" filaments of hamster jejunum brush borders that binds D-glucose and L-histidine. They postulate that "core" filaments act as a conduit for the Na^+-dependent active transport of all monosaccharides and amino acids. Further, they claim that this common binding protein accounts for the competitive inhibitory effects between intestinal sugar and amino acid transports. This proposed relationship between "core" binding and transport of solutes has been seriously questioned, however (Mitchell *et al.*, 1974; Hopfer and Sigrist-Nelson, 1974).

External to the microvillus membrane proper is a sialic acid-containing glycoproteinaceous fibrillar material (Groniowski *et al.*, 1969), the fuzzy coat or glycocalyx, which is approximately 100 Å in width (Ito, 1965). When the microvillus is viewed in the electron microscope as a negatively stained preparation, it appears to be studded with knobs about 60 Å in diameter (Johnson, 1967). These knobs are more prominent in the intestine than in the kidney (Berger and Sacktor, 1970). Johnson (1967) and Nishi *et al.* (1968) have reported that intestinal disaccharidases are localized in the knobs, hence external to the plasma membrane of the microvillus. Benson *et al.* (1971) have refuted this conclusion with a kinetic study showing that the removal of disaccharidase activities and the 60 Å particles from the membrane is not correlated.

In general, the basal-lateral membrane of the proximal tubular cell or the enterocyte resembles plasma membranes of other cell types. On the peritubular side the membrane abuts the basement membrane. The renal basal-lateral membrane forms many interdigitating ridges and processes that greatly enlarge the area of the basal and lateral surfaces and increase the lateral intercellular spaces. In contrast to the microvillus membrane, the basal-lateral membrane is devoid of a fuzzy coat and when viewed in the electron microscope is sharply delineated.

B. ISOLATION PROCEDURES

Miller and Crane (1961) were the first to isolate brush border membranes of the hamster intestinal mucosa as a morphologically distinct entity. Basically employing their method, brush border membranes from intestines of various vertebrate species have been prepared (for compilation, see Sacktor, 1976). It should be pointed out, however, that membranes isolated by these procedures are prominently contaminated by other cellular constituents, particularly DNA and RNA. The isolation technique has been significantly improved by Forstner et al. (1968a) and Porteous (1968), and brush border membranes essentially free from nucleic acids can now be prepared. For example, the sucrase:DNA ratio in a rat intestinal preparation (Forstner et al., 1968a) is more than a hundred times greater than was found in the less pure earlier preparations. Currently, the procedure as developed in Isselbacher's laboratory (Forstner et al., 1968a; Hopfer et al., 1973) is generally considered to yield the most satisfactory animal intestinal brush border membranes for transport studies. Schmitz et al. (1973) have reported a method for preparing human intestinal brush border membranes that may be applied to fresh or frozen intestine, to surgical specimens, or to peroral jejunal biopsies. Isolated guinea pig intestinal brush border membranes have been stored in glycerol at low temperatures for one year and have retained normal morphological appearance and capacity to transport vitamin B_{12} (Andersen et al., 1975).

For some transport studies, the isolated intact intestinal brush borders are disrupted and subfractionated, resulting in preparations of microvillus membrane vesicles devoid of the fibrillar residue. The microvillus membrane comprises approximately two-thirds of the total brush border membrane protein and most of the enzymic activities (Forstner et al., 1968a).

Preparations of the basal-lateral segments of the enterocyte plasma membrane relatively free of brush border segments have been described (Quigley and Gotterer, 1969; Douglas et al., 1972). The technique of free-flow electrophoresis of membranes (Heidrich et al., 1972) has been adopted to separate the basal-lateral membranes from brush border microvillus membranes of rat intestinal epithelial cells (Murer et al., 1974).

A variety of methods have been reported for isolating renal brush borders, and these have recently been described and compared (Sacktor, 1976). Most rely on the original observation of Thuneberg and Rostgaard (1968) that the preliminary disruption of the kidney cortex must be gentle to minimize the shearing of microvilli from the plasma membrane. Thus, the relatively large apical membrane of the tubular cell is dislodged intact and is readily separated from other cellular particulates. A detailed procedure for the preparation of rabbit renal brush border membranes employing sucrose density and multiple differential centrifugations has been reported (Berger and Sacktor, 1970; Aronson and

Sacktor, 1975). An electron micrograph of the isolated brush border membranes is shown in Fig. 1.

A technique for preparing the renal basal-lateral plasma membrane fraction has been described by Marx *et al.* (1972). Recently, this procedure has been significantly modified and improved (Liang and Sacktor, 1976a), resulting in membrane preparations with severalfold enhancements in the specific activities of marker enzymes relative to those in the homogenate. Moreover, both basal-lateral and brush border membranes can be prepared from the same animal (rabbit, dog). Free-flow electrophoresis (Heidrich *et al.*, 1972) has also been used to separate the two membranous entities from the rat renal cortex. It should be pointed out this latter method is clearly distinct from the separation method used in this reviewer's laboratory. By their technique, the plasma membranes are initially fragmented during homogenization of the cortex and the segments later separated by electrical charge. In contrast, the procedure of Thuneberg and Rostgaard depends basically on the gravitational separation of the predominantly nondisrupted brush border membranes from the smaller basal-lateral segments of the plasma membrane. We shall see, however, that despite the differences in procedure, the transport properties of the finally isolated membrane vesicles are in many ways comparable.

C.   CHEMICAL COMPOSITION

Protein constitutes 54% of the dry weight of the renal brush border membrane (Stevenson, 1973), a value similar to that found in liver plasma membranes (Emmelot and Bos, 1972). The intestinal microvillus membrane contains approximately 600 μg of lipid per milligram of protein (Forstner *et al.*, 1968b). Of the total lipid, about 20% is neutral lipid, 30% is phospholipid, and the remaining 50% is glycolipid. Compared to plasma membranes from other tissues, the brush border membrane possesses the greatest amount of glycolipid and the least phospholipid. Also characteristic of the brush border membrane is a high cholesterol:phospholipid ratio. Forstner *et al.* (1968b) have reported a value of 1.26 for moles of cholesterol per mole of phospholipid in the intestinal microvillus membrane. A molar ratio of only 0.5 is found in the basal-lateral segment of the enterocyte plasma membrane (Douglas *et al.*, 1972). This latter value is comparable with those reported for a variety of other plasma membranes (Steck and Wallach, 1970), but it contrasts with values (i.e., below 0.1) found in endoplasmic reticulum and mitochondria (Korn, 1969). The cholesterol:phospholipid molar ratio in the renal brush border membrane appears to be different from that in the intestinal membrane. Quirk and Robinson (1972) have reported a value of 0.65 in brush borders from rabbit kidney. This is due to a 2-fold greater amount of phospholipid in the renal preparation rather than a decrease in the cholesterol content.

Approximately 70% of the neutral lipid fraction of the intestinal microvillus membrane is cholesterol, and none of this is esterified (Forstner et al., 1968b). The remaining neutral lipids are mostly free fatty acids and diglycerides. Of the phospholipids in the intestinal microvillus membrane, phosphatidylethanolamine, phosphatidylcholine, phosphatidylserine, sphingomyelin, and lysophosphatidylcholine comprise, respectively, approximately 40, 21, 14, 7, and 2% of the total. The glycolipids of the intestinal brush border membrane have been analyzed by Forstner and Wherrett (1973). The major glycosphingolipids are ceramides (mono-, di-, and trihexosylceramides) and gangliosides. These investigators have also identified and estimated the sugar moieties of each class of glycolipid.

The basal-lateral membrane of the intestinal epithelial cell is similar to the brush border membrane in that both are rich in cholesterol and sphingolipids. However, the sphingolipids of the two membranes are markedly different (Lewis et al., 1975a). The majority of the sphingolipids in the basal-lateral membrane are tri- and tetrahexosylceramides and sphingomyelin. If the glycosphingolipids and sphingomyelin contribute most of the outward-facing lipid polar head groups on the surface of the epithelial cell, the outer aspect of the lipid bilayer on the basal-lateral and brush border surfaces must be very different. Moreover, free diffusion of membrane components as envisioned in the "fluid-mosaic" model of membrane organization clearly does not occur between the two segments of the intestinal epithelial cell plasma membrane. Lewis et al. (1975a) suggest that this limitation on free movement may be due to the presence of the terminal bar that encircles the cells just below the brush border.

D. ENZYMIC ACTIVITIES

The kidney and intestine possess analogous transepithelial transport systems by which solutes common to the tubular and intestinal lumen enter the cell via the luminal brush border membrane and exit from the cell via the basal-lateral membrane. It is not surprising, therefore, that the two brush border membranes and the two basal-lateral membranes have similar enzyme constituents. On the other hand, the intestinal brush border has, in addition, a major role in digestion. Therefore, it is to be expected that the intestinal membranes have hydrolytic enzymes that are not found in the renal membrane.

In the renal brush border membrane, several enzymes show characteristically large and comparable increases in specific activities relative to that in the cortical homogenase. As shown in Table I, these include the disaccharidases trehalase and maltase, γ-glutamyltranspeptidase, alkaline phosphatase, 5′-nucleotidase, and two aminopeptidases.

The disaccharidases serve as an excellent "enzyme marker" for the brush border membrane for they are localized exclusively in the membrane, as is evident by progressive increases in specific activities at each step in the purification of the brush border and by the very low specific activities of the enzymes in non-brush border fractions (Berger and Sacktor, 1970). Moreover, trehalase is not found in the renal medulla and papilla (Sacktor, 1968), nor in the glomerulus and interstitial areas of the cortex (Grossman and Sacktor, 1968; Stevenson, 1972). Trehalase has been reported in the kidneys of most mammals, including rabbit, mouse, dog, primates, and man. It is virtually absent, however, from the kidneys of the rat and cat (Sacktor, 1968). In these two species, the disaccharidase maltase is very active. The function of the disaccharidases in the renal brush border membrane has not been established. The possible role for the enzymes in glucose transport has been hypothesized (Sacktor, 1968; Sacktor and Berger, 1969).

γ-Glutamyltranspeptidase, which has been proposed to function in amino acid transport (Meister, 1973), is a valuable "enzyme marker" for the brush border membrane, particularly when the membrane is suspended in sucrose solutions of high molarities. However, an apparent

TABLE I
ENZYME ACTIVITIES LOCALIZED IN RENAL BRUSH BORDER MEMBRANES[a]

Enzyme	Homogenate	Brush border membranes	Relative specific activity
Trehalase	0.081[b]	1.18[b]	12–15
Maltase	0.051	0.95	14–22
γ-Glutamyltranspeptidase	0.37	5.93	14–18
Alkaline phosphatase	0.14	2.25	15–19
5′-Nucleotidase	0.013	0.22	17
Aminopeptidase (leucine)	0.17	2.50	15
Aminopeptidase (alanine)	0.25	4.58	19

[a] Data are for rabbit membrane preparations. For other species, see Sacktor (1976). Data presented are a composite of values reported by Berger and Sacktor (1970), Quirk and Robinson (1972), George and Kenny (1973), and Liang and Sacktor (1976a). The range of values cited for relative specific activities indicates the difference in values reported in the cited studies.

[b] Activities were measured at 37°C and are expressed as micromoles per minute per milligram of protein.

species-dependent variance in relative specific activity may exist for this enzyme, too. In the rat renal brush border membrane, a value of only 5 has been reported (Glossmann and Neville, 1972). This contrasts to 14–18 in the rabbit (Table I). The use of 5'-nucleotidase activity as a "marker" for renal brush border membranes suffers from the inability to discriminate unequivocally between 5'-nucleotidase and alkaline phosphatase activities (George and Kenny, 1973). Interestingly, 5'-nucleotidase, which is commonly used as an "enzyme marker" for plasma membranes of various cell types, is essentially absent from the basal-lateral segment of the renal tubular cell plasma membrane (Liang and Sacktor, 1976a). Alkaline phosphatase has been used as an "enzyme marker" for the renal brush border membranes by Kinne and co-workers (e.g., Heidrich et al., 1972). Complications with the use of this enzyme have been discussed elsewhere (Sacktor, 1976).

All the enzymes that have been cited (Table I) as associated with renal brush border membranes have been reported in intestinal brush borders. In addition, other enzymes, whose principal function seems to be directly related to digestive processes, have been localized in the intestinal membrane (Crane, 1975). The disaccharidases sucrase, isomaltase, lactase, and cellobiase, which are not found in renal brush borders (Sacktor, 1968), and maltase and trehalase, which are found in the renal membranes, are in intestinal brush borders. Sucrase, which usually serves as the "enzyme marker" for intestinal brush border membranes has a specific activity in purified rat intestinal brush borders almost 20 times that in mucosal scrapings (Forstner et al., 1968a). This specific activity is increased an additional 1.6 times when microvillus membranes are prepared from the isolated brush borders. Maltase is the most active intestinal disaccharidase. In the adult, lactase is the least active. The activity of trehalase varies 10-fold, depending on species (Benson et al., 1971; Forstner et al., 1968a; Schmitz et al., 1973). It is noteworthy that the highest intestinal trehalase activity, equal to that of sucrase, is found in the rat, the very species that has no trehalase in its kidney.

In addition to disaccharidases, other hydrolytic enzymes have been identified in intestinal brush border membranes. These include: aminopeptidases and enteropeptidase (enterokinase), which hydrolyze a variety of di-, tri-, and polypeptides (Rhodes et al., 1967; Maroux et al., 1973); glucoamylase (Alpers and Solin, 1970); phlorizin hydrolase (glycosylceramidase) (Leese and Semenza, 1973); lipase (Senior and Isselbacher, 1963); cholesterol esterase (David et al., 1966); and retinol hydrolase (Malathi, 1967). These enzymes are presumably involved in the terminal digestion of their respective substrates. Rosenberg et al. (1969) have reported that folate deconjugase, which releases folate from the polyglutamate form, is in the brush border membrane. Isolated intestinal brush borders are also able to acylate fatty acids, suggesting the presence of a thiokinase and of mono- and diglyceride acylases (Forstner *et al.*, 1965).

The primary "enzyme marker" for the basal-lateral membrane is Na^+K^+ ATPase activity. Quigley and Gotterer (1969) have isolated a plasma membrane fraction from rat intestine that contains 85% of the total enzyme activity with a 25- to 35-fold increase in specific activity relative to homogenates of mucosal scrapings. Subsequent studies by Fujita *et al.* (1971), Douglas *et al.* (1972), and Lewis *et al.* (1975b) showing relative enrichments of 11- to 20-fold in Na^+K^+ ATPase activity in different intestinal basal-lateral membrane preparations have confirmed the applicability of the enzyme as a "marker" for this membrane. Mitochondrial contamination is a major problem, DCCD-sensitive ATPase being enriched 3-fold. Brush border membranes are also found, trehalase and alkaline phosphatase indicating a 2-fold increase in relative specific activities (Lewis *et al.*, 1975b). In the kidney, partially purified preparations of the basal-lateral region of the plasma membrane also show increases in the specific activity of Na^+K^+ ATPase. For example, the crude plasma membranes from rat kidneys are enriched about 4 times in both Na^+K^+ ATPase and alkaline phosphatase (Heidrich *et al.*, 1972). After free-flow electrophoresis, membrane fragments rich in Na^+K^+ ATPase tend to separate from those rich in alkaline phosphatase. The specific activity of Na^+K^+ ATPase in the basal-lateral membrane fractions is enhanced an additional 2.5 times, so that the enzyme has a final relative specific activity of 10-fold the homogenate. In contrast, the specific activity of alkaline phosphatase in the basal-lateral membrane fractions decreases relative to the crude plasma membrane preparation, although the final specific activity of this brush border enzyme is still somewhat higher than that originally in the homogenate. The basal-lateral membrane preparation from rabbit renal cortex has a 7-fold increase in specific activity of Na^+K^+ ATPase relative to that in the cortex homogenate (Liang and Sacktor, 1976a). γ-Glutamyltranspeptidase activity is enhanced 3-fold, and mitochondrial contamination (succinic dehydrogenase activity) is prevalent.

Although it is quite clear that the major fraction of the total Na^+K^+ ATPase activity is associated with the basal-lateral segment of the plasma membrane, a small, but consistent fraction (about 15% with low specific activity) is found in brush border membrane preparations. Thus, there is a question as to whether the enzyme is an intrinsic component of the brush border membrane proper or of the tags of basal-lateral membrane, i.e., tight junctions, which remain attached to the brush border throughout homogenization and fractionation (Fig. 1). Favoring the former alternative is the study by Quigley and Gotterer (1972) suggesting that the two Na^+K^+ ATPase activities, one in the basal-lateral region and the other in the microvillus segment of the plasma membrane, have distinct kinetic properties.

Contrasting with enzymes that show 10- to 20-fold increases in relative specific activities and are localized predominantly in either the brush border or basal-lateral membranes, other enzymes are found in these preparations of plasma membranes that have final enrichments of only 2- to 5-fold and, therefore, are probably associated with subcellular fractions of the epithelial cell in addition to the plasma membrane. Most prominent of the enzymes of this latter type are ATPases and enzymes which catalyze the synthesis or degradation of cyclic nucleotides (Table II). Mg ATPase and HCO_3^--stimulated ATPase are localized in the brush border membrane. Here activities are enriched 3- to 4-fold those in the homogenate (Berger and Sacktor, 1970; Kinne-Saffran and Kinne, 1974b; Liang and Sacktor, 1976b). After free-flow electrophoresis of plasma membrane fragments, the distribution patterns of HCO_3^- ATPase follows that of alkaline phosphatase rather than that of Na^+K^+ ATPase (Kinne-Saffran and Kinne, 1974b). Mg ATPase and HCO_3^--stimulated ATPase are also found in renal cortical mitochondria. The

TABLE II

DISTRIBUTION OF ENZYME ACTIVITIES IN BRUSH BORDER AND BASAL-LATERAL
SEGMENTS OF RENAL PLASMA MEMBRANES

Enzyme	Specific activities		
	Homogenate	Brush border	Basal-lateral
γ-Glutamyltranspeptidase[a]	0.37	5.93	1.37
Na^+K^+ ATPase[a]	0.060	0.14	0.39
Mg ATPase[b]	0.069	0.22	—
HCO_3^- ATPase[b]	0.028	0.12	—
Ca ATPase[c]	0.17	0.29	0.68
Adenylate cyclase (basal)[d]	11	23	48
Adenylate cyclase (+F)[d]	73	190	325
Guanylate cyclase (latent)[d]	6.4	3.1	3.9
Guanylate cyclase (active)[d]	57.0	28.6	311.0
cAMP phosphodiesterase[e]	—	73	55
cGMP phosphodiesterase[e]	—	51	81

[a] μmoles/min/mg protein (Liang and Sacktor, 1976a).
[b] μmoles/min/mg protein (Liang and Sacktor, 1976b).
[c] mU/mg protein (Kinne-Saffran and Kinne, 1974a).
[d] pmoles/min/mg protein (Liang and Sacktor, 1976a).
[e] pmoles/min/mg protein (Filburn and Sacktor, 1976a); 1 μM cyclic AMP and cyclic GMP.

possibility that the activities in the brush border membranes may be accounted for by mitochondrial contamination of the brush border preparations has been ruled out (Liang and Sacktor, 1976b). A Ca-stimulated hydrolysis of ATP has been reported in renal plasma membranes (Berger and Sacktor, 1970; Kinne-Saffran and Kinne, 1974a). The enzyme shows an enrichment, relative to the homogenate, of 2 times in the brush border membrane and 4 times in the basal-lateral membrane. The electrophoretic distribution pattern resembles that of Na^+K^+ AT-Pase. It is noted, however, that Ca ATPase activity is assayed in the absence of added Mg. If exogenous Mg is present, the addition of Ca is inhibitory (Berger and Sacktor, 1970). Thus, the question as to whether the Ca-stimulated ATPase is distinct from the Mg ATPase is still equivocal. Complicating the situation further is the report of Melançon and DeLuca (1970) of an active, vitamin D-induced, Ca-stimulated Mg ATPase in purified preparations of intestinal brush borders. Nevertheless, these findings suggest a polarity of the renal tubular cell plasma membrane with respect to ATPases, Na^+K^+ ATPase, and, perhaps, Ca ATPase being concentrated in the basal-lateral region of the membrane, and HCO_3^- ATPase being predominant in the apical pole.

The enzymic polarity of the renal and intestinal epithelial cell may also be a factor in the hormonal regulation of transepithelial transport systems. Preparations of basal-lateral plasma membranes, having an enriched Na^+K^+ ATPase activity, show nearly comparable increases in the specific activity of adenylate cyclase (Table II) (Marx *et al.*, 1972; Parkinson *et al.*, 1972). The adenylate cyclase activity is sensitive to F^-, parathyroid hormone, calcitonin, vasopressin, and isoproterenol (Marx *et al.*, 1972). The renal membranes, from rat kidney, possess high-affinity receptor sites for salmon calcitonin. However, similar membrane preparations from man, dog, and cow do not possess high-affinity binding sites for this calcitonin and contain little, if any, calcitonin-sensitive adenylate cyclase (Marx and Aurbach, 1975). The presence of some adenylate cyclase activity in the brush border membrane region has not been ruled out. Wilfong and Neville (1970) report a 2- to 3-fold increase in specific activities of basal, parathyroid-, and vasopressin-stimulated adenylate cyclase in brush border membrane preparations relative to homogenates. Brush border membranes also possess high-affinity calcitonin binding sites and have more receptors per milligram of protein than do the basal-lateral membranes (Marx *et al.*, 1973). Para-thyroid hormone receptors are also found on both membranes (Shlatz *et al.*, 1975), Moreover, in histochemical studies, parathyroid hormone-activated adenylate cyclase is localized exclusively in the brush border membrane, no reaction precipitate is seen in the basal-lateral infoldings (Jande and Robert, 1974). Studies on the localization of guanylate cyclase also suggest differences that seemingly depend on the tissue of origin of the plasma membrane. Liang and Sacktor (1976a) find an exceedingly active guanylate cyclase in the renal basal-lateral membrane (Table II). The trace of activity found associated with the brush border region is fully explained by basal-lateral membrane contamination of the brush border membrane preparation. In contrast, de Jonge (1975) reports that guanylate cyclase is largely localized in the brush border membrane of intestinal epithelial cells, although some enzyme with high specific activity is associated with the serosal membrane. Cyclic nucleotide phosphodiesterases are found in both regions of the renal proximal tubule plasma membrane (Filburn and Sacktor, 1976a,b). When assayed at 1 μM cyclic nucleotide, the brush border region hydrolyzes cAMP at a faster rate than does the basal-lateral membrane. The converse is true for cGMP hydrolysis. Other kinetic parameters clearly distinguish the phosphodiesterases in the two membranes and differentiate the enzymes hydrolyzing cAMP from those hydrolyzing cGMP. cAMP-dependent and -independent protein kinases are associated predominantly with brush border membranes (Kinne et al., 1975b; George et al., 1976; Sacktor et al., 1976).

III.   Transport of D-Glucose by Membrane Vesicles

In general, two approaches have been taken to describe the molecular events involved in D-glucose transport. In one, the binding to the brush border membrane of phlorizin, the presumably nonpermeable competitive inhibitor of D-glucose transport, has been investigated to provide insight into the properties of the proposed D-glucose carrier (Bode et al., 1970; Glossmann and Neville, 1972; Chesney et al., 1974). To date, the problems inherent in solubilizing and purifying the membrane-bound carrier and in developing a rapid valid assay for carrier activity has limited progress. Efforts have been hampered additionally by the finding that intestinal brush border membranes hydrolyze phlorizin (Malathi and Crane, 1969), although the glycoside is not metabolized by renal membranes (Glossmann and Neville, 1972; Chesney et al., 1974). In the other approach, D-glucose uptake is measured directly. It is in these latter studies that advances in the understanding of sugar transport have recently taken rapid strides.

A.   Nature of the Uptake of D-Glucose by Brush Border Membranes

It was important to resolve the question whether the uptake of D-glucose by brush border membrane preparations represents membrane binding or sugar transport across the membrane into an intravesicular

space. Three lines of evidence suggest that the latter is correct. First,
when the isolated renal brush borders, illustrated in Fig. 1, are mechani-
cally agitated, the microvilli are sheared and the individual membranes
vesiculate (Fig. 2). The effect of the intravesicular space on D-glucose

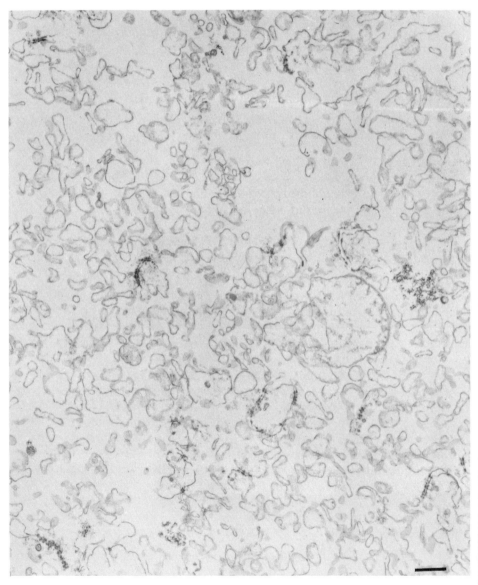

FIG. 2. Electron micrograph of the brush border membrane vesicles that are used in the
transport studies. Bar indicates 1 μm.

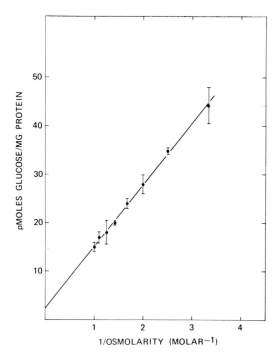

FIG. 3. The effect of medium osmolarity (reciprocal of intravesicular space) on D-glucose uptake into renal brush border membrane vesicles. From Beck and Sacktor (1975).

uptake has been determined. In an experiment shown in Fig. 3, Beck and Sacktor (1975) varied the intravesicular space by altering the medium osmolarity with sucrose, a relatively impermeable solute that is not hydrolyzed in the kidney (Sacktor, 1968). With a given concentration of D-glucose, the amount of sugar taken up at equilibrium should be dependent on the intravesicular space, and this volume should be inversely proportional to the medium osmolarity. As shown, D-glucose uptake is proportional to the inverse osmolarity and, thus, to the intravesicular space. Moreover, extrapolation to infinite medium osmolarity (zero space) results in negligible uptake. The very small calculated uptake at infinite medium osmolarity may suggest a slight binding of D-glucose to the membrane (Hopfer and Sigrist-Nelson, 1974) or, perhaps more likely, the slow leak of sucrose into the vesicle, thus negating zero intravesicular volume. Second, Aronson and Sacktor (1974) have reported that not only does phlorizin inhibit uptake of D-glucose by renal brush border membranes, but the glycoside essentially completely inhibits efflux of D-glucose from the membranes. If the interaction of D-glucose and brush border membrane were binding only, then it would be expected that phlorizin would displace the sugar, accelerating its release, providing phlorizin binding is competitive and the number of sites are limiting. The fact that phlorizin inhibits the release of D-glucose indicates that phlorizin reacts with the membrane at a site external to the site of D-glucose accumulation. Last, preloading of the membrane vesicles with D-glucose markedly stimulates the initial rate of D-glucose uptake (Aronson and Sacktor, 1974). The effect is stereospecific, as the rate of D-glucose uptake is not augmented by preincubation with L-glucose. Accelerated exchange diffusion (counter transport) cannot be explained by the binding hypothesis because preincubation with D-glucose would occupy binding sites and, if anything, would inhibit the uptake of additional D-glucose. On the other hand, models to explain accelerative exchange diffusion all involve the facilitated transport across a membrane.

Earlier proposals for the binding and/or "high affinity" uptake of D-glucose by brush border membrane preparations are also contradicted by subsequent studies with bacteria-free membranes (Mitchell *et al.*, 1974). The observation that the D-glucose taken up by the membrane vesicles is not metabolized (Aronson and Sacktor, 1974) further supports the view that the sugar is accumulated intravesicularly rather than being enzymically degraded.

B. THE NA$^+$ GRADIENT-DEPENDENT TRANSPORT OF D-GLUCOSE

The initial rate of uptake of D-glucose by intestinal (Hopfer *et al.*, 1973) and renal (Aronson and Sacktor, 1974, 1975), brush border membrane vesicles is enhanced by Na$^+$. This effect is specific for Na$^+$; other cations, e.g., Li$^+$, K$^+$, choline, and Tris, are ineffective. The Na$^+$-dependent enhancement of transport is stereospecific for D-glucose; uptake of L-glucose is not stimulated. In the absence of Na$^+$, the rates of uptake of D- and L-glucose are, in fact, similar. The studies also demonstrate that it is the presence of a Na$^+$ gradient that is crucial. Aronson and Sacktor (1975) have shown that the Na$^+$ gradient effect on D-glucose transport, measured as influx or efflux, can be dissected into a stimulatory effect of Na$^+$ on transport when sugar and Na$^+$ are on the same side of the membrane (*cis* stimulation) and an inhibitory effect of Na$^+$ on transport when sugar and Na$^+$ are on opposite sides of the membrane (*trans* inhibition). These findings also suggest symmetry of the D-glucose carrier at both sides of the brush border membrane.

Additional significant characteristics of the Na$^+$ gradient D-glucose uptake system are illustrated in Fig. 4. In this experiment by Aronson and Sacktor (1975), uptake of D-glucose by renal brush border membrane vesicles is measured during the time course of incubation, either in 300 mM buffered mannitol medium or in a medium in which mannitol

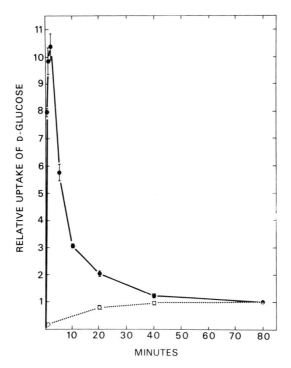

FIG. 4. The time course of the uptake of D-glucose into renal brush border membrane vesicles in the presence and in the absence of a Na$^+$ gradient. ●———●, 100 mM mannitol + 100 mM NaCl; ○···○, 300 mM mannitol. From Aronson and Sacktor (1975).

is replaced isosmotically by 100 mM NaCl at the initiation of incubation. In the absence of a Na$^+$ gradient, steady-state levels are reached in about 80 minutes. The presence of a Na$^+$ gradient between the external incubation medium and the intravesicular medium induces a marked stimulation of D-glucose transport. The initial (30 S) rate of uptake with the Na$^+$ gradient is 40 times the initial rate in the absence of the gradient. Accumulation of the sugar in the membrane vesicles is maximal at about 2 minutes. Afterward the amount of D-glucose in the vesicles decreases, indicating efflux of the sugar. The final level of uptake of the sugar in the presence and in the absence of the Na$^+$ gradient is identical, however, suggesting that equilibrium has been established. Moreover, at the peak of the "overshoot," at an incubation period of 2 min, the uptake of D-glucose is more than 10-fold the final equilibrium value. These results suggest that the imposition of a large extravesicular to intravesicular Na$^+$ gradient effects the transient move-ment of D-glucose into renal brush border membranes against its concentration gradient (uphill or active transport). A similar observation has been reported by Murer and Hopfer (1974) with intestinal brush border membrane vesicles. The "overshoot" is transient with these vesicular preparations because of the limited energy inherent in the salt gradient present at the initiation of the incubation and its dissipation with time. The dissipation of the salt gradient has been demonstrated directly by concomitant measurements of D-glucose and Na$^+$ uptakes into intestinal (Sigrist-Nelson et al., 1975) and renal (Kinne et al., 1975a) membrane vesicles. These findings show additionally that D-glucose is taken up into the same intravesicular space as Na$^+$.

Increasing the concentration of Na$^+$ increases the rate of D-glucose uptake (Aronson and Sacktor, 1975). With 100 mM NaCl, the rate of the sugar uptake is about 40 times the rate in the absence of Na$^+$. Even at this concentration, only partial saturability with respect to Na$^+$ is evident. Michaelis–Menten kinetics with respect to Na$^+$ is not strictly obeyed. Estimation of a concentration of Na$^+$ resulting in half-maximal activity, however, yields a value of 87 mM, determined with 50 μM D-glucose. Kinne et al. (1975a) have reported a K_m for Na$^+$ of 29 mM, with 1 mM sugar. Other kinetic studies show that increasing Na$^+$ in the extravesicular medium (enhancing the Na$^+$ gradient) lowers the apparent K_m of D-glucose for transport (Aronson and Sacktor, 1975). The calculated apparent K_m values are 500, 220, and 80 μM D-glucose at 10, 20, and 50 mM NaCl, respectively.

Transport of D-glucose by renal (Busse et al., 1972; Chesney et al., 1973; Aronson and Sacktor, 1974) and intestinal (Hopfer et al., 1973) brush border membranes is inhibited by phlorizin. However, in these studies significant inhibition of the uptake by isolated membranes required phlorizin concentrations of from 10^{-4} to 10^{-3} M, whereas concentrations of 10^{-5} to 10^{-7} M inhibit D-glucose reabsorption in vivo (Chan and Lotspeich, 1962). Aronson and Sacktor (1974) have suggested that this apparent discrepancy would be observed if only the Na$^+$-dependent component of D-glucose uptake is highly sensitive to phlorizin. That this is indeed the case has now been demonstrated. Phlorizin (1 mM) inhibits 97% of the Na$^+$-dependent uptake of 50 μM D-glucose, whereas the same concentration inhibits only 59% of the Na$^+$-independent uptake (Aronson and Sacktor, 1975). In the presence of the Na$^+$ gradient, kinetics consistent with competitive inhibition is found, with a K_i for phlorizin of 7 μM. The K_i for phlorizin corresponds exceptionally well with the dissociation constant of 7–8 μM, which has been reported for the Na$^+$-dependent high-affinity binding site in similar preparations of rabbit renal brush border membranes (Chesney et al., 1974; Mitchell et al., 1974), although it is somewhat higher than the dissociation constants of 0.2 (Glossmann and Neville, 1972) to 3.4 μM (Bode et al., 1970) that have been reported for rat renal brush border membranes.

The uptake of D-glucose, at a given concentration of sugar, by brush border membrane vesicles reflects the sum of contributions from a Na$^+$-dependent transport system and a Na$^+$-independent system (Aronson and Sacktor, 1975). The relative stimulation of D-glucose uptake by Na$^+$ decreases as the sugar concentration increases. It is suggested, however, that at physiological concentrations of D-glucose the asymmetry of Na$^+$ across the brush border membrane fully accounts for uphill D-glucose transport in the proximal tubule. Busse *et al.* (1975) have reported that the two transport systems differ in pH optimum in addition to their known differences in Na$^+$ requirement and phlorizin sensitivity. They also propose that the renal membrane possesses only a single carrier species for D-glucose functioning in two interchangeable conformational states rather than two transfer systems working independently.

A transport system for D-glucose, derived from disaccharides, which is different from the Na$^+$ gradient-dependent D-glucose system, has been described in hamster intestine by Ramaswamy *et al.* (1974). The transport of D-glucose from sucrose is substantially independent of Na$^+$ and phlorizin. In the absence of Na$^+$, D-glucose released from sucrose does not mix with a pool of added free hexose, but is directly transferred. The D-glucose moieties in maltose, isomaltose, and trehalose act similarly to those in sucrose. However, the extent of D-glucose uptake is not related to disaccharidase activity. These authors conclude that intestinal brush border membrane disaccharidases may subserve a translocating "carrier" function for part of the products of their enzymic action.

C.   ENERGETICS OF THE NA$^+$ GRADIENT-DEPENDENT TRANSPORT OF D-GLUCOSE

The specific effect of the Na$^+$ gradient in stimulating the transport of D-glucose across the isolated brush border membrane is consistent with the Na$^+$ gradient hypothesis formulated by Crane (1962) and Schultz and Curran (1970) for intestinal sugar transport. Although the precise mechanism by which Na$^+$ enhances D-glucose transport is not known, the proposal suggests that the Na$^+$ electrochemical gradient across the cell membrane drives the uptake of D-glucose, the translocation of the sugar being coupled in some manner to the flux of Na$^+$. An important aspect of the driving force is the question of whether Na$^+$-dependent D-glucose transport is an electroneutral or an electrogenic process. If electroneutral, then the positive charge associated with Na$^+$ flux is compensated by the cotransport of an anion or the countermovement of a cation via the same carrier. If, however, the transport process is electrogenic, then charge compensation is not made via the glucose carrier, but at a different site in the membrane. In the latter case, Na^+-dependent D-glucose transport should be influenced by an electrochemical potential across the membrane. This question has been examined recently in both intestinal (Murer and Hopfer, 1974) and renal (Beck and Sacktor, 1975) brush border membrane vesicles.

Two approaches have been taken to regulate experimentally the membrane potential across the brush border membrane. These are: the use of anions of different modes of permeability, and the utilization of specific ionophores and proton conductors. With renal luminal membrane preparations, Beck and Sacktor (1975) have found that the imposition of a salt gradient with either Na_2SO_4 or sodium isethionate, in contrast to one with NaCl (see Fig. 4), does not result in the accumulation of D-glucose above equilibrium. With either salt, however, the initial rate of D-glucose uptake is stimulated by the presence of Na^+, when compared to the rate in the absence of Na^+, but it is significantly less than that with NaCl. Both sulfate and isethionate anions are relatively impermeable to the luminal membrane of the proximal tubule. Therefore, little development of electrochemical potential is to be expected for driving an electrogenic Na^+-dependent D-glucose uptake. Since the same Na^+ chemical gradient is present when Na_2SO_4 or sodium isethionate is used as when NaCl is used, it is evident that the electrochemical potential generated in part by the anion is of considerable significance in the control of D-glucose transport against its concentration gradient. This view is supported additionally when salt gradients of the lipophillic anions NO_3^- and SCN^- are used. With these salts, the transient "overshoot" of D-glucose uptake is greater and/or faster than that with NaCl. The NO_3^- and SCN^- anions penetrate biological membranes in the charged form at pH 7.5, and both are known to stimulate Na^+ transport in the toad urinary bladder to a greater extent than Cl^- (Singer and Civan, 1971). In the experiments with brush border membranes, if the Na^+-stimulated D-glucose uptake is electrogenic, diffusion of the anions into the vesicles will influence D-glucose uptake by producing an electrochemical membrane potential (negative inside). Since in the proximal tubule of the rabbit Cl^- is 3 times more permeable than Na^+ (Schafer et al., 1974), presumably Cl^- enters the intravesicular space more rapidly than Na^+ and permits development of an electrochemical potential (interior negative). Further, SCN^- and NO_3^-, which are probably more permeable than Cl^-, will facilitate the more rapid or greater development of an electrochemical potential. Murer and Hopfer (1974) have also reported that D-glucose uptake into intestinal microvillus membranes is enhanced by NaSCN relative to NaCl.

In addition, Beck and Sacktor (1975) have shown that with Na^+ salts whose mode of membrane translocation is electroneutral, i.e., acetate and bicarbonate, or one which on entering the vesicle dissociates to yield a proton, i.e. phosphate, there is no accumulation of D-glucose above the equilibrium value. These findings suggest that only anions that penetrate the brush border membrane and generate an electrochemical potential, negative on the inside, permit the uphill Na^+-dependent transport of D-glucose.

This suggestion is supported by determining how alterations in the electrochemical potential of the membrane induced by specific ionophores (Cockrell *et al.*, 1967) and a protein conductor affect the uptake of the sugar (Beck and Sacktor, 1975). As illustrated in Fig. 5, valinomycin, an ionophore that mediates electrogenic K^+ movements, supports the Na^+-dependent accumulation of D-glucose, provided a K^+ gradient (vesicle > medium) is present. In contrast, nigericin, which mediates an electroneutral exchange of Na^+ for K^+, does not. Na^+-dependent D-

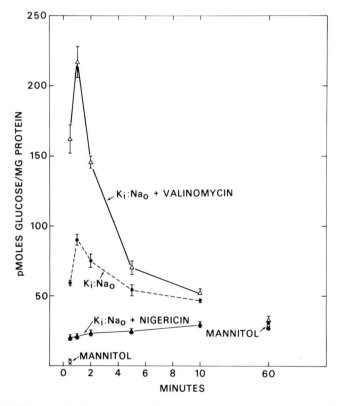

FIG. 5. Effect of the ionophores valinomycin and nigericin on the Na^+ gradient-dependent uptake of D-glucose into renal brush border membrane vesicles. From Beck and Sacktor (1975).

glucose uptake is diminished by ionophores that allow Na⁺ to pass
through the membrane via another channel, either electrogenically, e.g.,
gramicidin, or electroneutrally, e.g., nigericin. The electrogenic proton
conductor, carbonyl cyanide *p*-fluoromethoxyphenyl hydrazone, enhances D-glucose uptake in the presence of a proton gradient (vesicle >
medium) in renal (Beck and Sacktor, 1975) and intestinal (Murer and
Hopfer, 1974) brush border preparations. It is important to note that the
ionophores do not affect the nonspecific permeability properties of the
brush border membrane, as the equilibrium values are not altered (Beck
and Sacktor, 1975), nor is there a loss in the ability to discriminate
between D- and L-glucose (Hopfer, 1975).

These results indicate that the Na⁺-dependent transport of D-glucose
into renal and intestinal brush border membrane vesicles is an electrogenic process and that changing the electropotential of the membranes,
i.e., making the interior more negative, stimulates the Na⁺-dependent
transport of D-glucose. This proposal receives strong corroboration from
the experiments illustrated in Fig. 6. Beck and Sacktor (1976) have
varied the ratio of the initial concentration of K⁺ inside the vesicle to
that outside the vesicle, thus establishing a membrane potential, the
magnitude of which is dependent on the initial ratio. Addition of
valinomycin to the reaction medium allows K⁺ to move down its
concentration gradient. The simultaneous addition of D-glucose and Na⁺
induces transport of the sugar. The uptake is linearly related to the log
$[K^+_i]:[K^+_o]$ and, therefore, assuming that the Nernst relationship is
applicable, proportional to the membrane potential.

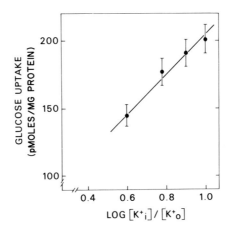

Fɪɢ. 6. Effect of the membrane potential on the uptake of D-glucose into renal brush
border membrane vesicles. From Beck and Sacktor (1976).

Hopfer (1975) has reported that the Na^+ gradient-dependent transport of D-glucose is greater in intestinal microvillus membranes derived from alloxan-diabetic rats than in vesicles from normal animals. He suggests that the difference is due to an ability of the membranes from diabetic animals to maintain a higher driving force for active D-glucose transport, not to changes in the glucose "carrier." The membranes from the diabetic animals have a decreased D-glucose-independent Na^+ conductance, which can be increased to normal levels by monactin or gramicidin.

D. SPECIFICITIES OF THE Na^+-DEPENDENT AND -INDEPENDENT SUGAR TRANSPORT SYSTEMS

The Na^+-dependent D-glucose transport system in the isolated renal brush border membranes possesses the sugar specificities characteristic of the more physiological intact system. Of the D-glucose analogs tested, only D-galactose and α-methyl-D-glucoside inhibit the Na^+-dependent transport of D-glucose (Aronson and Sacktor, 1975). None of the other sugars tested, including L-glucose, D-mannose, D-fructose, D-xylose, 2-deoxy-D-glucose inhibits the Na^+-dependent uptake. A slight inhibition is found with 3-O-methyl-D-glucose. In contrast, the Na^+-independent transport system in renal brush border membranes shows a general lack of specificity with respect to the various analogs. Except for L-glucose, all the sugars inhibit D-glucose uptake. However, D-galactose and α-methyl-D-glucoside are markedly less effective as inhibitors of the Na^+-independent uptake than as inhibitors of the Na^+-dependent system. Kleinzeller (1970) has suggested that in rabbit renal cortical slices the structural requirements for the Na^+-dependent active sugar transport system are a D-pyranose or furanose ring, a hydrophilic group on C-2, a hydroxyl group on C-3 in the same configuration as in D-glucose, a hydroxyl group on C-6, but not a hydroxyl group on C-1. The results with rabbit renal luminal membranes are generally consistent with this view with the additional specifications that the ring must be in the pyranose form and the hydroxyl group on C-2 must be in the D-glucose rather than in the D-mannose configuration. Silverman *et al.* (1970) have also stressed the distinction between the D-glucose and D-mannose transport systems in the dog *in vivo*. The findings with isolated renal brush borders are also in general accord with the elegant stopflow microperfusion experiments in the proximal tubule of the intact rat kidney (Ullrich *et al.*, 1974).

The uptake of D-glucose in intestinal microvillus membranes, but not of L-glucose, is inhibited by D-galactose (Hopfer *et al.*, 1973). Conversely, D-glucose inhibits the uptake of D-galactose. The mutual interaction of D-galactose and D-glucose is also found in renal brush border membranes (Sacktor *et al.*, 1974). Moreover, the inhibitions are competitive in nature. Therefore, the data support the view that D-glucose and D-galactose have common or closely associated carrier sites on the brush border membranes. In contrast, brush border membranes from rat intestine have a transport system for D-fructose that is distinct from that for D-glucose (Sigrist-Nelson and Hopfer, 1974). Uptake of D-fructose is unaffected by Na$^+$, phlorizin, D-glucose, or D-galactose.

E.   UPTAKE OF D-GLUCOSE BY BASAL-LATERAL MEMBRANES

Basal-lateral membranes, like brush border membranes, tend to vesiculate when isolated (Fig. 7). The mechanism of D-glucose transport in basal-lateral membranes, however, has not been elucidated as well as that in apical membranes. The difficulties stem in part from the significant contamination of the basal-lateral membrane preparations with brush border membranes and mitochondrial fragments. For example, in intestinal basal-lateral membranes prepared by free-flow electrophoresis (Murer *et al.*, 1974) the specific activities of Na$^+$K$^+$ ATPase is increased 5 times that in the homogenate of epithelial cells; but, alkaline phosphatase, the brush border "marker," is also enriched 2-fold. Mitochondrial contamination of renal basal-lateral membrane preparations may be as high as 20–30% (Liang and Sacktor, 1976a). Moreover, the intravesicular volume of the renal brush border membrane vesicle may be 3 times larger per milligram of protein than that of the basal-lateral membrane vesicle (Kinne *et al.*, 1975a). Thus, vesicular volume contamination is even greater than is indicated by "enzyme marker" contamination. Despite these complications, preliminary studies suggest that the D-glucose transport system in the basal-lateral segment of the epithelial cell plasma membrane differs from that in the luminal region.

When the results reported by Murer *et al.* (1974) and Kinne *et al.* (1975a) for intestinal and renal preparations, respectively, are recalculated and reexamined (Table III), the following tentative conclusions are reached by this reviewer. (1) The initial (30 second) rates of uptake of D-glucose, in the presence of 100 mM Na$^+$, are the same in intestinal brush border and intestinal basal-lateral membrane vesicles. The rates in renal brush border membrane vesicles may be greater than in renal basal-lateral vesicles, but this finding is equivocal because the intravesicular volume of the brush border membrane is 3-fold that of the basal-lateral membrane, and it is known (Aronson and Sacktor, 1975) that the rate of D-glucose uptake increases with expanded intravesicular volume. (2) The uptake of D-glucose is stimulated by Na$^+$, relative to K$^+$, to a greater extent in brush border than in basal-lateral membrane vesicles.

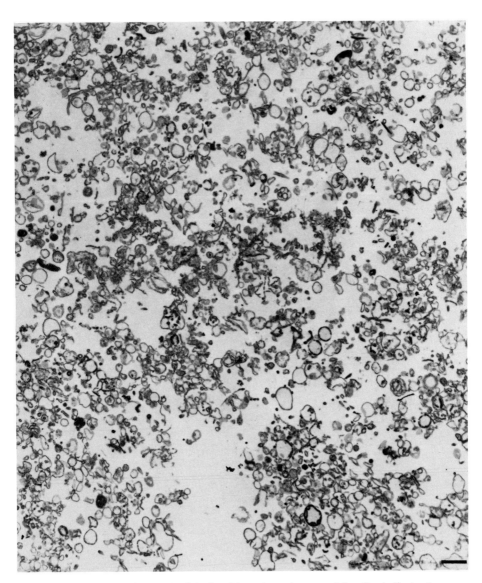

FIG. 7. Electron micrograph of the basal-lateral membrane vesicles. Bar indicates 1 μm. From Liang and Sacktor (1976a).

Whether the relatively smaller Na$^+$-dependent enhancement in the rate of D-glucose transport observed in basal-lateral membranes represents an intrinsic property of the transport system in these membranes or merely contamination of the preparations by the Na$^+$-dependent system of brush border membranes cannot be decided definitively with the

TABLE III
COMPARISON OF THE RATES OF UPTAKE OF D- AND L-GLUCOSE IN RENAL AND
INTESTINAL BASAL-LATERAL AND BRUSH BORDER MEMBRANES[a]

	Intestinal		Renal	
Incubation	Brush border	Basal-lateral	Brush border	Basal-lateral
D-Glucose + Na$^+$	0.91	0.85	2.88	0.91
D-Glucose + K$^+$	0.49	0.69	0.51	0.61
D-Glucose + Na$^+$ + phlorizin	0.26	0.76	0.54	0.50
L-Glucose + Na$^+$	0.29	0.45	0.20	0.45

[a] Values are reported as nanomoles per milligram of protein in 30 seconds. Concentrations of D- and L-glucose are 1 mM, and Na$^+$ and K$^+$ are 100 mM. The phlorizin concentrations are 0.5 mM and 0.1 mM, respectively, for intestinal and renal preparations. Values are recalculated from the data reported by Murer et al. (1974) and Kinne et al. (1975a).

evidence available at this time. (3) The Na$^+$-independent rates of D-glucose uptake are about equal in the two types of membrane vesicles. (4) The uptake of D-glucose, in the presence of Na$^+$, is more sensitive to phlorizin in brush border membranes than in basal-lateral membranes. (5) The initial rates of D-glucose uptake in both membranes is faster than those of L-glucose. (6) The rates of uptake of L-glucose may be greater in the basal-lateral membrane than in the brush border membrane. In addition, an "overshoot," if present in the basal-lateral membranes is considerably less than in the brush border membranes. Further, the D-glucose transport system in brush border and in basal-lateral membranes differ in apparent activation energies (Kinne et al., 1975a).

In a somewhat different approach, Bihler and Cybulsky (1973) have blocked the active sugar transport system (Na$^+$ and phlorizin sensitive) of isolated mouse epithelial cells with HgCl$_2$ and have shown that the uptake of D-mannose, D-fructose, and 2-deoxy-D-glucose are not inhibited by D-glucose and D-galactose. The uptakes of D-glucose and D-galactose in cells poisoned with HgCl$_2$ are not sensitive to Na$^+$ or to phlorizin. These authors postulate that uptake of sugars in the presence of HgCl$_2$ is mediated via the basal-lateral portion of the enterocyte. In the kidney of the dog, Silverman (1974), using the multiple indicator dilution technique in vivo, has distinguished sugars being transported across the luminal membranes from those being transported across the antiluminal membranes. He suggests that for the brush border membrane the specificity characteristics consist of a pyranose ring, hydroxyl groups on C-3 and C-6 orbited as in the configuration of D-glucose. For the antiluminal membrane, the specificities are a pyranose ring, hydroxyl groups on C-1 and C-2, and hydroxyl groups, if present on C-3 and C-6, oriented equatorially as in the configuration of D-glucose.

F. MECHANISM OF THE TRANSEPITHELIAL TRANSPORT OF D-GLUCOSE

If these findings suggesting polarity of the transport function are further substantiated at the membrane level, it is postulated that the transcellular "active" transport of D-glucose consists of a Na^+ gradient-dependent uphill influx at the brush border end and a Na^+-independent downhill efflux of sugar at the basal-lateral region of the epithelial cell. Figure 8 illustrates diagrammatically a tentative model for the Na^+-coupled D-glucose transport in the proximal tubule or intestine. Na^+ and D-glucose are translocated from the lumen across the brush border membrane into the cell by an electrogenic process, with the transmembrane electrochemical potential (interior cell negative) providing the driving force. This electrochemical membrane potential may be maintained in part by an active Cl^- pump transporting the anion into the cell (Field *et al.*, 1971), the extrusion of H^+ from the cell across the luminal membrane by a HCO_3^--stimulated ATPase (Liang and Sacktor, 1976b), and by the extrusion of Na^+ from the cell across the basal-lateral membrane by a ouabain-sensitive Na^+K^+ ATPase localized in this membrane (Quigley and Gotterer, 1969; Heidrich *et al.*, 1972). D-Glucose exits from the cell via the basal-lateral membrane, presumably by a downhill Na^+-independent process. Thus, the asymmetric distribution of Na^+ across the epithelial cell and the electrochemical potential across the brush border membrane provide the energy needed to transport D-glucose against its concentration gradient.

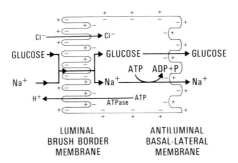

FIG. 8. Diagrammatic model for D-glucose transport across the proximal tubule or intestinal epithelial cell. From Beck and Sacktor (1975).

IV. Transport of Amino Acids by Membrane Vesicles

A. NATURE OF THE NA⁺ GRADIENT-DEPENDENT UPTAKE OF AMINO
ACIDS

Amino acid transport has been examined in a wide variety of preparations, including the intact animal, intestinal and renal tubular segments, and renal cortical slices. Micropuncture studies of the rat nephron *in vivo* indicate that the main site of amino acid reabsorption takes place in the proximal tubule (Eisenbach *et al.*, 1975). On the other hand, there is nearly a complete void of published information on the mechanisms of amino acid transport with isolated membrane preparations. Hillman and Rosenberg (1970) have described a rat kidney brush border membrane preparation which reportedly binds L-proline. "Binding" of L-proline is enhanced by Na⁺. Although their preparations contain some intact brush borders as seen by phase microscopy, it is monitored biochemically erroneously and is found to be enriched in the non-brush border membrane "marker," Na⁺K⁺ ATPase. Moreover, their argument to distinguish between surface binding and transport is not persuasive. Faust and Shearin (1974) have reported the binding of L-histidine to "core" filaments of jejunum brush borders, but the significance of this binding to transport has been largely discounted (Mitchell *et al.*, 1974; Hopfer and Sigrist-Nelson, 1974). Very recently, Sigrist-Nelson *et al.* (1975) and investigators in our laboratory have focused attention on amino acid transport using the same well-characterized brush border membrane preparations that have been used for studies of sugar transport.

Several observations clearly indicate that the measured uptakes of amino acids by brush border membranes represent transport into membrane vesicles, but not membrane binding. (1) At equilibrium, the uptake of L-alanine by intestinal (Sigrist-Nelson *et al.*, 1975) and renal (Fass *et al.*, 1976) brush border membrane vesicles, and of L-proline, L-glutamate, glycine, and L-arginine by renal brush border membrane vesicles (Hammerman and Sacktor, 1976), is decreased with increased osmolarity, as predicted for osmotically active vesicles. (2) Accelerated exchange diffusion (countertransport) is observed (Sigrist-Nelson *et al.*, 1975; Hammerman and Sacktor, 1976). (3) The uptakes of a given concentration of the different amino acids as well as D-glucose at equilibrium are approximately the same, suggesting a common intravesicular space (Hammerman and Sacktor, 1976). (4) Lastly, the amino acids exhibit the "overshoot" phenomenon, indicating uptake above equilibrium followed by efflux to reach equilibrium (Sigrist-Nelson *et al.*, 1975; Fass *et al.*, 1976; Hammerman and Sacktor, 1976).

The transport of L-alanine into renal brush border membrane vesicles exhibits Na^+-dependent and -independent components (Fass *et al.,* 1976). As illustrated in Fig. 9, in the absence of Na^+ the initial rate of uptake is essentially linearly related to the concentration of L-alanine from 20 μM to 100 mM, perhaps suggesting passive diffusion. In the presence of a Na^+ gradient, L-alanine uptake is enhanced. If at each L-alanine concentration the Na^+-free uptake is subtracted from the uptake obtained in the presence of Na^+, a curve is described that is consistent with a proposal for a Na^+-dependent L-alanine transport system in the kidney that saturates at about 2 mM and has an apparent K_m of 300 μM (at 60 mM Na^+).

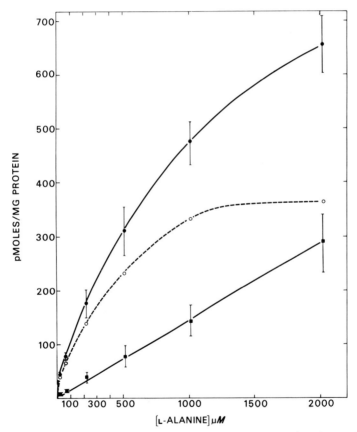

FIG. 9. The uptake of L-alanine into renal brush border membrane vesicles, with and without a Na^+ gradient: ●——●, 60 mM Na^+; ○---○, 60 mM Na^+ − 0 mM Na^+; ■——■, 0 mM Na^+. From Fass *et al.* (1976).

The Na^+-dependent transport system is stereospecific, the uptake of
L-alanine being distinguished by several criteria from that of D-alanine.
Stereospecificity between the L- and D-isomers of alanine are also found
in intestinal brush border membranes (Sigrist-Nelson et al., 1975) and
the L- and D-isomers of various other amino acids in renal membrane
vesicles (Hammerman and Sacktor, 1976).

Increasing the Na^+ gradient, adding NaCl extravesicularly from 7.5 to
100 mM, increases the initial rate of L-alanine uptake 2- to 5-fold with no
evidence for saturation with respect to Na^+ (Fass et al., 1976). Other
cations, e.g., K^+ and choline, do not stimulate uptake. A slight stimulation, perhaps of statistical significance, is observed with Li^+. A Li^+
gradient reportedly also effects a 2-fold increase in the rate of L-alanine
uptake into intestinal membrane vesicles (Sigrist-Nelson et al., 1975).
The specificity of Na^+ on the transport of different amino acids in renal
brush border membrane vesicles is compared in Table IV. It is evident
that the effect of the Na^+ gradient depends on the nature of the amino
acid. The Na^+ gradient stimulates the rates of uptake of neutral and
acidic amino acids, glycine, and imino acids (Hammerman and Sacktor,
1976). The uptake of L-proline, like that of D-glucose, shows a marked
Na^+ gradient dependency. In contrast, the uptake of the basic amino
acid L-arginine is inhibited by Na^+, as well as by other cations
(Hammerman and Sacktor, 1976). A Li^+ gradient, but not that of K^+,
increases moderately the uptake rates of L-proline and L-glutamate. The
rate of L-glutamate uptake is also enhanced by a choline gradient. Other
studies show that the kinetic effect of increasing Na^+ in the extravesicular medium (enlarging the Na^+ gradient) is to decrease the apparent K_m
of L-alanine or L-proline for transport (Fass et al., 1976; Hammerman
and Sacktor, 1976).

TABLE IV

EFFECT OF Na^+ AND OTHER CATIONS ON THE INITIAL RATE OF UPTAKE OF DIFFERENT
AMINO ACIDS IN RENAL BRUSH BORDER MEMBRANE VESICLES[a]

Cation	L-Alanine	L-Proline	L-Glutamate	Glycine	L-Arginine
None	100	100	100	100	100
Na^+	275	1143	377	268	68
K^+	99	87	132	127	71
Li^+	141	174	210	147	56
Choline	113	107	183	125	59

[a] Values are relative to the uptakes in the absence of added cation (300 mM mannitol).
The concentrations of amino acid and cations for each amino acid series were constant,
although they were not necessarily the same for the different amino acids. Data are from
Fass et al. (1976) and Hammerman and Sacktor (1976).

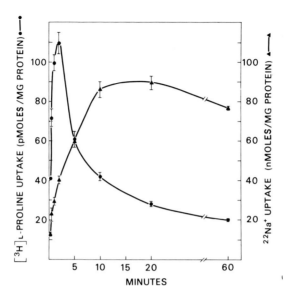

FIG. 10. The simultaneous uptake of L-proline and Na$^+$ into renal brush border membrane vesicles. From Chernoff and Sacktor. (1976).

A typical experiment describing the effect of the Na$^+$ gradient on the uptake of the amino acid L-proline is illustrated in Fig. 10. The initial (30-second) rate of uptake is at least 10-fold that in the absence of salt gradient. Accumulation of L-proline by the renal membrane vesicles reaches a maximum in about 2 minutes. Thereafter, the concentration of amino acid in the membrane vesicles decreases, indicating efflux. The final level of uptake of L-proline is reached in approximately 60 minutes. This value is the same in the presence and in the absence of the Na$^+$ gradient, suggesting that equilibrium has been established. At the peak of the "overshoot," the uptake of L-proline is often more than 5 times the equilibrium value. In analogy to the case with D-glucose, the presence of an "overshoot" with L-proline indicates the continuing uptake of the amino acid into the membrane vesicles after the intravesicular concentration of L-proline has reached the concentration of L-proline in the extravesicular medium, i.e., uphill or active transport. This phenomenon implies the persistence of the coupled Na$^+$ gradient. That this is indeed so is evident when the uptakes of L-proline and Na$^+$ are measured simultaneously (Chernoff and Sacktor, 1976). The data in Fig. 10 show that Na$^+$ uptake into the membrane vesicles persists beyond the time that the intravesicular concentration of L-proline first reaches the amino acid concentration in the medium. Other experiments demonstrate that the energy inherent in the large extravesicular to intravesicular Na^+ gradient can drive the transient movements of L-alanine, L-glutamate, and glycine, in addition to that of L-proline, against their respective concentration gradients into renal brush border membrane vesicles (Hammerman and Sacktor, 1976; Fass *et al.,* 1976).

The Na^+ gradient-dependent transport of amino acids in renal brush border membrane vesicles is an electrogenic process and is regulated by the electrochemical membrane potential. The ionophore gramicidin enhances membrane conductance for Na^+ by pathways other than by the amino acid system, dissipates the electrochemical membrane potential, and decreases the "overshoot" uptakes of L-proline, L-glutamate, and glycine (Hammerman and Sacktor, 1976). As shown in Fig. 11, the ionophore, valinomycin, which mediates electrogenic K^+ movements, enhances the Na^+ gradient-dependent accumulation of L-proline, provided a K^+ gradient (vesicle > medium) is present. In contrast, the ionophore nigericin, which mediates an electroneutral exchange of Na^+ for K^+ does not. Therefore, these findings suggest that changing the electrochemical potential across the vesicular membrane, i.e., making the interior negative, stimulates the Na^+-dependent transport of L-proline (Hammerman and Sacktor, 1976) by a mechanism similar to that for D-glucose.

B. INTERACTIONS OF AMINO ACID AND SUGAR TRANSPORTS

Demonstration of the role of the Na^+ gradient in the uptakes of both amino acid and D-glucose by isolated brush border membrane may also be relevant to the well known mutual interaction of amino acid and sugar transports in intestine (Schultz and Curran, 1970) and kidney (Genel *et al.,* 1971). Several mechanisms have been proposed to explain this phenomenon, including formation of toxic metabolites, competition for metabolic energy, stimulation of efflux from the cell, allosteric interactions for a common polyfunctional carrier, and competition of the sugar and amino acid transport systems for Na^+. Experiments by Murer *et al.* (1975) and by Fass *et al.,* (1976) with intestinal and renal brush border membrane vesicles, respectively, bear on this question. The following findings are reported: (1) Uptake of D-glucose is inhibited by the simultaneous flow of L-alanine into the vesicles. The inhibition is dependent on the presence of Na^+. (2) Uptake of L-alanine is not affected by D-glucose in the absence of a Na^+ gradient, but in the presence of the gradient the sugar significantly inhibits the uptake of the amino acid. (3) Addition of L-alanine to membranes preincubated with D-glucose causes efflux of the sugar. (4) The ionophores monactin and valinomycin prevent the transport interactions of D-glucose and L-alanine. The action of the latter ionophore requires K^+, in accordance

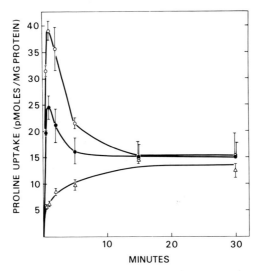

FIG. 11. Effect of the ionophores valinomycin (○) and nigericin (Δ), on the uptake of L-proline into K⁺-loaded renal brush border membrane vesicles. From Hammerman and Sacktor (1976).

with its known specificity. Thus, it is of considerable significance that the interactions of amino acids and sugar first reported with relatively intact preparations is also seen with brush border membrane vesicles. Moreover, the first three postulates cannot apply to the transport across the isolated purified membrane which lacks respiratory and glycolytic enzymes and into which uptakes of solutes are insensitive to metabolic energy in the form of ATP (Aronson and Sacktor, 1974). The finding that D-glucose and L-alanine do not compete in the absence of Na^+ argues counter to the simple allosteric interaction of carriers. On the other hand, the inhibition observed in the presence of Na^+ is consistent with the view of competition for Na^+. This hypothesis is presently expanded by suggesting that sugars and amino acids are coupled electrically and compete for the electrochemical Na^+ gradient or membrane potential.

C. Specificities of the Amino Acid Transport Systems

The specificities of the amino acid transport systems in the kidney have attracted much attention because of clinical significance to the understanding of metabolic disorders, e.g., cystinuria, imino glycinuria, Hartnup's disease, and conditions such as Fanconi syndrome (Scriver and Rosenberg, 1973). Studies in man and intact animals, with isolated renal tubules and cortical slices, have indicated that the kidney is able to distinguish between neutral, basic, and acidic amino acids as well as proline and glycine (Young and Freedman, 1971; Kamin and Handler, 1951; Holtzapple *et al.*, 1970). However, with these physiological preparations it is not possible to determine the precise site where recognition occurs. In contrast, studies of amino acid transport systems at the membrane level now permits a direct examination of this question.

Figure 12 summarizes recent observations by Hammerman and Sacktor (1976) and by Fass *et al.*, (1976) on the specificities of amino acid transport systems as found in rabbit renal brush border membranes. In these studies competition between the uptake of the labeled transported amino acid and the unlabeled test amino acid is measured in the presence and in the absence of a Na^+ gradient. When Na^+ is omitted, no selective competition is found among amino acids, except for the basic amino acids, i.e., L-arginine, L-lysine, and L-ornithine, whose transports do not require Na^+. Thus, in the absence of the Na^+ gradient, the uptake of L-arginine is strongly inhibited by L-arginine, L-lysine, and L-ornithine. Other test amino acids have little, if any, effect. In the presence of the Na^+ gradient, the uptake of the acidic amino acid, L-glutamate, is inhibited only by L-glutamate and L-aspartate. It is not inhibited by neutral and basic amino acids, nor imino acids and glycine. The uptake of the imino acid, L-proline, is strongly inhibited by L-proline and L-hydroxyproline, weakly inhibited by L-leucine and L-phenylalanine, but is not inhibited significantly by the basic and acidic amino acids. Uptake of L-alanine is strongly inhibited by other neutral amino acids, including glycine. Acidic and basic amino acids have no effect on L-alanine uptake, but the imino acids do inhibit moderately. Uptake of glycine is strongly inhibited by neutral amino acids and imino

TRANSPORT AMINO ACID	TEST AMINO ACID									
	NEUTRAL GROUP				IMINO ACIDS		DIBASIC GROUP		ACIDIC GROUP	
	L-ALA	L-LEU	L-PHE	GLY	L-P-OH	L-PRO	L-ARG	L-LYS	L-ASP	L-GLU
L-ALANINE	++	++	++	++	+	+	−	−	−	−
L-ARGININE	±	±	±	±	−	−	++	++	±	±
L-GLUTAMATE	±	±	±	−	−	−	±	±	++	++
GLYCINE	++	+	++	++	++	++	−	−	±	±
L-PROLINE	±	+	+	±	++	++	−	−	±	±

++ STRONGLY INHIBITED   + WEAKLY INHIBITED   − NOT INHIBITED

FIG. 12. Scheme showing the specificities of amino acid transport systems in renal brush border membrane vesicles. From Hammerman and Sacktor (1976) and Fass *et al.* (1976).

acids. The uptake of glycine, however, is insensitive to the copresence of acidic and basic amino acids. These findings suggest that the ability of the proximal tubule to transport amino acids selectively may be ascribed to an intrinsic property of the brush border membrane. Further, on the basis of amino acid specificity, the brush border membrane appears to possess at least five distinct amino acid transport systems.

V.   Transport of Ions by Membrane Vesicles

Studies on the transport of ions by isolated renal and intestinal brush border or basal-lateral membranes lag behind comparable investigations on sugar and amino acid transport systems. Except for the elegant work on Na^+ and K^+ translocation mediated by the Na^+K^+ ATPase in plasma membranes, which has been considered extensively elsewhere and will not be discussed in this review, information on the transport of other ions is fragmentary.

A.   MEMBRANE TRANSPORT OF CA^{2+}

As noted above, Ca ATPase has a distribution pattern in rat renal plasma membrane fractions resembling that for Na^+K^+ ATPase; namely, localized predominantly in the basal-lateral membrane (Kinne-Saffran and Kinne, 1974a). They have conjectured that the Ca^{2+}-stimulated ATPase is involved in the active transtubular transport of Ca^{2+} in a manner analogous to that indicated for Na^+K^+ ATPase and the translocation of Na^+ from cell to plasma. According to this hypothesis, at the brush border membrane an electrochemical potential exists that favors the influx of Ca^{2+} into the cell, because the interior of the cell is negative relative to the tubular lumen and because the concentration of intracellular Ca^{2+} is less than that in the filtrate (Borle, 1971). Thus, Ca^{2+} by following its electrochemical potential can cross the brush border membrane by a downhill mechanism. On the other hand, Kinne-Saffran and Kinne (1974a) suggest that at the basal-lateral region of the tubular cell Ca^{2+} has to overcome an electrochemical potential difference between the cellular and interstitial fluids. This requires an uphill transport mechanism. Presumably, this is mediated by the Ca ATPase. That isolated renal plasma membranes can, indeed, accumulate Ca^{2+} has been shown by Moore et al. (1974). Uptake of Ca^{2+} is dependent on Mg^{2+} and ATP. The K_m for Ca^{2+} is 19 μM and the K_m for MgATP is 0.55 mM. The V for the system is 1.2 nmoles of Ca^{2+}/mg per minute. The replacement of KCl in the medium with NaCl is strongly inhibitory. In contrast to the report of Kinne-Saffran and Kinne (1974a), Moore et al. (1974) find that Ca^{2+} enhances the Mg ATPase in their basal-lateral membrane preparations. Ca^{2+} (20 μM) induces an extra ATPase amounting to 35 nmoles of P_i/mg per minute. It is noted, however, that the optimal Ca^{2+} concentrations for Ca^{2+} uptake and ATP hydrolysis differ.

The localization of Ca ATPase and the mechanism of Ca^{2+} transport in the intestine seemingly differs from that in the kidney. Kinetic studies have led Patrick (1973) to conclude that in the intestine entry across the brush border membrane is rate-limiting for Ca^{2+} absorption. Moreover, Ca ATPase is found in highly purified brush border membrane preparations from rat (Martin et al., 1969) and chick (Melançon and DeLuca, 1970; Holdsworth, 1970). Significantly, vitamin D elicits a marked increase in brush border Ca ATPase activity (Martin et al., 1969). The time course of the appearance of Ca ATPase activity correlates with the increase in Ca^{2+} transport (Melançon and DeLuca, 1970). Additionally, Ca^{2+} has little effect on ATPase in vitamin D-deficient chicks but strikingly stimulates ATPase in vitamin D-replete animals. Norman et al. (1970) have reported that cholecalciferol also increases the level of alkaline phosphatase in chick (rachitic) intestinal brush border membranes. Other brush border enzymes, i.e., the disaccharidases, are not increased. The simultaneous time course of appearance of increased levels of brush border alkaline phosphatase and of increased rates of Ca^{2+} transport, measured in vitro across ileal segments, have prompted these investigators to suggest a functional involvement of alkaline phosphatase in vitamin D-mediated Ca^{2+} transport. Ca ATPase activity is also found in the basal-lateral segments of the plasma membrane of rat intestine (Birge et al., 1972). The ATPase in the basal-lateral membrane, but not in the brush border membrane, is inhibited by ethacrynic acid, but not ouabain, and is activated by Na^+. These authors claim that the basal-lateral Ca ATPase may be part of the translocation system for Ca^{2+}, in the intestine, and Na^+ may have a role in activating the enzyme.

B.   MEMBRANE TRANSPORT OF BICARBONATE

In the kidney, 80–90% of the filtered bicarbonate is reabsorbed in the proximal tubule (Gottschalk et al., 1960), and acidification of the tubular fluid is a prominent feature of renal function (Rector, 1973). This focuses attention on the possible role of the proximal tubule brush border membrane in these transport processes. Indeed, the presence of a HCO_3^--stimulated ATPase in a membrane fraction rich in microvilli has been reported (Kinne-Saffran and Kinne, 1974b). The kinetic properties of the enzyme have been investigated (Liang and Sacktor, 1976b), and these studies provide evidence relevant to the possible interrelationships between membrane HCO_3^--stimulated ATPase, proton secretion, and bicarbonate reabsorption in the renal tubule.

The ATPase in renal brush border membranes is stimulated 60% by 50 mM HCO_3^-. The K_a for HCO_3^- is 36 mM. Kinetic studies of the "HCO_3^--ATPase" indicate that HCO_3^- had no effect on the K_m for ATP and ATP did not alter the K_a for HCO_3^-. Several anions, notably SO_3^{2-}, also accelerate the rate of dephosphorylation of ATP. The V for "SO_3^{2-}-ATPase" is 5-fold greater than that for "HCO_3^--ATPase." Other anions, including Cl^- and phosphates, do not enhance ATPase activity. Thus, of the anions present in the glomerular filtrate in appreciable concentrations, only HCO_3^- stimulates the luminal membrane enzyme. The anion-stimulated ATPase activity increases sharply from pH 6.1 to 7.1 and moderately with higher pH. The renal ATPase is relatively insensitive to oligomycin and quercetin. Carbonyl cyanide p-trifluoromethoxy phenylhydrazone (FCCP) increases the basal rate of the membranal ATPase, suggesting that the ATPase activity is limited by transmembrane H^+ flux. Carbonic anhydrase significantly increases the HCO_3^--stimulated ATPase activity. This increment is blocked by Diamox.

The findings that carbonic anhydrase increases the rate of the brush border membrane HCO_3^--stimulated ATPase and that this enhancement is blocked by Diamox may be relevant to proposed mechanisms of H^+ and bicarbonate transport. In the intact dog, 40% of the filtered bicarbonate is excreted when carbonic anhydrase is inhibited by Diamox (Berliner, 1952). Diamox prevents acidification of the filtrate in the proximal tubule *in situ* (Clapp *et al.*, 1963), and it inhibits the secretory rate of H^+ in perfused tubules (Ullrich *et al.*, 1975). As illustrated diagrammatically in Fig. 13, carbonic anhydrase in the proximal tubular

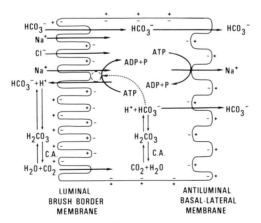

FIG. 13. A diagrammatic model for bicarbonate reabsorption in the renal proximal tubular cell and the postulated role of the HCO_3^--stimulated ATPase. From Liang and Sacktor (1976b).

cell has a dual localization: approximately 90% of the activity is found in the cytosol; the remainder is localized in the brush border membrane (Maren and Ellison, 1967). According to one generally accepted hypothesis for bicarbonate transport (Rector, 1973), extrusion of H^+ from cell to lumen favors the conversion of HCO_3^- to H_2CO_3 in the glomerular filtrate. The brush border carbonic anhydrase enhances the breakdown of this H_2CO_3 to CO_2 and H_2O. The CO_2, thus formed, is transported across the brush border membrane into the cell, where it is hydrated by the cytosolic carbonic anhydrase. Dissociation of the H_2CO_3 generates intracellular HCO_3^- and H^+. A significant share of the bicarbonate that is reabsorbed from the glomerular filtrate has been attributed to H^+ secretion by this mechanism (Rector et al., 1965). It is now further postulated, as diagrammed in Fig. 13, that the brush border ATPase is involved in the extrusion of H^+ from cell to lumen and that intracellular HCO_3^- by stimulating this ATPase augments translocation of H^+ across the membrane. Thus, reabsorbed bicarbonate, in the form of HCO_3^-, may act as a positive effector promoting the reabsorption of additional bicarbonate.

Other evidence is available which lends support for this hypothesis. That a "pump" mechanism is needed to extrude H^+ from proximal tubular cell to lumen via the brush border membrane is indicated from findings that the transmembrane electrochemical potential of the brush border is positive on the outside and negative on the inside (Beck and Sacktor, 1975; Maruyama and Joshi, 1972; Fromter and Gessner, 1975). In other membrane systems, ATPases are known to couple ATP hydrolysis to H^+ translocation against electrochemical gradients (Mitchell, 1973). The present finding that in brush border membranes the proton conductor FCCP increased the basal rate of dephosphorylation of ATP by about 25% is consistent with the presence of a membranal ATPase whose activity is limited by transmembrane H^+ flux. This argues for a role for the enzyme in the transport of H^+. In addition, Diamox, which inhibited the HCO_3^--stimulated ATPase in brush border membranes also reduces the lumen-positive active transport potential in loops of proximal tubules (Fromter and Gessner, 1975). Strengthening the hypothesis further is the suggestion that the bicarbonate species which is transported across brush border membrane vesicles is probably CO_2 (Beck and Sacktor, 1975). Last, Pitts and Alexander (1945) from clearance measurements in dogs have first postulated an exchange of cellular H^+ for filtered Na^+, and this view is supported by stop-flow microperfusion studies in rats (Ullrich et al., 1975). Moreover, studies in which isolated kidneys are perfused with HCO_3^--free media or with media containing HCO_3^- + Diamox show that reabsorption of bicarbonate accounts for a small but significant fraction of the Na^+ reabsorbed

(Besarab *et al.*, 1975). Thus, exchange of H^+ for Na^+ may represent one of the mechanisms for maintaining cellular electroneutrality. Indeed, experiments with brush border membrane vesicles do indicate a coupling of the transports of the two cations (Chernoff and Sacktor, 1976).

C. NA^+ TRANSPORT IN MEMBRANES

Uptake of Na^+ by renal brush border membrane vesicles occurs into an osmotically active space as well as by apparent "binding" (Chernoff and Sacktor, 1976). Uptake is initially rapid and reaches a steady state in 40 minutes (Fig. 10). The K_m is 1 mM and V is 1.65 nmoles/mg per minute. The electroneutral ionophore nigericin enhances the initial rate of Na^+ uptake 2-fold in both K^+- and H^+-loaded membrane vesicles. "Overshoots" of 1.5 and 3 times the equilibrium level are observed in these respectively loaded vesicles. Chernoff and Sacktor (1976) also find that increasing the H^+ gradient (vesicle > medium) stimulates the uptake of Na^+ and effects a gradient-dependent transient accumulation above the equilibrium value. The transient nature of this accumulation of Na^+ against its concentration gradient suggests that the effect of the pH gradient is not one of enhanced "binding" but of an electroneutral H^+-Na^+ exchange.

The pumping of Na^+ across the basal-lateral membrane from the epithelial cell to the blood, mediated by the Na^+K^+ ATPase, has been reviewed elsewhere.

D. HORMONAL REGULATION OF MEMBRANE TRANSPORT

Hormones, e.g., parathyroid (Chase and Aurbach, 1967), calcitonin (Marx *et al.*, 1972), vasopressin (Dousa *et al.*, 1972), and catecholamines (Gill and Casper, 1971), acting via cyclic AMP are known to affect the transports of phosphate (Agus *et al.*, 1971), calcium (Agus *et al.*, 1973), Na^+ (Agus *et al.*, 1973; Fulgraff and Meiforth, 1974), sugars (Rea and Segal, 1973), and amino acids (Weiss *et al.*, 1972), all reabsorbed across the brush border membrane. Basal-lateral membranes possess hormone receptors and hormone-sensitive adenylate cyclase (Marx *et al.*, 1972). The function of receptors on the brush border membrane is puzzling in view of suggestions that the bulk of the adenylate cyclase is in the contraluminal membrane. A presumptive locus of cyclic AMP action, however, is the brush border membrane. This membrane binds cyclic AMP (Insel *et al.*, 1975) and possesses multiple protein kinases which phosphorylate endogenous as well as exogenous proteins (Kinne *et al.*, 1975b; George *et al.*, 1976; Sacktor *et al.*, 1976). In the toad bladder, vasopressin-induced changes in solute transport have been implicated in alterations in the state of phosphorylation of membrane protein (Walton *et al.*, 1975). Presumably, the same is true for the hormonal control of transport in renal and intestinal epithelial cells. The mechanisms of this regulation are still to be elucidated.

REFERENCES

Agus, Z. S., Puschett, J. B., Senesky, D., and Goldberg, M. (1971). *J. Clin. Invest.* **50,** 617–626.
Agus, Z. S., Gardner, L. B., Beck, L. H., and Goldberg, M. (1973). *Am. J. Physiol.* **224,** 1143–1148.
Alpers, D. H., and Solin, M. (1970). *Gastroenterology* **58,** 833–842.
Andersen, K.-J., von der Lippe, G., Mørkrid, L., and Schjønsby, H. (1975). *Biochem. J.* **152,** 157–159.
Aronson, P. S., and Sacktor, B. (1974). *Biochim. Biophys. Acta* **356,** 231–243.
Aronson, P. S., and Sacktor, B. (1975). *J. Biol. Chem.* **250,** 6032–6039.
Beck, J. C., and Sacktor, B. (1975). *J. Biol. Chem.* **250,** 8674–8680.
Beck, J. C., and Sacktor, B. (1976). In preparation.
Benson, R. L., Sacktor, B., and Greenawalt, J. W. (1971). *J. Cell Biol.* **48,** 711–716.
Berger, S. J., and Sacktor, B. (1970). *J. Cell Biol.* **47,** 637–645.
Berliner, R. W. (1952). *Fed. Proc., Fed. Am. Soc. Exp. Biol.* **11,** 695–700.
Basarab, A., Silva, P., Ross, B., and Epstein, F. H. (1975). *Am. J. Physiol.* **228,** 1525–1530.
Bihler, I., and Cybulsky, R. (1973). *Biochim. Biophys. Acta* **298,** 429–436.
Birge, S. J., Jr., Gilbert, H. R., and Avioli, L. V. (1972). *Science* **176,** 168–170.
Bode, F., Baumann, K., Frasch, W., and Kinne, R. (1970). *Pfluegers Arch.* **315,** 53–65.
Borle, A. B. (1971). *In* "Cellular Mechanisms for Calcium Transfer and Homeostasis" (G. Nichols, Jr. and R. H. Wasserman, eds.), p. 151. Academic Press, New York.
Busse, D., Elsas, L. J., and Rosenberg, L. E. (1972). *J. Biol. Chem.* **247,** 1188–1193.
Busse, D., Jahn, A., and Steinmaier, G. (1975). *Biochim. Biophys. Acta* **401,** 231–243.
Chan, S. S., and Lotspeich, W. D. (1962). *Am. J. Physiol.* **203,** 975–979.
Chase, L. R., and Aurbach, G. D. (1967). *Proc. Natl. Acad. Sci. U.S.A.* **58,** 518–525.
Chernoff, A., and Sacktor, B. (1976). In preparation.
Chesney, R. W., Sacktor, B., and Rowen, R. (1973). *J. Biol. Chem.* **248,** 2182–2191.
Chesney, R. W., Sacktor, B., and Kleinzeller, A. (1974). *Biochim. Biophys. Acta* **332,** 263–277.
Clapp, J. R., Watson, J. F., and Berliner, R. W. (1963). *Am. J. Physiol.* **205,** 693–696.
Cockrell, R. S., Harris, E. J., and Pressman, B. C. (1967). *Nature (London)* **215,** 1487–1488.
Crane, R. K. (1962). *Fed. Proc., Fed. Am. Soc. Exp. Biol.* **21,** 891–895.
Crane, R. K. (1975). *In* "Intestinal Absorption and Malabsorption" (T. Z. Csaky, ed.), pp. 127–142. Raven, New York.
David, J. S. K., Malathi, P., and Ganguly, J. (1966). *Biochem. J.* **98,** 662–668.
de Jonge, H. R. (1975). *FEBS Lett.* **53,** 237–242.
Douglas, A. P., Kerley, R., and Isselbacher, K. J. (1972). *Biochem. J.* **128,** 1329–1338.
Dousa, T. P., Walter, R., Schwartz, I. L., Sands, H., and Hechter, O. (1972). *Adv. Cyclic Nucleotide Res.* **1,** 121–135.
Eichholz, A., and Crane, R. K. (1965). *J. Cell Biol.* **26,** 687–691.
Eisenbach, G. M., Weise, M., and Stolte, H. (1975). *Pfluegers Arch.* **357,** 63–76.
Emmelot, P., and Bos, C. J. (1972). *J. Membr. Biol.* **9,** 83–104.

Fass, S., Hammerman, M., and Sacktor, B. (1977). In press.

Faust, R. G., and Shearin, S. J. (1974). *Nature (London)* **248**, 60–61.

Field, M., Fromm, D., and McColl, I. (1971). *Am. J. Physiol.* **220**, 1388–1396.

Filburn, C. F., and Sacktor, B. (1976a). *Arch. Biochem. Biophys.* **174**, 249–261.

Filburn, C. F., and Sacktor, B. (1976b). In preparation.

Forstner, G. G., and Wherrett, J. R. (1973). *Biochim. Biophys. Acta* **306**, 446–459.

Forstner, G. G., Riley, E. M., Daniels, S. J., and Isselbacher, K. J. (1965). *Biochem. Biophys. Res. Commun.* **21**, 83–88.

Forstner, G. G., Sabesin, S. M., and Isselbacher, K. J. (1968a). *Biochem. J.* **106**, 381–390.

Forstner, G. G., Tanaka, K., and Isselbacher, K. J. (1968b). *Biochem. J.* **109**, 51–59.

Fromter, E., and Gessner, K. (1975). *Pfluegers Arch.* **357**, 209–224.

Fujita, M., Matsui, H., Nagano, K., and Nakao, M. (1971). *Biochim. Biophys. Acta* **233**, 404–408.

Fulgraff, G., and Meiforth, A. (1974). *Naunyn-Schmiedeberg's Arch. Pharmacol.* **283**, 425–429.

Genel, M., Rea, C. F., and Segal, S. (1971). *Biochim. Biophys. Acta* **241**, 779–788.

George, E. R., Balakir, R. A., Filburn, C. R., and Sacktor, B. (1976). In preparation.

George, S. G., and Kenny, A. J. (1973). *Biochim. J.* **134**, 43–57.

Gill, J. R., Jr., and Casper, A. G. T. (1971). *J. Clin. Invest.* **50**, 1231–1240.

Glossmann, H., and Neville, D. M., Jr. (1972). *J. Biol. Chem.* **247**, 7779–7789.

Gottschalk, C. W., Lassiter, W. E., and Mylle, M. (1960). *Am. J. Physiol.* **198**, 581–585.

Groniowski, J., Biczyskowa, W., and Walski, M. (1969). *J. Cell Biol.* **40**, 585–601.

Grossman, I. W., and Sacktor, B. (1968). *Science* **161**, 571–572.

Hammerman, M., and Sacktor, B. (1976). Submitted for publication.

Heidrich, H. G., Kinne, R., Kinne-Saffran, E., and Hannig, K. (1972). *J. Cell Biol.* **54**, 232–245.

Hillman, R. E., and Rosenberg, L. E. (1970). *Biochim. Biophys. Acta* **211**, 318–326.

Holdsworth, E. S. (1970). *J. Membr. Biol.* **3**, 43–53.

Holtzapple, P., Rea, C., Bovee, K., and Segal, S. (1970). *J. Lab. Clin. Med.* **75**, 818–825.

Hopfer, U. (1975). *Proc. Natl. Acad. Sci. U.S.A.* **72**, 2027–2031.

Hopfer, U., and Sigrist-Nelson, K. (1974). *Nature (London)* **252**, 422.

Hopfer, U., Nelson, K., Perrotto, J., and Isselbacher, K. J. (1973). *J. Biol. Chem.* **248**, 25–32.

Insel, P., Balakir, R., and Sacktor, B. (1975). *J. Cyclic Nucleotide Res.* **1**, 107–122.

Ito, S. (1965). *J. Cell Biol.* **27**, 475–491.

Jande, S. S., and Robert, P. (1974). *Histochemistry* **40**, 323–327.

Johnson, C. F. (1967). *Science* **155**, 1670–1672.

Kamin, H., and Handler, P. (1951). *Am. J. Physiol.* **164**, 654–661.

Kinne, R., Murer, H., Kinne-Saffran, E., Thees, M., and Sachs, G. (1975a). *J. Membr. Biol.* **21**, 375–395.

Kinne, R., Shlatz, L. J., Kinne-Saffron, E., and Schwartz, I. L. (1975b). *J. Membr. Biol.* **24**, 145–159.

Kinne-Saffran, E., and Kinne, R. (1974a). *J. Membr. Biol.* **17**, 263–274.

Kinne-Saffran, E., and Kinne, R. (1974b). *Proc. Soc. Exp. Biol. Med.* **146**, 751–753.

Kleinzeller, A. (1970). *Biochim. Biophys. Acta* **211**, 264–276.

Korn, E. D. (1969). *Fed. Proc., Fed. Am. Soc. Exp. Biol.* **28**, 6–11.

Leese, H. J., and Semenza, G. (1973). *J. Biol. Chem.* **248**, 8170–8173.

Lewis, B. A., Gray, G. M., Coleman, R., and Michell, R. H. (1975a). *Biochem. Soc. Trans.* **3**, 752–753.

Lewis, B. A., Elkin, A., Michell, R. H., and Coleman, R. (1975b). *Biochem. J.* **152**, 71–84.

Liang, C. T., and Sacktor, B. (1976a). In preparation.
Liang, C. T., and Sacktor, B. (1976b). *Arch. Biochem. Biophys.* **176**, 285–297.
Malathi, P. (1967). *Gastroenterology* **52**, 1106.
Malathi, P., and Crane, R. K. (1969). *Biochim. Biophys. Acta* **173**, 245–256.
Maren, T. H., and Ellison, A. C. (1967). *Mol. Pharmacol.* **3**, 503–508.
Maroux, S., Louvard, D., and Baratti, J. (1973). *Biochim. Biophys. Acta* **321**, 282–295.
Martin, D. L., Melancon, M. J., Jr., and DeLuca, H. F. (1969). *Biochem. Biophys. Res. Commun.* **35**, 819–823.
Maruyama, T., and Joshi, T. (1972). *Biochim. Biophys. Acta* **282**, 214–225.
Marx, S. J., and Aurbach, G. D. (1975). *Endocrinology* **97**, 448–453.
Marx, S. J., Fedak, S. A., and Aurbach, G. D. (1972). *J. Biol. Chem.* **247**, 6913–6918.
Marx, S. J., Woodward, C., and Aurbach, G. D. (1973). *J. Biol. Chem.* **248**, 4797–4802.
Maunsbach, D. B. (1973). In "Handbook of Physiology" (Am. Physiol. Soc., J. Orloff and R. W. Berliner eds.), Sect. 8, pp. 31–79. Williams & Wilkins, Baltimore, Maryland.
Meister, A. (1973). *Science* **180**, 33–39.
Melançon, M. J., Jr., and DeLuca, H. F. (1970). *Biochemistry* **9**, 1658–1664.
Miller, D., and Crane, R. K. (1961). *Biochim. Biophys. Acta* **52**, 293–298.
Mitchell, M. E., Aronson, P. S., and Sacktor, B. (1974). *J. Biol. Chem.* **249**, 6971–6975.
Mitchell, P. (1973). *FEBS Lett.* **33**, 267–274.
Moore, L., Fitzpatrick, D. F., Chen, T. S., and Landon, E. J. (1974). *Biochim. Biophys. Acta* **345**, 405–418.
Murer, H., and Hopfer, U. (1974). *Proc. Natl. Acad. Sci. U.S.A.* **71**, 484–488.
Murer, H., Hopfer, U., Kinne-Saffran, E., and Kinne, R. (1974). *Biochim. Biophys. Acta* **345**, 170–179.
Murer, H., Sigrist-Nelson, K., and Hopfer, U. (1975). *J. Biol. Chem.* **250**, 7392–7396.
Nishi, Y., Yoshida, T. O., and Takesue, Y. (1968). *J. Mol. Biol.* **37**, 441–494.
Norman, A. W., Mircheff, A. K., Adams, T. H., and Spielvogel, A. (1970). *Biochim. Biophys. Acta* **215**, 348–359.
Parkinson, D. K., Ebel, H., Dibona, D. R., and Sharp, G. W. G. (1972). *J. Clin. Invest.* **51**, 2292–2298.
Patrick, G. (1973). *Nature (London)* **243**, 89–91.
Pitts, R. F., and Alexander, R. S. (1945). *Am. J. Physiol.* **144**, 239–254.
Porteous, J. W. (1968). *FEBS Lett.* **1**, 46–49.
Quigley, J. P., and Gotterer, G. S. (1969). *Biochim. Biophys. Acta* **173**, 456–468.
Quigley, J. P., and Gotterer, G. S. (1972). *Biochim. Biophys. Acta* **255**, 107–113.
Quirk, S. J., and Robinson, G. B. (1972). *Biochem. J.* **128**, 1319–1328.
Ramaswamy, K., Malathi, P., Caspary, W. F., and Crane, R. K. (1974). *Biochim. Biophys. Acta* **345**, 39–48.
Rea, C. F., and Segal, S. (1973). *Biochim. Biophys. Acta* **311**, 615–624.
Rector, F. C., Jr. (1973). In "Handbook of Physiology" (Am. Physiol. Soc., J. Orloff and R. W. Berliner, eds.), Sect. 8, pp. 431–454. Williams & Wilkins, Baltimore, Maryland.
Rector, F. C., Jr., Carter, N. W., and Seldin, D. W. (1965). *J. Clin. Invest.* **44**, 278–290.
Rhodes, J. B., Eichholz, A., and Crane, R. K. (1967). *Biochim. Biophys. Acta* **135**, 959–965.
Rosenberg, I. H., Streiff, R. R., Godwin, H. A., and Castle, W. B. (1969). *N. Engl. J. Med.* **280**, 985–988.
Rostgaard, J., Kristensen, B. I., and Nielsen, L. E. (1972). *J. Ultrastruct. Res.* **38**, 207.
Sacktor, B. (1968). *Proc. Natl. Acad. Sci. U.S.A.* **60**, 1007–1014.
Sacktor, B. (1976). In "Mammalian Cell Membranes" (G. A. Jamieson and D. M. Robinson, eds.), Vol. 4. Butterworth, London (in press).

Sacktor, B., and Berger, S. J. (1969). *Biochem. Biophys. Res. Commun.* **35**, 796–800.

Sacktor, B., Chesney, R. W., Mitchell, M. E., and Aronson, P. S. (1974). *In* "Recent Advances in Renal Physiology and Pharmacology" (L. G. Wesson and G. M. Fanelli, Jr., eds.), pp. 13–26. Univ. Park Press, Baltimore, Maryland.

Sacktor, B., Balakir, R. A., and Filburn, C. F. (1976). In preparation.

Schafer, J. A., Troutman, S. L., and Andreoli, T. E. (1974). *J. Gen. Physiol.* **64**, 582–607.

Schmitz, J., Preiser, H., Maestracci, D., Ghosh, B. K., Cerda, J. J., and Crane, R. K. (1973). *Biochim. Biophys. Acta* **323**, 98–112.

Schultz, S. G., and Curran, P. F. (1970). *Physiol. Rev.* **50**, 637–718.

Scriver, C. R., and Rosenberg, L. E. (1973). "Amino Acid Metabolism and Its Disorders." Saunders, Philadelphia, Pennsylvania.

Senior, J. R., and Isselbacher, K. J. (1963). *J. Clin. Invest.* **42**, 187–195.

Shlatz, L. J., Schwartz, I. L., Kinne-Saffran, E., and Kinne, R. (1975). *J. Membr. Biol.* **24**, 131–144.

Sigrist-Nelson, K., and Hopfer, U. (1974). *Biochim. Biophys. Acta* **367**, 247–254.

Sigrist-Nelson, K., Murer, H., and Hopfer, U. (1975). *J. Biol. Chem.* **250**, 5674–5680.

Silverman, M. (1974). *Biochim. Biophys. Acta* **332**, 248–262.

Silverman, M., Aganon, M. A., and Chinard, F. P. (1970). *Am. J. Physiol.* **218**, 743–750.

Singer, I., and Civan, M. M. (1971). *Am. J. Physiol.* **221**, 1019–1026.

Steck, T. L., and Wallach, D. F. H. (1970). *Methods Cancer Res.* **5**, 93–153.

Stevenson, F. K. (1972). *Biochim. Biophys. Acta* **282**, 226–233.

Stevenson, F. K. (1973). *Biochim. Biophys. Acta* **311**, 409–416.

Thuneberg, L., and Rostgaard, J. (1968). *Exp. Cell Res.* **51**, 123–140.

Thuneberg, L., and Rostgaard, J. (1969). *J. Ultrastruct. in. Res.* **29**, 578.

Trier, J. S. (1968). *In* "Handbook of Physiology" (Am. Physiol. Soc., G. F. Code, ed.), Sect. 6, Vol. III, pp. 1125–1175. Williams & Wilkins, Baltimore, Maryland.

Ullrich, K. J., Rumrich, G., and Kloss, S. (1974). *Pfluegers Arch.* **351**, 35–48.

Ullrich, K. J., Rumrich, G., and Baumann, K. (1975). *Pfluegers Arch.* **357**, 149–163.

Walton, K. G., DeLorenzo, R. J., Curran, P. F., and Greengard, P. (1975). *J. Gen. Physiol.* **65**, 153–177.

Weiss, I. W., Morgan, K., and Phang, J. M. (1972). *J. Biol. Chem.* **247**, 760–764.

Wilfong, R. F., and Neville, D. M., Jr. (1970). *J. Biol. Chem.* **245**, 6106–6112.

Young, J. A., and Freedman, B. S. (1971). *Clin. Chem.* **16**, 245–266.

Membranes and Energy Transduction in Bacteria [1]

FRANKLIN M. HAROLD

Division of Molecular and Cellular Biology,
National Jewish Hospital and Research Center,
and Department of Microbiology and Immunology,
University of Colorado Medical School,
Denver, Colorado

> The growth of our knowledge is the result of a process closely resembling what Darwin called "natural selection"; that is, the natural selection of hypotheses: our knowledge consists, at every moment, of those hypotheses which have shown their (comparative) fitness by surviving so far in their struggle for existence. . . .
>
> *Karl Popper*

[1] Abbreviations: $\Delta\psi$, membrane potential; ΔpH, pH gradient; Δp, proton-motive force. These are related by: $\Delta p = \Delta\psi - (2.3RT/F) \Delta pH \cong \Delta\psi - 60 \Delta pH$. ANS, 1-anilino-8-naphthalene sulfonate; DCCD, N,N'-dicyclohexylcarbodiimide; CCCP, carbonylcyanide-m-chlorophenylhydrazone; HOQNO, hydroxyquinoline-N-oxide; PEP, phosphoenolpyruvic acid. EDTA, ATP, GTP, DNA, NAD(H), and NADP(H) have their usual meanings.

I. The Revolution in Membrane Biology

The study of bacterial bioenergetics, long overshadowed by molecular genetics, has flowered prodigiously in the past decade. The impetus came partly from the introduction of new and powerful tools—mutants defective in energy coupling, ionophores, and membrane vesicles. Equally significant has been the emergence of a unifying conceptual framework that links bacterial bioenergetics to that of mitochondria, chloroplasts, muscle, and nerve. Broadly stated, it is increasingly recognized that biochemical reactions may be so organized within membranes as to bring about the translocation of molecules, ions, or chemical groups across the membrane; that some of these reactions lead to the separation of electrical charges within and across the membrane; and that the recombination of charges underlies the performance of osmotic, chemical, and mechanical work.

The roots of these ideas reach back more than half a century (Robertson, 1968), but they found little welcome among biochemists or microbiologists until quite recently. The decisive event was the formulation by Peter Mitchell of his chemiosmotic hypothesis (1961), which sharpened the contrast between the traditional biochemistry of soluble enzymes and metabolic intermediates, and a new order of vectorial pathways linked by topology and ion gradients. This provocative proposal instigated a furious debate, now in its second decade, which has many of the hallmarks that Thomas Kuhn (1970) found characteristic of scientific revolutions. It has generated a quite excessive volume of print, some personal animosities, at least six more or less distinct models of energy coupling, but also a very respectable body of sound experimental work. Predictably, the controversy failed to produce consensus but is gradually being transcended by a new generation of investigators and problems.

The chemiosmotic theory has been thoroughly expounded both by its author (Mitchell, 1966, 1968, 1970a,b) and by others (Greville, 1969; Harold, 1972; Hamilton, 1975) and need not be recapitulated here. But it may be useful to highlight a few concepts that tend to become blurred, if only to render the meaning of words as sharp as possible. Chemiosmotic theory is not primarily about oxidative phosphorylation but about transport—its molecular basis and fundamental significance in the workings of cells. Historically, it grew out of Mitchell's dissatisfaction with existing concepts of "active transport," as perusal of his earlier papers (e.g., Mitchell, 1957, 1962a,b) makes quite clear. The essential idea is that many, if not all, enzyme-catalyzed reactions have a direction in space; this is not macroscopically visible in solution but may become apparent when enzymes are incorporated anistropically within a solid structure ("vectorial metabolism"). Some metabolic pathways mediate "primary" transport, reactions so articulated as to bring about the translocation of one of the participating particles or groups from one side of a membrane to the other (Mitchell, 1967). Primary transport processes can generate a concentration gradient or, in the case of ions, an electrochemical potential gradient; reactions that thus convert chemical energy into osmotic (more precisely, electrochemical) potential are the "chemiosmotic" reactions that lend their name to the theory. There are in addition various kinds of "secondary" transport processes, not covalently connected with any metabolic reaction; these include uniport, symport, and antiport carriers that depend upon ion gradients for the performance of work (Mitchell, 1967, 1970b, 1973b).

The proposed explanation for ATP synthesis in oxidative phosphorylation, like that for nutrient accumulation, grows logically from the concept of chemiosmotic reactions. An ion circulation actuated by a chemiosmotic reaction—expulsion of protons, for example—can "drive" the accumulation of nutrients by carriers of appropriate design. Likewise, a pair of reversible chemiosmotic reactions that translocate the same ion may be linked by an ion current so that one appears to "drive" the other (Mitchell, 1962a, 1966, 1968). In neither case need there be any close chemical or physical link between the reaction that generates the current and that which consumes it, but both must be localized in the same, topologically closed vesicle.

The object of this essay is to survey what is known of the mechanisms by which bacterial membranes generate useful energy and perform the work of chemical synthesis, transport, and movement. Let me state at the outset that I am among those who find the general framework of chemiosmotic theory intellectually and esthetically satisfying. But I would emphasize that, thanks to the work of many laboratories over the past five years, this position relies far less than formerly upon intuitive appeal but is founded on an increasingly solid experimental base. Chemiosmotic theory may not be the last word on how cells generate and utilize energy, but a strong case can now be made that any serious attempt to understand bacterial physiology must incorporate the insights to which this theory led.

I did not fully appreciate the magnitude of the task until it was too late to abandon it. Coverage of the literature extends to the summer of 1975. However, to keep the list of citations within bounds I have relied almost entirely on previous reviews for work done prior to 1973, and often cite the most recent report rather than that describing the original discovery. To those whose contributions were short-changed or inadvertently overlooked I would here like to offer my apologies.

II. Bacterial Energy Economy

A. The Role of Membranes

ATP and other "high–energy" compounds have been traditionally assigned a unique role in cellular economics (Lipmann, 1941). Energy-yielding reactions were seen as producing ATP, some by substrate-level phosphorylations catalyzed by soluble enzymes, others by membrane-bound electron transport. Energy-consuming reactions were considered to be driven by ATP (or by thermodynamically equivalent compounds, such as GTP or NADH); and ATP itself held pride of place as the universal energy currency. One of the major achievements of bioenergetics has been the recognition that this description is seriously oversimplified. Numerous studies, first with mitochondria and chloroplasts, later with bacteria, left no doubt that some membrane functions can be energized by electron transport directly, without the intermediacy of ATP. In keeping with concepts and nomenclature derived from the study of intermediary metabolism the linkage was envisaged as an energized state of the membrane, generally designated "~," which is in equilibrium with ATP but can also serve directly as an alternative form of energy currency (Ernster and Lee, 1964; Slater, 1971).

The general significance of energy coupling at the membrane level became apparent when membrane vesicles were seen, not only to "conserve energy" in some manner related to phosphorylation, but to perform physiologically useful work. To microbiologists, at least, the most compelling instance was the discovery (Kaback and Stadtman, 1966) that lysozyme-EDTA vesicles are devoid of soluble enzymes and metabolites yet accumulate sugars and amino acids at the expense of respiration; the linkage between transport and metabolism is clearly effected at the membrane itself without involvement of ATP (Kaback, 1972, 1974). French-press vesicles, whose polarity is inverted, carry out oxidative phosphorylation and transhydrogenation, and the analogous light-driven functions are performed by chromatophores. Characteristically all these functions are subject to uncoupling by ionophores, a hallmark of processes that depend upon the energized state. Studies with inhibitors and mutants show that even in intact cells much of the work of transport, phosphorylation, and motility is effected by the energized state of the membrane; that this can be generated both by electron transport and from ATP; and that these two energy currencies are interconvertible through the ubiquitous Mg^{2+}-dependent ATPase complex.

The great diversity of bacteria is in part a reflection of the variety of energy-yielding reactions they employ. We thus find a range of metabolic economies, some of which are illustrated in Fig. 1.

1. Fermentative Metabolism

Streptococcus faecalis and *S. lactis* (Fig. 1a) have a particularly simple metabolic pattern. When grown on glucose they are devoid of cytochromes and do not carry out oxidative phosphorylation but rely entirely on fermentative metabolism: the Embden–Meyerhof pathway of

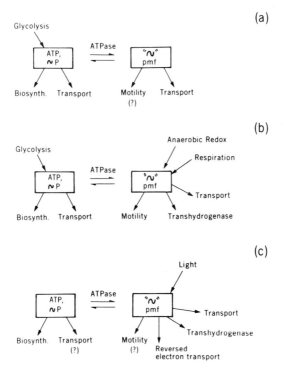

FIG. 1. Some bacterial energy economies. (a) Fermentative metabolism in organisms such as streptocci or clostridia. (b) Metabolism of facultative anaerobes, such as *Escherichia coli*. (c) Metabolism of photosynthetic bacteria.

glycolysis or the catabolism of arginine to ornithine. Thus all work functions ultimately depend upon ATP. The role of ATPase in generating the energized state is well established (Harold, 1972, 1974; Abrams, 1976; Abrams and Smith, 1974; Hamilton, 1975), but some transport processes require ATP more directly (Section IV,C). *Clostridium perfringens*, a strict anaerobe, probably has a very similar metabolic pattern (Riebling *et al.*, 1975).

It should perhaps be mentioned that some strains of *S. faecalis* do utilize fumarate as terminal electron acceptor for redox pathways, and even make cytochromes when supplied with heme; these presumably exhibit the more complex metabolic economy of facultative anaerobes (Ritchey and Seeley, 1975). Clostridia, however, appear to lack membrane-bound electron transport pathways that could generate an energized state (Dekker *et al.*, 1970; Barker, 1972).

2. *Fermentation and Respiration as Alternative Energy Donors*

Escherichia coli is a much more versatile organism that grows aerobically by oxidative phosphorylation, and anaerobically either by fermentation or by redox pathways that employ nitrate or fumarate as electron acceptors. The evidence that redox reactions and ATP are alternative means of generating the energized state (Fig. 1b) has been thoroughly discussed in recent reviews (Harold, 1972, 1974; Hamilton, 1975; Konings and Boonstra, 1976) and need not be recapitulated. Here again, some transport processes require ATP and other phosphoryl donors directly.

Is the ability to generate an energized state essential for growth? The behavior of mutants defective in the ATPase suggest that this is the case. It will be recalled that these mutants grow on glucose aerobically, with a growth yield similar to that of the parent strain anaerobically, but fail to grow on substrates that must be respired because oxidative phosphorylation is blocked (Butlin *et al.*, 1971; Cox and Gibson, 1974). The point is that mutants of the *uncA* type did not grow at all under anaerobic conditions; *uncB* mutant did. The paradox appears to have been resolved with the discovery (Rosenberg *et al.*, 1975) that this anaerobic growth depends upon the cell's ability to synthesize fumarate reductase, which affords an alternative pathway for energizing the membrane. Mutants that lack both the *uncB* function and fumarate reductase do not grow anaerobically, presumably because all means to generate the energized state have been blocked.

The pattern of Fig. 1b is a common one and probably holds for all the familiar facultative and strict aerobes, including chemolithotrophs (Suzuki, 1974). It also describes many strictly anaerobic bacteria that obtain energy from redox reactions including the sulfate-reducing bacteria or *Veillonella* (Konings *et al.*, 1975; Konings and Boonstra, 1976).

3. Photosynthetic Bacteria

Bacterial chromatophores exhibit much the same pattern of linkage between the photosynthetic apparatus and work functions as that described above for membranes of aerobes (Fig. 1c). An ATPase is part of the chromatophore membrane and serves as coupling factor both for the synthesis of ATP (photophosphorylation) and for its utilization as an energy donor for transhydrogenase or reversed electron transport. The latter functions are of particular importance for the generation of reducing power (Section V,B). The green and purple sulfur bacteria are strict anaerobes but the nonsulfur purple bacteria, such as *Rhodospirillum rubrum* can grow either anaerobically in the light or aerobically in the dark; the same ATPase serves for oxidative and photosynthetic phosphorylation (Baltscheffsky *et al.*, 1971; Gest, 1972; Baltscheffsky and Baltscheffsky, 1974; Parson, 1974; Lien and Gest, 1973; Gromet-Elhanan, 1974; see also Section V,A). Movement of metabolites across chromatophore membranes has apparently not been studied, but Hellingwerf *et al.* (1975) have described accumulation of amino acids by vesicles of *Rhodospirillium rubrum* whose polarity is like that of the parent cells. In vesicles from cells grown anaerobically in the light, uptake was supported by light; in vesicles from cells grown aerobically, uptake was supported by respiration.

A unique pattern is exhibited by certain extreme halophiles. *Halobacterium halobium* and its relatives respire and carry out oxidative phosphorylation, but when grown in the light under low oxygen tension they synthesize a purple pigment, bacteriorhodopsin, which constitutes a novel mechanism for transducing the energy of light into work functions (Oesterhelt and Stoeckenius, 1973; Danon and Stoeckenius, 1974). That coupling again takes place at the membrane level is shown particularly by the report (MacDonald and Lanyi, 1975; Kanner and Racker, 1975) that illuminated membrane vesicles accumulate amino acids and rubidium. Thus in these organisms, as in the *Athiorhodaceae*, respiration and light are probably alternative means of energizing the membrane.

B.   Energized State and Proton-Motive Force

The "energized state of the membrane" is a neutral term widely used by students of membrane physiology to discuss energy coupling but avoid dispute. We must now ask what physical reality the energized state represents, and this is, of course, the most contentious issue in bioenergetics. Traditionally the coupling between, say, respiration and phosphorylation or transport was envisaged in terms of high-energy intermediates. Boyer and others (Boyer, 1974; Weiss, 1973) prefer to think of conformational energized states transmitted by a matrix of adjoining macromolecules. Kaback (1972; Kaback and Hong, 1973) once championed a redox model, now withdrawn (Kaback, 1974), with features of both kinds of coupling. Straub (1974) proposed energy coupling by phonons, Caserta and Cerrigni (1973) a piezoelectric model, Green and his associates described in detail first the electromechano-chemical model (Green, 1974), then the paired-moving-charge model (Green and Reible, 1974, 1975; Green et al., 1975). Williams (1974, 1975) and Robertson and Boardman (1975) attribute energy coupling to the action of anhydrous protons within the hydrophobic phase of the membrane. And to chemiosmoticists it has been obvious all along that the energized state is the proton-motive force across the membrane.

We shall return to some of these proposals below in the context of particular physiological functions. Here we are concerned only with the energized state in the relatively specific sense discussed above (Fig. 1). In my judgment, evidently not universally shared, the experimental evidence strongly supports the thesis that the energized state is always associated with the existence of ΔpH, $\Delta\psi$, or both across the membrane, and that in prokaryotes at least these arise from the vectorial transloca-tion of protons. A summary of the evidence follows, with emphasis on bacterial systems.

1. *Metabolic reactions that energize the membrane also generate a proton-motive force across it.* In streptococci, glycolysis is accompanied by electrogenic proton extrusion and results in a ΔpH of about one unit (interior alkaline) and $\Delta\psi$ from -45 to -180 mV (interior negative) depending on conditions and method of measurement. Arginine fermen-tation generates $\Delta\psi$ but, for reasons never properly explained, no ΔpH (Harold, 1972; Harold and Altendorf, 1974; Laris and Pershadsingh, 1974; Kashket and Wilson, 1974; Riebling et al., 1975).

Respiring cells of *Staphylococcus aureus, E. coli,* and other bacteria extrude protons electrogenically and attain a Δp near -200 mV, much of it in form of a membrane potential (Hamilton, 1975; Lawford and Haddock, 1973; Griniuviene et al., 1974; Meyer and Jones, 1973). Membrane vesicles likewise extrude protons electrogenically; there seems to be little or no ΔpH but a large membrane potential as measured by K^+ distribution in presence of valinomycin, uptake of lipid-soluble cations and fluorescence quenching (Harold and Altendorf, 1974; Hamil-ton, 1975; Hirata et al., 1973; Altendorf et al., 1974, 1975; Griniuviene et al., 1975; Hertzberg and Hinkle, 1974).

Formation of ΔpH, $\Delta\psi$, and Δp by illuminated chromatophores has been extensively documented and the associated proton movements have been followed by rapid kinetic techniques (Jackson and Dutton, 1973; Cogdell et al., 1973; Cogdell and Crofts, 1974; Gromet-Elhanan and Leiser, 1973; Casadio et al., 1974; Schuldiner et al., 1974). Bacteriorhodopsin also extrudes protons with generation of $\Delta\psi$ (Oesterhelt and Stoeckenius, 1973; Racker and Stoeckenius, 1974; MacDonald and Lanyi, 1975; Kanner and Racker, 1975).

2. *The polarity of the proton-motive force corresponds to that of the energized membrane.* The vectorial nature of many energy-linked functions is obvious: cells, for example, accumulate amino acids but extrude protons and Ca^{2+}. In sonic vesicles, or those prepared by use of a French press, the polarity is inverted: both respiration and ATP hydrolysis lead to the uptake of protons with formation of a membrane potential interior positive (Hertzberg and Hinkle, 1974; Gorneva and Ryabova, 1974). Chromatophores also show this polarity, in contrast to the parent cells.

3. *Both the energized state and the proton-motive force require a topologically closed structure.* This is a crucial assertion since, were it proved to be false, the chemiosmotic theory would have to be abandoned. It is the general experience that the coupling between respiration or photosynthesis and such functions as ATP synthesis, transhydrogenase, proton translocation or fluorescence quenching are seen only in vesicular structures but claims to the contrary have appeared in the literature. For instance, Hunter and his associates (Hunter and Capaldi, 1974; Hunter et al., 1974) reported that submitochondrial particles prepared with lysolecithin are nonvesicular but still carry out at least partial reactions of oxidative phosphorylation. Cole and Aleem (1973) described oxidative phosphorylation by an apparently soluble preparation from *Thiobacillus*. It will also be recalled that Reeves et al. (1972) claimed that *E. coli* vesicles could extrude protons and quench ANS fluorescence even after the vesicular structure had been disrupted by detergents, an inconsistency not yet cleared up.

4. *Reagents and conditions that dissipate the proton-motive force deenergize the membrane.* Examples include proton-conducting uncouplers, valinomycin plus K^+ and certain other ionophores. The interpretation of experiments with ionophores has been discussed elsewhere (Harold, 1972; Henderson, 1971; Harold and Altendorf, 1974; Harold et al., 1974; Hamilton, 1975; McLaughlin and Eisenberg, 1975). The special case of colicins will be considered in Section VII.

Membrane vesicles prepared from certain mutants deficient in the ATPase exhibit an unexpected defect in coupling respiration to transport. This turns out to be due to the high proton conductance of these membranes; treatment with DCCD "seals" the membrane and restores coupling functions (Rosen, 1973; Rosen and Adler, 1975; Altendorf *et al.*, 1974) (Section III,D). It is noteworthy that energy-linked functions always require the membrane to be impermeable to protons but not necessarily impermeable to other ions, such as K^+. However, it need not follow that only increased proton conductance can bring about "uncoupling" (e.g., Hatefi *et al.*, 1975).

5. *Indicators of the energized state respond to ΔpH or $\Delta\psi$.* Quenching and enhancement of dye fluorescence often serves to signal the energized state of the membrane but can also be elicited by manipulation of ΔpH or $\Delta\psi$ and is increasingly used to measure these parameters quantitatively (for recent examples, see Laris and Pershadsingh, 1974; Casadio *et al.*, 1974; Kashket and Wilson, 1974; Barsky *et al.*, 1975; Griniuviene *et al.*, 1975). The reliability of these procedures has been assessed by Rottenberg (1975). In chromatophores, shifts in the spectra of carotenoids and chlorophyll report the membrane potential (Jackson and Dutton, 1973; Cogdell and Crofts, 1974; Casadio *et al.*, 1974; Barsky *et al.*, 1975; Rottenberg, 1975).

6. *The energized state can be produced by imposing an artificial $\Delta\psi$, ΔpH, or Δp across the membrane.* In membrane vesicles, as in whole cells, accumulation of sugars and amino acids occurs in response to artificial gradients in the absence of any source of metabolic energy (Section IV,A). Such nonmetabolic "active transport," like that supported by metabolism, is abolished by proton conductors but is unaffected by metabolic inhibitors. Moreover, it has now been shown that in bacterial cells and in chromatophores ATP synthesis can be elicited by a nonmetabolic Δp (Section V,A). That this is true for mitochondria and chloroplasts has been known for a decade.

In this connection I would like to join Hamilton's plea (1975) for greater rigor in the use of chemiosmotic terms. The pH gradient ΔpH, electrical potential $\Delta\psi$ and the proton-motive force Δp (or the electrochemical potential of H^+, $\Delta\bar{\mu}_{H^+}$) are clearly defined entities (Mitchell, 1966, 1968, 1970b) that can be discussed even by those who question their physiological role. By contrast the popular but undefined "proton gradient" means exactly what the author wants it to mean. A more serious difficulty arises in the description of experiments, such as those cited above, in which imposition of an artificial ΔpH or $\Delta\psi$ elicits some physiological response, such as transport. What is the driving force— ΔpH, $\Delta\psi$, or Δp? This question can be approached experimentally, but not many studies have attempted to assess the contributions of ΔpH, $\Delta\psi$, and Δp (but see Kashket and Wilson, 1973, 1974; Hamilton, 1975; Gromet-Elhanan and Leiser, 1975; Leiser and Gromet-Elhanan, 1975; Casadio *et al.*, 1974; Schuldiner *et al.*, 1974).

To sum up: There is mounting evidence that bacteria do generate a proton-motive force by the vectorial, electrogenic translocation of protons; that a proton-motive force can support the physiological functions normally energized by metabolism; and that any condition that abolishes Δp also abolishes the energized state. Does this then establish the identity of the qualitative, abstract "energized state" with the quantitative and tangible proton-motive force? Perhaps not quite. The molecular mechanisms by which protons are extruded and the work of transport, phosphorylation, or movement are performed, are in no case fully understood. Thus, while there is no operational way at present to distinguish between the Δp *across* the membrane and an energized state of membrane proteins, it is not inconceivable that this may be possible in future. The physical meaning, if any, of this distinction will probably be clarified only when precise molecular mechanisms replace our present usage.

But we have come a long way toward an overall understanding of bacterial energy metabolism. Bacteria employ two fundamentally different classes of reactions to make energy available (Fig. 1). One class consists of macroscopically scalar reactions that generate ATP and other "energy-rich" compounds by substrate-level phosphorylation. Glycolysis, arginine fermentation, and the bizarre ATP-yielding processes of clostridia (Barker, 1972; Dekker *et al.*, 1970) are of this kind. Energy-rich compounds function in intermediary metabolism and also support particular transport processes (Section IV,C,D), and future research may reveal additional membrane functions. The second class consists of pathways that translocate protons vectorially across a membrane to generate a proton circulation. Aerobic and anaerobic redox chains, photosynthesis, bacteriorhodopsin, and perhaps others yet to be discovered belong in this category. The proton circulation directly supports many transport processes, transhydrogenase, and (at least in *E. coli*) the flagellar motor. Probably all bacteria possess the proton-translocating ATPase which links cytoplasmic ATP to the proton circulation. And it would appear that for prokaryotes the proton is the characteristic coupling ion, possibly the only one.

III. Proton-Translocating Pathways

It is one thing to identify the respiratory chain, the photosynthetic apparatus, or the ATPase complex as pathways that translocate protons, and quite another to specify at the molecular level how they do it. In this respect research on bacterial systems, with the notable exception of light-dependent ones, lags behind that with mitochondria; a coherent picture is possible only by appealing to analogy.

A. REDOX CHAINS

It seems now to be generally accepted that in mitochondria the passage of two reducing equivalents from NADH to oxygen is accompanied by the electrogenic translocation of six protons: two each in the regions defined by NADH and the nonheme iron-sulfur centers; ubiquinone and cytochrome b; and cytochrome c to oxygen. A functional ATPase is not required, nor has any other ancillary device been found necessary for proton transport. The general principle may be that of the redox loop (Mitchell, 1966) whereby in effect at each coupling site two H travel outward across the membrane by a hydrogen carrier; two electrons pass back by an electron carrier; and two protons are liberated into the medium. But the molecular mechanism of these translocations remains very much in doubt (for recent discussions of the mitochondrial redox chain, see Wikström, 1973; Hinkle, 1973; Harmon et al., 1974; Baltscheffsky and Baltscheffsky, 1974; Skulachev, 1974; Papa et al., 1974, 1975; Dutton and Wilson, 1974, Mitchell, 1975b). To mention but one of several unresolved problems, potential hydrogen carriers are found in the first two sites but not in the third. Mitchell (1975b) has suggested a solution to this and related issues but its presentation is beyond the scope of an article on bacterial energy metabolism.

Bacterial respiratory chains resemble that of mitochondria in general structure and presumably serve the same basic function, namely, the electrogenic transport of protons. But the constitution of bacterial chains is far more variable, particularly in the terminal segment, and for each organism varies further with physiological conditions. Others are better qualified than I to review this voluminous and confused literature (Jurtshuk et al., 1975; Haddock and Jones, 1976); a few points must suffice here. Among the familiar chemoheterotrophs a number have chains that include cytochromes c and either aa_3 or o as terminal oxidase; these have three coupling sites (*Mycobacterium phlei, Micrococcus lysodeikticus, Paracoccus denitrificans, Pseudomonas* sp.). Others lack cytochrome c (*E. coli, Bacillus subtilis, B. megaterium*) and probably have only two sites (Lawford and Haddock, 1973; Jones et al., 1975). The first two sites involve flavoprotein, nonheme iron, quinone, and cytochromes b as do the mitochondrial ones. Under conditions of slow growth cytochrome d becomes the main terminal oxidase and only a single coupling site appears to be present (Meyer and Jones, 1973; Pudek and Bragg, 1974; Ashcroft and Haddock, 1975).

There is ample evidence that respiring cells of *E. coli* and many other bacteria do translocate protons electrogenically. In fact, the ratio of protons extruded to oxygen consumed is probably the best index of the number of coupling sites (Meyer and Jones, 1973; Lawford and Haddock, 1973; Hertzberg and Hinkle, 1974; Jones *et al.*, 1975). The ability of vesicles to extrude protons indicates that no soluble constituents are needed, nor is a functional ATPase. But the uncertainty of the sequence of carriers means that the loops drawn in Fig. 2 are little more than a guess. There is some evidence that the first loop involves NADH dehydrogenase, with a second loop further down the chain; lactate feeds electrons into that second loop only, presumably at the level of quinone (Poole and Haddock, 1974, 1975a; Hertzberg and Hinkle, 1974; Bragg and Hou, 1974). Cytochromes of the *b* type, multiple in bacteria (Hendler *et al.*, 1975) as in mitochondria, constitute the electrogenic arm of the second loop. Existence of a third loop is doubtful (Lawford and Haddock, 1973; Jones *et al.*, 1975), but it is interesting that Cox and Gibson (1974) cite evidence for involvement of ubiquinone both before cytochrome *b* and after; if true, this could be the hydrogen carrier of a third loop. In this connection one wonders how and where electrons enter the respiratory chain in "reconstituted" vesicles in which lactate dehydrogenase is localized at the outer surface (Futai, 1974b; Short *et al.*, 1974, 1975).

Equally tentative looped chains could be drawn for organisms with three coupling sites, particularly *Paracoccus denitrificans* (John and Whatley, 1975) and *Rhodospirillum* (Baccarini-Melandri *et al.*, 1973; King and Drews, 1975), whose respiratory chains are strikingly similar

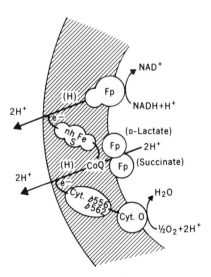

FIG. 2. Possible respiratory loops in *Escherichia coli*. A tentative scheme showing two loops; oxidation of NADH involves both loops, oxidation of lactate or succinate only the second.

to that of mitochondria. In no case is there an obvious hydrogen carrier for the third loop.

Anaerobic redox chains are characteristic of many bacteria. One such is the oxidation of formate by *E. coli* with nitrate as terminal acceptor, a particularly simple and well characterized chain that now includes the cytochromes *b*, quinone, nonheme iron, and selenium as well as molybdenum (MacGregor, 1975; Enoch and Lester, 1975). The chain translocates four protons, but the orientation of the nitrate reductase within the membrane is not yet unequivocally established (Kemp *et al.*, 1975; B. A. Haddock, personal communication). A very different anaerobic chain oxidizes NADH with fumarate as acceptor, without the participation of hemoproteins (Singh and Bragg, 1975). This pathway energizes the membrane and supports transport (Singh and Bragg, 1975; Rosenberg *et al.*, 1975), but proton translocation has not yet been measured. Finally, mention might be made of the redox chains of strict anaerobes, such as *Desulfovibrio* and other sulfate-reducing bacteria (LeGall and Postgate, 1973; Konings and Boonstra, 1976), whose loops are not yet ready for stringing.

B. The Photosynthetic Apparatus

We are considerably better informed concerning the mechanism of proton translocation in bacterial photosynthesis, thanks to sophisticated studies on chromatophores of *Rhodospirillum rubrum* and *Rhodopseudomonas capsulata*.

Chromatophores do not exist as such in cells but arise by comminution of a membranous structure that is thought to be continuous with the cytoplasmic membrane, and become inverted in the process. When illuminated, chromatophores take up protons by an electrogenic process closely associated with cyclic electron flow, generating a membrane potential (interior positive) and, under conditions that allow charge compensation, a pH gradient as well (Baltscheffsky *et al.*, 1971; Gest, 1972; Parson, 1974; Crofts *et al.*, 1974). Removal of the ATPase does not impair electron flow.

How is proton translocation brought about? Primary charge separation occurs in the photosynthetic reaction center buried within the membrane, a subject recently reviewed (Parson, 1974; Parson and Cogdell, 1975). Suffice it to recall that absorption of a quantum of light ejects an electron from a special chlorophyll molecule; the electron reduces the primary acceptor, probably a nonheme-iron center complexed with quinone, and the chlorophyll is reoxidized at the expense of cytochrome c_2. These components are so arranged that an electric field arises. An electron transport chain that includes quinone, cytochrome *b*, and an antimycin-sensitive site carries the electron back to cythchrome c_2 to complete the circuit (Jackson and Dutton, 1973; Cogdell *et al.*, 1973; Crofts *et al.*, 1974). Direct proof of charge separation by the reaction center has been reported by Drachev *et al.* (1975): Isolated reaction center preparations were incorporated into either liposomes or planar bilayer membranes; in the presence of an electron donor on one side and of a lipid-soluble hydrogen carrier (CoQ or vitamin K_3), an electric current was found to flow across the membrane.

Charge separation in illuminated chromatophores manifests itself as proton uptake, which was resolved into a fast and a slow phase. Analysis by laser flash and rapid kinetic techniques showed convincingly that the initial rapid uptake H^+ is an integral part of the reduction of the "secondary acceptor," probably quinone; this takes place at the outer surface of the chromatophore membrane, with electrons donated by the primary acceptor and protons from the medium (Fig. 3). The slow phase of proton uptake was attributed, albeit less confidently, to a second proton translocation involving cytochrome b and an unidentified hydrogen carrier Z (Cogdell *et al.*, 1973; Cogdell and Crofts, 1974). Two molecules of cytochrome c_2 are localized at the inner surface of the chromatophore membrane (Dutton *et al.*, 1975; Prince *et al.*, 1975), and their oxidation closes the cycle. The tentative scheme shown in Fig. 3 includes both the first loop after Prince *et al.* (1975) and also the more uncertain second loop (Cogdell *et al.*, 1973; Cogdell and Crofts, 1974; Crofts *et al.*, 1974).

It should be emphasized here that the light reaction must be oriented so as to pass across the membrane: cytochrome c_2 was trapped within the chromatophores, loosely bound to the membrane; in the intact cells

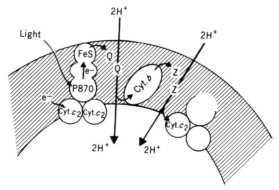

FIG. 3. Possible pathway for proton translocation during cyclic electron flow in chromatophores of *Rhodopseudomonas spheroides*. After Prince *et al.* (1975) and Crofts *et al.* (1974) with permission.

it is localized in the periplasmic space (Prince *et al.*, 1975). The protons come from the aqueous phase on the opposite side. Thus in this case, at least, we are dealing with vectorial reactions that connect the aqueous phases across the membrane, as envisaged in the chemiosmotic theory, rather than being confined to the hydrophobic phase of the membrane itself.

Nonsulfur purple bacteria grow either photosynthetically in the light or heterotrophically in the dark. In the latter case they do not make the photosynthetic reaction center, but rather a complete respiratory chain with a terminal cytochrome oxidase (Baccarini-Melandri *et al.*, 1973; Oelze and Kamen, 1975, King and Drews, 1975). Adaptation of cells from photosynthetic to respiratory growth involves loss of the reaction center and acquisition of cytochrome oxidase but at least one each of the existing cytochromes *b* and *c* are conserved in their original orientation (Connelly *et al.*, 1973; Jones and Plewis, 1974). Studies on transport of electrons and protons in photosynthesis thus bear on the orientation of the respiratory chain as well.

The purple and green sulfur bacteria have not been as fully studied, but it is likely that both the photochemical reaction and subsequent electron transport are generally similar to those outlined above (Parson and Cogdell, 1975; Dutton and Leigh, 1973; Knaff and Buchanan, 1975).

C. BACTERIORHODOPSIN

The purple photoreceptor pigment of *Halobacterium halobium* is chemically the simplest known proton pump. The purple patches contain but a single kind of protein, associated with retinal (bacteriorhodopsin), together with lipids. The retinal is bound as a protonated Schiff base to a lysine residue of the protein and is also complexed with aromatic amino acids that form a hydrophobic pocket around it (Lewis *et al.*, 1974; Lozier *et al.*, 1975). The bacteriorhodopsin molecules are arrayed in a single layer with their long axis spanning the membrane (Henderson, 1975; Blaurock, 1975; Henderson and Unwin, 1975).

Upon illumination of membrane fractions or cells the pigment is bleached, with vectorial release of a proton to the medium side; regeneration of the original pigment consumes a proton from the cytoplasm. One proton is ejected for each photon absorbed (Oesterhelt and Hess, 1974; Oesterhelt *et al.*, 1973; Lozier *et al.*, 1975). Bacteriorhodopsin thus functions as a light-driven proton pump, which can perform various kinds of work including transport and ATP synthesis (Oesterhelt and Stoeckenius, 1973; Danon and Stoeckenius, 1974; MacDonald and Lanyi, 1975).

Direct evidence for electrogenic proton transport comes from experiments in which bacteriorhodopsin was incorporated into liposomes or planar lipid bilayer membranes. Illumination was shown to result in vectorial proton transport across the membrane, variously detected as $\Delta\psi$, ΔpH, or by the flow of an electric current (Kayushin and Skulachev, 1974. Drachev et al., 1974; Racker and Stoeckenius, 1974). In fact, bacteriorhodopsin transferred protons from an aqueous suspension into an octanol phase, as detected by the generation of a Volta potential (Boguslavsky et al., 1975). The effects of temperature and lipid composition in such reconstituted preparations suggested that proton translocation involves some kind of channel mechanism rather than a mobile carrier (Racker and Hinkle, 1974).

By means of low-temperature and laser-flash spectroscopy, Stoeckenius and his associates were able to resolve the cycle of bleaching and regeneration into a series of spectral intermediates and to identify the steps at which the uptake and release of protons take place (Lozier et al., 1975). At the structural level they envisage a chain of proton-exchanging groups across the membrane, either through the bacteriorhodopsin molecule or along its surface; each group would be protonated and deprotonated once in the cycle. The only candidate chemically identified so far is the Schiff base that links retinal to the protein; this undergoes rapid exchange with deuterium in the light (Lewis et al., 1974) and was found to be protonated in one of the intermediates, unprotonated in another. Lozier et al. (1975) suggest that it is at this strategically located group that energy input occurs, perhaps by a transient shift of the pK when light is absorbed; appropriate conformation changes would ensure unidirectional proton transfer.

D. ATPASE AND PYROPHOSPHATASE

Bacterial membranes, like those of mitochondria and chloroplasts, often appear in photomicrographs to be studded with knobs that project into the cytoplasm. These can be identified with the Mg-dependent ATPase complex (Abrams and Smith, 1974; Abrams, 1976; Pedersen, 1975a). For the mitochondrial enzyme there is now very strong evidence that hydrolysis of ATP is accompanied by electrogenic transport of protons across the membrane, away from the knobbed side; the stoichiometry is probably two protons per ATP hydrolyzed (Thayer and Hinkle, 1973; Moyle and Mitchell, 1973b). Several laboratories have described proton translocation by purified ATPase incorporated into artificial planar or vesicular lipid membranes (Kagawa et al., 1973; Skulachev, 1974; Drachev et al., 1974), leaving little doubt that proton transport is an intrinsic function of this enzyme complex and requires no exogenous components such as respiratory carriers.

Evidence from bacterial systems is still somewhat meager. Chromatophores of *R. rubrum* (Scholes *et al.*, 1969) and inverted membrane vesicles of *E. coli* (Hertzberg and Hinkle, 1974; West and Mitchell, 1974a) translocate protons electrogenically when hydrolyzing ATP but the stoichiometry is uncertain. Since whole membranes were studied there also remains some possibility that components outside the ATPase complex proper are involved in proton transport, but participation of cytochromes is ruled out by the finding that streptococci extrude protons during ATP hydrolysis (Harold and Papineau, 1972b). We shall proceed on the premise that the bacterial ATPase complex, like the mitochondrial one, functions physiologically as a proton-translocating pathway.

As information accumulates about molecular characteristics, the family resemblance between the ATPase complexes of bacteria, mitochondria, and chloroplasts becomes ever more apparent (Abrams, 1976; Pedersen, 1975a). In all cases the enzyme complex comprises two distinct regions—the headpiece, F_1, which can often be dissociated from the membrane by washing with buffers of low ionic strength; and the membrane portion, or basepiece, F_0. The ATPase of *S. faecalis* includes a third element, the protein nectin, which links the headpiece to the membrane; in other bacteria this function may be performed by a subunit of the headpiece. As a rule only the membrane-bound enzyme is inhibited by DCCD or by oligomycin; the DCCD-binding site is part of the membrane portion of the complex (Abrams and Smith, 1974; Abrams, 1976; Simoni and Postma, 1975).

The molecular constitutions of some solubilized bacterial ATPase headpieces are compared in Table I. The purified ATPase of *E. coli*, presently the subject of intense scrutiny, is made up of five distinct subunits in the proportions $\alpha_3\beta_3\gamma\delta\epsilon$. Enzymes of this composition can reassociate with the depleted membranes with reconstitution of coupling functions (Futai *et al.*, 1974; Bragg *et al.*, 1973; Bragg and Hou, 1975; Smith and Sternweis, 1975). A somewhat different preparative procedure yields headpieces that lack the δ subunit (Hanson and Kennedy, 1973; Kobayashi and Anraku, 1974; Nelson *et al.*, 1974; Futai *et al.*, 1974); these do not rebind to the residual membranes. It thus seems likely that the δ subunit is involved in binding the headpiece to the membrane portion and is functionally equivalent to the nectin of *S. faecalis*. Trypsin stimulates ATPase activity and removes the δ and ϵ subunits, as well as part of the γ subunit. Thus δ or ϵ, or perhaps both, may be equivalent to the inhibitory subunits of mitochondrial and chloroplast ATPases. The active site of the enzyme is associated with

TABLE I

SOME ATPase HEADPIECES OF BACTERIA AND ORGANELLES[a]

Source	Molecular weight $\times 10^{-3}$	Subunits and molecular weight $\times 10^{-3}$					Proposed structure	Bound nucleotides	Inhibitors	References
		α	β	γ	δ	ϵ				
Escherichia coli	360–390	56.8	51.8	32.2	20.9	13.2	$\alpha_3\beta_3\gamma\delta\epsilon$	ATP, ADP	DCCD, azide	(1, 5)
Salmonella typhimurium	—	56.8	51.8	30.9	21.5	13.2	$\alpha_3\beta_3\gamma\delta\epsilon$	—	—	(1)
Alcaligenes faecalis	—	59	54	43	—	12	—	—	—	(2)
Micrococcus lysodeikticus	345	52	47	41	28.5	—	$\alpha_3\beta_3\gamma\delta$	—	DCCD	(3)
Rhodospirillum rubrum	350	54	50	32	13	7.5	—	ATP, ADP	DCCD, oligomycin	(4)
Streptococcus faecalis	385	60	55	37	20 (nectin)	13	$\alpha_3\beta_3\gamma\delta\epsilon$	ATP, ADP	DCCD	(5)
Liver mitochondria	384	62.5	57	36	12	7.5	$\alpha_3\beta_3\gamma\delta\epsilon$	ATP, ADP	DCCD, oligomycin	(6)
Chloroplasts	325	62	59	43	21	14	$\alpha_3\beta_3\gamma\delta\epsilon$	ATP, ADP	DCCD	(7)

[a] References: (1) Bragg and Hou, 1975; (2) Adolfsen et al., 1975; (3) Andreu and Muñoz, 1975; (4) Johansson and Baltscheffsky, 1975; Lutz et al., 1974; (5) Abrams, 1976; Abrams et al., 1975, and personal communication; (6) Pedersen, 1975a.

the α and β subunits (Bragg and Hou, 1975; Futai *et al.*, 1974; Nelson *et al.*, 1974; Smith and Sternweis, 1975).

While it is not certain that the *E. coli* ATPase is representative of bacterial ATPases generally, this does appear increasingly likely. Recent work on the ATPase of *S. faecalis*, for example (Abrams, 1976; Abrams *et al.*, 1975), makes this enzyme appear much more like that of *E. coli* than had formerly been thought. Loss of the minor subunits during purification probably accounts for some of the differences between ATPase preparations.

A number of mutants defective in the ATPase complex have been described (reviewed by Cox and Gibson, 1974; Simoni and Postma, 1975), many of them with apparent lesions in the headpiece. The original *uncA* strain, for instance, lacks ATPase activity but produces an inactive headpiece; a related strain *unc405*, also lacks ATPase activity and apparently produces headpieces that are defective and found in the cytoplasm (Cox *et al.*, 1974). Other varieties were noted by Kanner *et al.* (1975) and by Daniel *et al.* (1975). In no case is it yet possible to relate the genetic lesion to a particular subunit, although Bragg *et al* (1973) reported reproducible alteration of the γ subunit in *etc* mutants.

The membrane portion of the ATPase complex is much less well known although its functional importance is clear from the effects of inhibitors and mutations. DCCD is known to react with a binding site in the membrane and inhibits ATP hydrolysis secondarily; release of the headpiece from the membrane relieves the inhibition (Abrams and Smith, 1974). A number of mutants whose ATPase is resistant to DCCD have been isolated; some of these mutants still hydrolyze ATP but cannot couple this to energy-linked functions (Abrams, 1976; Cox and Gibson, 1974; Simoni and Postma, 1975; Kanner *et al.*, 1975). We do not yet know how many components the basepiece comprises nor precisely what they do, but it is fairly certain that a general role of the basepiece in bacteria, as in mitochondria (Mitchell, 1973a) is to control the access of protons to the catalytic site.

This insight stemmed from efforts to clear up the following paradox. The ATPase complex should not be required to link respiration to transport or transhydrogenase (Section II,B) and indeed this linkage is normal in mutants such as *uncA*. Unexpectedly, however, membrane vesicles prepared from several other ATPase mutants (DL-54, NR70) proved to be severely defective in energy coupling; coupling could be restored by treating the vesicles with DCCD (Simoni and Schallenberger, 1972; other references cited in Simoni and Postma, 1975). Closer study revealed that the vesicles, and to a lesser extent mutant cells, are highly and specifically permeable to protons; treatment with DCCD seals the leak (Rosen, 1973; Altendorf *et al.*, 1974). It had been found earlier that removal of the ATPase from mitochondrial or chloroplast membranes renders these permeable to protons and again treatment with DCCD seals the leak. To account for these results Mitchell (1973a) proposed that part of the basepiece serves as a specific proton-conducting channel or ionophore which passes protons across the hydrophobic barrier to the catalytic site at the interface of headpiece and membrane. Reaction with DCCD blocks the channel. In the normal, intact enzyme complex proton translocation is tightly coupled to ATP hydrolysis; DCCD, by blocking the proton channel, renders the complex physiologically nonfunctional. In mutants such as DL-54 or NR70 the proton channel is exposed, perhaps because the particular subunit that plugs the channel comes off the membrane, resulting in complete uncoupling (Fig. 4A).

Precisely what is meant by "exposure" of the proton channel remains to be determined. It may well result from a change in conformation of the headpiece rather than its loss (Rosen and Adler, 1975). Curiously, treatment of membrane vesicles with chaotropic agents also renders them proton permeable and again treatment with DCCD restores a tight seal (Patel et al., 1975).

Assuming the preceding argument to be generally correct, we must still inquire just how the hydrolysis of ATP brings about the electrogenic movement of protons and conversely, how a proton-motive force can reverse the reaction and accomplish ATP synthesis (Section V,A). It is also necessary to account for such features as the various exchange reactions, the presence of bound nucleotides, and the fact that hydrolysis of ATP and its synthesis differ kinetically and also in their response to certain inhibitors (Pedersen, 1975a). Two distinct models have begun to emerge.

1. Mitchell's views (1973a, 1974) are based squarely on the concept of vectorial metabolism and assign a major role to the molecular channels that guide the participants to the catalytic site. The later of two versions is shown schematically in Fig. 4. It is proposed that ATP finds access to the active center by a channel specific for ATP in a state of protonation and salt formation that corresponds to the neutral species ADPOP; similarly, other channels through the headpiece would specify states corresponding to ADPO$^-$ and PO$^-$. Water and protons pass to the catalytic site by specific channels through the basepiece but cannot enter from the cytoplasmic side. It is important that the stoichiometry and specificity of ion translocation are imposed by the orientation and properties of the channels that lead participating molecules to the catalytic site, rather than by the site itself.

At the catalytic site Mitchell envisages a nucleophilic substitution reaction at a pentavalent transitional phosphorus configuration, oriented

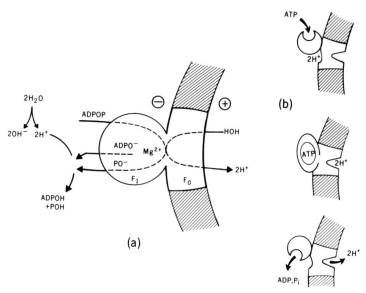

FIG. 4. Possible models for the proton-translocating ATPase. (a) Chemiosmotic mechanism after Mitchell (1974), with permission. (b) Proton translocase mechanism with conformational changes. The reaction is reversible, but for clarity the arrows point in the hydrolytic direction. For explanation see text.

in a specific manner with respect to the proton-motive field (Mitchell, 1974) (Fig. 4). In the hydrolytic reaction, ADPOP is hydroxylated from the right to yield the transitional intermediate, which then cleaves with release of the second proton. Thus the ATPase does not actually translocate protons from left to right but rather O^{2-} from right to left across the catalytic center. Similarly, synthesis of ATP is seen as involving transfer of O^{2-} from left to right: PO^-, trapped at the catalytic center, would be successively protonated to POH and POH_2^+ by protons from the right, present on that side at a high electrochemical potential. The POH_2^+ reacts with ADP, releasing water toward the right. Mitchell's proposal has been severely criticized by Boyer (1975a) and by Williams (1975) as being both chemically and thermodynamically implausible, and the objections were answered by Mitchell (1975a). Significantly, neither critic offers an alternative proposal to accommodate what seems to be the chief physiological role of ATPase, namely, the translocation of protons.

2. An alternative mechanism for the ATPase complex can be based on the idea that ATP hydrolysis induces conformational changes in the enzyme complex, the net result of which is the vectorial release of protons. Skulachev (1974) described this in terms of a rotating "proton

translocase," and a somewhat different version is shown schematically in Fig. 4b, which retains the concept of the proton well (Mitchell, 1968, 1975a). Binding of ATP to a specific site on the headpiece would cause a conformational change in the basepiece such that a proton-binding site of low pK_a is exposed at the other surface in the bottom of the well. Hydrolysis of the bound ATP (in a vectorial manner) is accompanied by further conformational changes, which release the protons and restore the initial state. A model of this kind would correspond to the "conformational" hypothesis of oxidative phosphorylation (Section V,A).

Chromatophores of *R. rubrum* possess not only an orthodox ATPase but also a quite distinct energy-linked pyrophosphatase. Illumination of chromatophores in presence of P_i, without ADP, leads to accumulation of pyrophosphate; the enzyme also catalyzes energy-linked exchange reactions (Baltscheffsky *et al.*, 1971; Keister and Raveed, 1974). Conversely, hydrolysis of pyrophosphate generates ΔpH and $\Delta\psi$ (Barsky *et al.*, 1975) and is accompanied by electrogenic proton translocation with a stoichiometry of $H^+/PP_i = 0.5$ (Moyle *et al.*, 1972). This enzyme appears so far to be confined to the Athiorhodaceae and may possibly be a metabolic fossil, recalling an evolutionary stage when pyrophosphate rather than ATP played the central role in energy metabolism (Baltscheffsky *et al.*, 1971).

IV.   The Work of Transport

The cytoplasmic membrane is at once the barrier that separates cytoplasm from medium and the link between them. Traffic across the membrane is not a matter of "selective permeability" but of transport: with a few exceptions, such as water and ammonia, passage of metabolites occurs by the agency of specific transport systems. Bacteria, being free-living, produce a large number of transport systems of diverse kinds whose substrates range from trace metals and vitamins through the major nutrients to transforming DNA and the precursors of extracellular macromolecules. Transport has recently been well served by reviews differing in scope and orientation (Boos, 1974a,b; Harold, 1974; Harold and Altendorf, 1974; Kaback, 1974; Oxender, 1974; Oxender and Quay, 1976; Roseman, 1972); those by Hamilton (1975) and Simoni and Postma (1975) are particularly pertinent in the present context.

This section is concerned with transport as an energy transduction, the performance of work that is useful to the cell. A few bacterial transport systems merely facilitate diffusion from one side of the membrane to the other, as does the glycerol carrier of *E. coli* (Richey and Lin, 1972) or that for lactic acid in *S. faecalis* (Harold and Levin, 1974), but most are obviously geared to the performance of osmotic work that is oriented in space. Bacteria provide many examples, often spectacular, of "active transport": In *E. coli* amino acids and β-galactosides accumulate in the cytoplasm by a factor of 1 to 3 × 10³, galactose by 10⁵, and the K⁺ concentration may exceed that of the medium by 10⁶. By contrast Na⁺ and Ca²⁺ are expelled from the cells against the electrochemical potential gradient. Group translocations, such as uptake of sugars by the PEP-dependent phosphotransferase system, do not conform to the thermodynamic definition of active transport but accomplish the same physiological end. Bacteria probably allocate a substantial fraction of their energy budget to the work of transport, estimates ranging from a quarter to over one half depending on conditions (Forrest and Walker, 1971; Stouthamer, 1973). The molecular mechanisms involved have been brilliantly illuminated by the concept of secondary coupling via an ion circulation (Mitchell, 1970a,b, 1973b), but it is also quite clear now that this is by no means the only device employed by bacteria to perform the work of transport.

A. COUPLING OF TRANSPORT TO METABOLISM VIA THE PROTON CIRCULATION

According to the chemiosmotic theory, transport systems are linked to the metabolic machinery in an indirect manner, via the proton circulation. The vectorial orientation of the proton-translocating pathways ultimately accounts for the direction of transport, as shown schematically in Fig. 5. Cationic metabolites (K⁺, lysine) can respond directly to the membrane potential, interior negative. Anionic metabo-

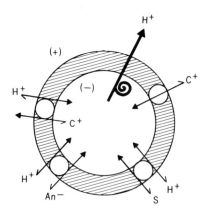

FIG. 5. Secondary coupling of transport carriers to the proton circulation according to chemiosmotic theory. The primary proton pump (mechanism unspecified) is vectorial; the secondary carriers are reversible. Metabolites: S, uncharged; C⁺, cationic; An⁻, anionic.

lites (e.g., phosphate or glutamate) would be transported as the uncharged acids and accumulate in response to ΔpH, interior alkaline. Uncharged metabolites (β-galactosides, proline) would travel by symport with protons, accumulating in response to the total proton-motive force; and antiport carriers link extrusion of Na^+ or Ca^{2+} to the entry of H^+ (Fig. 5). Kinetic and thermodynamic aspects of the proposed carriers have been analyzed by Mitchell (1966, 1968, 1970a,b, 1973b).

How truly does Fig. 5 portray the transport of metabolites by bacteria? After a period of confusion and controversy (see Boos, 1974a,b; Harold, 1972, 1974; Kaback and Hong, 1973; Kaback, 1974; Lombardi et al., 1974; Hamilton, 1975; Simoni and Postma, 1975), there seems now to be fairly general consensus on the broad principles. A respectable number of bacterial transport systems do seem to be energized by the proton circulation (Table II) including the classical lac permease of E. coli. But there remain some difficult puzzles plus an array of transport systems that do not appear to be related to the proton circulation at all (Section IV,C). It should also be emphasized that the molecular nature of translocation itself remains virtually unknown.

The mounting evidence that respiration, photosynthesis, and ATP hydrolysis generate a proton-motive force of the requisite magnitude and polarity was summarized in Section II,B; note that a Δp of −240 mV would in principle account for a concentration gradient of 10^4 by electrogenic translocation of one proton. We have also outlined reasons for attributing some kinds of uncoupling to dissipation of the proton-motive force. In addition, there are two lines of evidence that bear directly on the coupling of transport carriers to the proton circulation.

1. Accumulation of Metabolites in Response to an Artificial Proton-Motive Force

Cells of S. faecalis or S. lactis are readily deprived of metabolic energy by starvation; addition of valinomycin then induces efflux of K^+, thus creating a membrane potential interior negative. This procedure was shown to elicit accumulation of thiomethylgalactoside (Kashket and Wilson, 1973) and of threonine and other neutral amino acids (Asghar et al., 1973). In the former case it was clearly shown that the driving force is in fact the total Δp, not Δψ alone: under appropriate conditions accumulation could be elicited by imposing ΔpH rather than Δψ and the time-course of galactoside accumulation could be quantitatively correlated with the rise and decay of the proton-motive force (Kashket and Wilson, 1973). Mutants lacking the transport systems did not respond to the potential gradients (Kashket and Wilson, 1973; Asghar et al., 1973).

Analogous experiments were performed with membrane vesicles of E. coli, in which uptake of thiomethylgalactoside, proline, glycine, lysine,

TABLE II
Energy Sources for Some Bacterial Transport Systems[a]

Energy donor	Escherichia coli	Streptococcus faecalis	Staphylococcus aureus
Proton circulation	β-Galactosides	β-Galactosides	
	Galactose		
	Arabinose		
	Glucose-6-P		
	Alanine	Alanine	
	Glycine	Glycine	Glycine
	Serine	Serine	
	Threonine	Threonine	
	Proline	Cycloleucine	Isoleucine
	Phenylalanine	(Phenylalanine)	
	Cysteine	(Tyrosine)	
	Lysine	(Methionine)	Lysine
	Gluconic acid	(Histidine)	Glutamic acid
	Others[b]		Others[b]
ATP (or derivative)	Arginine	Glutamic acid	
	Histidine	Aspartic acid	
	Isoleucine		
	Methionine		
	Glutamine		
	Diaminopimelic acid		
	Ornithine		
	Glycylglycine		
	Ribose		
	Galactose		
	β-Methylgalactoside		
	Phosphate	Phosphate	
	K^+	K^+?	
	Others[c]	Na^+?	

[a] For references, see text.
[b] Most if not all the transport systems of membrane vesicles that can be supported by respiration may be of this kind.
[c] Presumably all transport systems that include a periplasmic binding protein.

and other metabolites was coupled to an artificial membrane potential. Control experiments were performed to ensure that transport was mediated by the physiological transport systems and did not involve participation of either the ATPase or the respiratory chain (Hirata *et al.*, 1973, 1974a; Altendorf *et al.*, 1974) but uptake in response to an imposed ΔpH was not documented. These findings have been confirmed by Kaback (1974) and by Kasahara and Anraku (1974). Very recently Hirata *et al.* (1976) duplicated all these experiments with vesicles of a thermophilic bacterium and succeeded in showing accumulation of alanine in response to ΔpH.

Further evidence comes from intact cells. West and Mitchell (1972) induced accumulation of lactose by *E. coli* cells rendered permeable to K$^+$, in response to an imposed ΔpH. In *Staphylococcus aureau* Niven and Hamilton (1974) induced lysine uptake by a membrane potential and showed that the extent of accumulation corresponds quantitatively to the potential gradient; glutamate uptake, by contrast, was elicited only by imposing an appropriate pH gradient in a manner compatible with the hypothesis that it is the uncharged species, glutamic acid, that traverses the membrane (Niven and Hamilton, 1974; Hamilton, 1975). They were also able to induce accumulation to isoleucine and glycine, apparently in response to Δp.

The import of these experiments is clear. They leave little doubt that a proton-motive force can, in fact, drive accumulation by the physiological transport carriers in a manner that is qualitatively—and in one case (Kashket and Wilson, 1973, 1974) quantitatively—consistent with the chemiosmotic theory. They thus argue strongly against any coupling hypothesis of the chemical or conformational type which requires tight physical articulation between the transport carrier and the major energy-yielding pathways.

2. Symport with Protons

Coupling of transport systems to the proton circulation implies in most cases either symport or antiport of substrate with one or more protons. There are not many bacterial systems in which this prediction has been experimentally verified. The most extensive data were obtained for the uptake of thiomethylgalactoside and lactose by the *lac* permease of *E. coli*, in which a stoichiometry of 1:1 was demonstrated; proton movement is electrogenic (West and Mitchell, 1972, 1973). Mutants defective in the coupling of β-galactoside transport to metabolism still translocated sugar but not protons (West and Wilson, 1973), nor did they respond to an artificial potential gradient (Hirata *et al.*, 1974a). Since these mutations map in the *y* gene it is likely that both proton and substrate associate with a single polypeptide, but it is not obvious why growth on certain fatty acids should repair the genetic lesion (Wong and MacLennan, 1973). Movement of protons together with thiomethylgalactoside has also bee noted in *S. lactis* (Kashket and Wilson, 1973); with various sugars in *E. coli* (Henderson and Skinner, 1974) and with alanine in vesicles (Hirata *et al.*, 1976).

There are a number of examples of proton uptake by symport with anionic substrates: gluconate (Robin and Kepes, 1973), succinate (Gutowski and Rosenberg, 1976a), glucose 6-phosphate (Essenberg and

Kornberg, 1975), and inorganic phosphate (F. M. Harold and H. Rosenberg, unpublished), all in *E. coli*; in *Staphylococci*, protons enter with glutamate (Gale and Llewellyn, 1972). Stoichiometries are approximate but suggest that proton movements maintain electroneutrality. The relevance of these proton symports to energy coupling must be considered with care. In staphylococci, Niven and Hamilton (1974) showed that uptake of glutamate can be driven by an artificial ΔpH, but it is not certain that this reflects the physiological transport carrier nor that in metabolizing cells the concentration gradient for glutamate is established by the pH gradient. Uptake of phosphate by *E. coli* via a transport system that involves a binding protein occurs by symport with protons, yet in this case the energy source is ATP rather than the proton-motive force (F. M. Harold and H. Rosenberg, unpublished).

Antiport with protons has so far been observed only for the movement of Na^+ out of *S. faecalis* (Harold and Papineau, 1972b) and *E. coli* (West and Mitchell, 1974b) and again the role of the proton flux as a driving force is in doubt (Section IV,C).

This somewhat meager evidence receives good backing from work with eukaryotic microorganisms. These are beyond the scope of this article but have been fully discussed by Hamilton (1975).

To summarize the bacterial case in terms of the most thoroughly studied instance, the *lac* system: There is strong evidence that *E. coli* generates a Δp of the polarity and magnitude needed to account for accumulation *in vivo*; that translocation of lactose or thiomethylgalactoside is accompanied by electrogenic symport with one proton; that anything that dissipates Δp severs the link between metabolism and accumulation; that genetic dissociation of proton movement from that of lactose does likewise; and that an externally applied proton-motive force is sufficient to drive accumulation in the absence of metabolism. If all this still falls short of rigorous proof that the proton-motive force is both the necessary and sufficient link between transport and metabolism, it is certainly a very strong case. For this transport system and, with reservations also for less exhaustively studied systems listed in Table II, energy coupling via the proton-motive force is the only hypothesis now available that is compatible with the experimental findings.

B.   PROTON-COUPLED TRANSPORT: SOME CURRENT CONUNDRUMS

The recent literature records many observations that were not easily understood in terms of chemiosmotic theory and were sometimes thought to be in direct conflict with this interpretation. Herewith a collection of puzzles, some recently resolved but others still very much *sub judice*, which bear on the application of chemiosmotic principles. A somewhat different perspective will be found in reviews by Boos (1974a), Hamilton (1975), and Simoni and Postma (1975), which deal more specifically with the controversy over energy coupling by redox carriers.

1. Valinomycin-Induced K^+ Accumulation by Membrane Vesicles

In the presence of valinomycin and other K^+-conducting ionophores, respiring membrane vesicles accumulate K^+ at a high rate and against a large concentration gradient. Conflicting interpretations were placed on this finding: According to Lombardi et al. (1973) the ionophores allow K^+ access to a transport system that carries it inward to generate a membrane potential, interior positive. The chemiosmotic interpretation sees K^+ accumulation simply as ionophore-mediated translocation in response to the electrical potential generated by proton extrusion, interior negative. Recent evidence that valinomycin does in fact serve as a K^+ conductor in E. coli vesicles, as in all other systems, and that the potential gradient is interior negative (Altendorf et al., 1975) would appear to have resolved this issue in favor of chemiosmotic orthodoxy. However, it remains to be explained why valinomycin does not induce K^+ accumulation in vesicles prepared from certain mutants deficient in K^+ transport (Bhattacharyya et al., 1971).

2. Energy Sources for Transport in Vesicles

The observation that D-lactate is a far better energy source for transport than is NADH, even though the latter is more rapidly oxidized, was one of the pillars supporting the idea that transport carriers are energized by a special redox pathway distinct from the main respiratory chain (Kaback and Hong, 1973). It now seems clear that the relative efficacies of energy sources reflect first of all the accessibility of the dehydrogenase: lactic dehydrogenase, normally localized at the inner surface, is accessible by a carrier for lactic acid. But there is no NADH carrier; exogenous NADH can support transport only by slow diffusion across the membrane to the inner surface (Hampton and Freese, 1974). Internally generated NADH is as effective an energy source as is D-lactate (Futai, 1974a).

Many unanswered questions remain, however. The cytochrome complement of membrane vesicles is completely reduced both by D-lactate and external NADH, even though only the former supports transport. Does this mean that external NADH feeds electrons into the chain past the point of proton extrusion? A deeper conundrum is illustrated by the following observation (Lombardi and Kaback, 1972): Succinate is almost as effective as D-lactate as an energy source for lysine accumulation, but far less effective than lactate in supporting uptake of proline. Additional examples of this kind are cited by Kaback (1974); they are not immediately explicable in chemiosmotic terms and rather suggest coupling of particular dehydrogenases and transport carriers. The situation in reconstituted vesicles, in which lactic dehydrogenase indubitably localized at the outer surface drives transport, also has yet to be clarified (Futai, 1974b; Short *et al.*, 1974, 1975).

3. Is Translocation Itself Energy Requiring?

Some years ago Koch (1971) described a procedure by which *E. coli* cells could be totally depleted of energy reserves. Such cells showed a greatly reduced rate of hydrolysis of *o*-nitrophenylgalactoside, a process that requires the *lac* carrier to translocate but not to accumulate the substrate; Koch concluded that translocation itself must somehow depend on metabolic energy, in conflict with chemiosmotic theory. The conflict was resolved when Cecchini and Koch (1975) found that hydrolysis was greatly stimulated by addition of a proton conductor, and offered the following explanation: Galactoside enters by symport with protons; the energy-depleted cells are unable to expel the protons, therefore entry of even a few molecules of galactoside generates an electrical potential, interior *positive*, which restricts entry of any further galactoside. Proton conductors facilitate exit of the protons and thus relieve the restriction on the rate of nitrophenylgalactoside entry. This important study may well have a bearing on some puzzling findings with membrane vesicles.

Schuldiner *et al.* (1975a,b) described a series of elegant experiments with dansylgalactosides, fluorescent lactose derivatives that bind to the *lac* transport system in *E. coli* membrane vesicles but are not accumulated. The basic observation is that in presence of an energy source there is a sharp increase in both the fluorescence yield and fluorescence polarization. These fluorescence parameters were shown to reflect, not transport of the substrate but its binding to the carrier. The effects can be elicited both by metabolic substrates and by an artificial membrane potential. Rudnick *et al.* (1975) described an analogous series of experiments with a photosensitive galactoside; photoinactivation of the *lac* transport system was again dependent upon availability of an energy source, metabolic or artificial. Since in these cases binding of the substrate to the carrier does not occur unless the membranes are energized, the authors suggest that the carrier becomes available only when a potential gradient has been established. Translocation itself thus becomes an energy-dependent process. The finding of Cecchini and Koch (1975) suggest an alternative interpretation: if binding of the dansylgalactoside, for example, effectively moves a proton across the barrier a potential (interior positive) would arise that would restrict binding of additional molecules.

4. Efflux of Transport Substrates in Response to Metabolic Inhibitors

Kaback and his associates have reported many instances of the following kind. Vesicles respiring D-lactate accumulate lactose, and this accumulation is blocked both by oxamate (an inhibitor of D-lactic dehydrogenase) and by cyanide; if the vesicles are allowed to accumulate lactose first, inhibition of respiration by cyanide induces efflux of lactose—but inhibition by oxamate does not (Kaback, 1972, 1974; Kaback and Hong, 1973). If accumulation depends solely on maintenance of the proton-motive force by oxidation of lactate one would expect all inhibitors to cause efflux or, at the least, to behave alike.

The explanation is far from clear, but there are some observations that may be pertinent. Altendorf *et al.* (1975) found that preincubation of vesicles with oxamate blocked subsequent generation of the membrane potential by lactate as measured either by uptake of lipid-soluble cations or of rubidium in presence of valinomycin. If, however, the vesicles were preincubated with lactate (as in the efflux experiments) subsequent addition of oxamate was much less effective in collapsing the potential. Addition of a proton conductor did collapse the potential, and is also known to elicit efflux of lactose and other metabolites. Evidently, efflux of accumulated metabolites requires that two conditions be fulfilled: the metabolic membrane potential must be collapsed and there must be charge compensation for any protons that exit by symport with the metabolite in question. It remains to be seen whether such a chemiosmotic rationalization suffices to explain what is certainly a very puzzling body of data.

Apropos efflux, it is interesting that the apparent K_m for lactose efflux is much higher than that for influx, both in cells and in vesicles. To the extent that efflux is mediated by the *lac* carrier, symport with protons outward to generate a diffusion potential (interior negative) may explain some of these observations.

5. Accumulation of Anionic and Cationic Metabolites

According to the chemiosmotic view of transport, anions are translocated by symport with protons on carriers specific for the uncharged acid; distribution between cells and medium would thus reflect the pH inside and out (Fig. 5). There is good evidence that uptake of phosphate and carboxylic acids by mitochondria conforms to this expectation, but this is not always true for bacteria. Postponing consideration of ATP-driven systems (Section IV,C), let us glance at anion transport systems that do depend on the proton circulation.

Distributions of lactic acid in *S. faecalis* (Harold and Levin, 1974) and of glutamic acid in *S. aureus* (Niven and Hamilton, 1974) can be correlated with measured pH gradients across the membrane, but for other transport systems this seems not to be the case. Uptake of gluconate by *E. coli* is accompanied by a single proton yet attains a concentration gradient of 100 in vesicles, as much as 500 in whole cells (Robin and Kepes, 1973, 1975; Pouyssegur *et al.*, 1974), a gradient too steep to be explained by ΔpH of a unit or less. Succinate is another apparent example of electroneutral symport with protons (Gutowski and Rosenberg, 1976b), yet membrane vesicles achieve a concentration gradient of 50 (Rayman *et al.*, 1972). Glucose-6-phosphate travels with one proton and concentration gradients in cells and vesicles are of the order of 10 to 20 (Dietz, 1972; Essenberg and Kornberg, 1975). The possible existence of a substantial pH gradient across the membrane of respiring cells and vesicles should be reconsidered, but it may also be that Na^+, K^+, or even an excess of protons are translocated so that the transport overall bears a net positive charge. Such a process has, in fact, been proposed by Cockburn *et al.* (1975) for the accumulation of phosphate and glutamate by yeast.

Uptake of K^+ and other inorganic cations by cells seems to require ATP (Section C), but those ion movements that occur in membrane vesicles should be explicable in terms of the proton-motive force. Valinomycin-mediated uptake of K^+ was discussed above but one wonders how Na^+ is expelled from the vesicles (Lombardi *et al.*, 1973). If, as West and Mitchell (1974b) suggest, a Na^+/H^+ antiporter is involved establishment of a pH gradient, interior alkaline, would be required; a $Na^+/2H^+$ antiporter could respond to the electrical potential. Another cation that is normally extruded from bacterial cells is calcium. Rosen and McClees (1974) have shown that inverted membrane vesicles of *E. coli* accumulate Ca^{2+} in response to the proton-motive force (interior positive) generated either by respiration or by ATP hydrolysis. A possible mechanism is $Ca^{2+}/2H^+$ antiport, driven by the pH gradient (interior acid). Finally, respiring vesicles accumulate Mn^{2+} (Bhattacharyya, 1975) presumably in response to $\Delta\psi$. All these systems obviously need closer study than they have yet received.

6. Do Na^+ or K^+ Serve as Coupling Ions?

In mammalian cells a Na^+ pump and symport with Na^+ are important elements of metabolite transport. Are bacteria limited to protons or do they make use of other ions as well?

Uptake of anionic metabolites often requires K^+, for reasons that are none too clear (Eagon and Wilkerson, 1972; Thompson and MacLeod, 1974; Willecke *et al.*, 1973); I know of no case of either symport or antiport of any metabolite with K^+. One way in which K^+ may function is through the control of cytoplasmic pH: K^+ can exchange for protons that enter the cell by symport with anionic metabolites and thus increases the capacity of the cell (Harold and Altendorf, 1974). The stimulation by K^+ of phosphate and glutamate accumulation by *S. faecalis* is a recent illustration of this indirect role (Harold and Spitz, 1975). By way of contrast, uptake of Mg^{2+} together with citrate in *B. subtilis* appears to be a genuine case of symport (Willecke *et al.*, 1973; Oehr and Willecke, 1974).

Quite a number of bacterial transport systems require Na^+ (Harold, 1972; Hamilton, 1975). Recent examples include the uptake of glutamate by *E. coli* vesicles (Miner and Franck, 1974; Kahane *et al.*, 1975), of citrate by vesicles of *K. aerogenes* (Johnson *et al.*, 1975) and of proline in membrane vesicles of *M. phlei* (Hirata *et al.*, 1974b). Oddly, in membrane vesicles of *E. coli* the uptake of proline is inhibited by Na^+. Sodium ion is also required for the uptake of several amino acids by a marine pseudomonad (Thompson and MacLeod, 1973; Sprott *et al.*, 1975). The role of Na^+ is not known; in some cases it alters the affinity of transport, in others the rate but in no case could dependence of accumulation on the Na^+ gradient be demonstrated. Indeed, it is uncertain whether or not Na^+ is translocated with the metabolite at all.

The only exception so far is the recent paper by MacDonald and Lanyi (1975) on the accumulation of leucine by illuminated membrane vesicles of *Halobacterium halobium*. Uptake of leucine was shown to depend on the Δp generated by bacteriorhodopsin and also required a high extracellular level of Na^+. Addition of a pulse of Na^+ in the dark-induced transient leucine uptake and the authors suggest that this may reflect electrogenic symport of amino acid with Na^+. It is conceivable that the Na^+ gradient induced a Δp which is the actual driving force but the observation that the Na^+ effect was not abolished by proton conductors speaks against this suggestion.

With the possible exception of halophiles it still appears that bacteria utilize only protons as physiological coupling ions. Eukaryotic microorganisms also utilize protons (Hamilton, 1975), and one wonders at what stage in cellular evolution the use of Na^+ for energy coupling makes its debut.

C. ATP-DEPENDENT TRANSPORT SYSTEMS

Transport systems that are linked to the proton circulation can be recognized, at least in a preliminary fashion, by quite simple criteria, such as the utilization of glycolysis and respiration as alternative energy sources, or inhibition by proton conductors, whichever is the energy source. The discovery (Berger, 1973) that many bacterial transport systems (Table II) depend upon ATP rather than Δp stemmed from this approach. It surely constitutes one of the most significant advances in this field and promises to have far-reaching implications for transport in eukaryotic systems as well.

1. Binding Proteins and the Role of ATP

Uptake of a number of metabolites by gram-negative bacteria is impaired after osmotic shock. In many instances this has been found to reflect loss of a small protein, localized in the periplasmic space, which binds the metabolite with high affinity and specificity. Some two dozen of these periplasmic binding proteins have now been isolated, and the extensive literature describing their purification, characteristics, and function has been reviewed repeatedly (Boos, 1974a,b; Oxender, 1974; Oxender and Quay, 1975; Rosen and Heppel, 1973). These proteins typically have molecular weights between 20,000 and 40,000; they have no known enzymic activities but bind one or two molecules of a particular metabolite per protein monomer. For a number of transport systems, including those for galactose, glutamine, histidine, sulfate, and others, the binding protein is an essential component of the transport system. In others (succinate, lysine, methylgalactoside, phosphate) reduced transport activity persists even in mutants devoid of binder. Precisely what is the role of the binding proteins in transport is not known but it seems fair to conclude that they largely determine the specificity and affinity of the process. A number of these systems are now known to comprise additional, membrane-bound, proteins (Fournier and Pardee, 1974; Kustu and Ames, 1974; Lo and Sanwal, 1975; Robbins and Rotman, 1975), reinforcing the general feeling that the binding proteins recognize the substrate but do not carry it across the membrane. According to Robbins and Rotman (1975), the binding protein somehow makes possible a specific and dramatic increase in affinity that is necessary for active transport to take place.

We can thus distinguish two classes of transport systems in gram-negative bacteria, the "shockable" systems that involve a periplasmic binding protein and the "shock-resistant" ones that depend on carrier proteins tightly associated with the cytoplasmic membrane. The numerous transport activities of membrane vesicles belong to the latter class. Berger and Heppel (1974; Berger, 1973) have now shown that these two classes differ also with respect to metabolic coupling: In E. coli uptake of proline, serine, cysteine, and others is mediated by carriers resistant to osmotic shock. Accumulation of these metabolites was inhibited by proton conductors whether respiration or glycolysis provided metabolic energy; in a mutant devoid of ATPase, oxidizable substrates such as lactate or ascorbate supported accumulation, but glycolysis did not; finally accumulation driven by respiration was resistant to arsenate. These characteristics point to energy coupling via the proton-motive force, though the authors (Berger and Heppel, 1974) prefer to speak of the energized state. By contrast the uptake of glutamine, arginine, histidine, and others, all of which require periplasmic binding proteins, was resistant to proton conductors; in mutants lacking the ATPase transport was supported by glycolysis only, not be respiration. Energy coupling was dissociated by arsenate. Berger and Heppel (1974; Berger, 1973) concluded that the latter transport systems specifically depend upon ATP or an unidentified metabolite derived from ATP.

The roster of members of this class (Table II) has grown rapidly to include galactose, ribose, isoleucine, and several other amino acids, phosphate and probably K^+ (Berger and Heppel, 1974; Curtis, 1974; Cowell, 1974; Wilson, 1974; Kobayashi et al., 1974; Wood, 1975; Kadner and Winkler, 1975; F. M. Harold and H. Rosenberg, unpublished. Almost certainly all the systems that involve binding proteins will prove to be ATP linked and there will be some which do not involve a classical binder. Aside from dependence upon ATP, these systems appear to have two characteristic kinetic features: energy coupling enhances entry of the substrate rather than reducing exit; and transport is unidirectional inward, without exchange or counterflow (Parnes and Boos, 1973; Wilson, 1974; Boos, 1974b).

So long as the identity of the immediate energy donor remains unknown speculation about the mechanism of energy coupling seems premature. The intracellular product is usually, if not always, chemically unaltered but present at a very much higher concentration (some 10^5-fold for galactose). But whether we must identify thirty or more individually powered carriers, or some kind of communal ATP-linked pump remains to be established. As the late Hercule Poirot would have said, it gives one furiously to think.

2. ATP-Linked Transport Systems in Gram-Positive Bacteria

Gram-positive bacteria have no periplasmic binding proteins, but also employ ATP as energy donor for transport. Accumulation of phosphate and of arsenate by S. faecalis is strictly unidirectional and dependent upon ATP generation; it attains a concentration gradient of 400 or more, a gradient too large to be explained by the modest ΔpH across the membrane. Indeed under carefully controlled conditions it was possible to collapse the proton motive force entirely without any inhibition of phosphate or arsenate uptake. It was therefore concluded that the energy source is either ATP or an unidentified metabolite thereof. The transport system for glutamate and aspartate is another of this kind but uptake of thiomethylgalactoside, methionine, histidine, and others was a function of the proton-motive force (Harold and Spitz, 1975).

A complication in these experiments deserves mention since it may prove to be common. Conditions were found which render phosphate uptake subject to inhibition by proton conductors after all, and this was tentatively traced to their effect on the cytoplasmic pH (Harold and Spitz, 1975). Maintenance of the cytoplasmic pH near neutrality, particularly in a glycolytic organism, depends upon the capacity to extrude protons. Thus the proton circulation may sometimes be required for transport, not as an energy source but to maintain a suitable environment.

The accumulation of K^+ by *S. faecalis* also illustrates the interplay between ATP and the proton-motive force in transport. Movement of K^+ across the membrane is strictly dependent upon metabolic generation of ATP. Studies with mutants, ionophores and inhibitors led to the conclusion that the primary process is the electrogenic extrusion of protons mediated by the membrane-bound ATPase; K^+ accumulates in response to the electrical potential whereas Na^+ exits by electroneutral exchange for protons (Harold and Papineau, 1972b). However, K^+ is clearly not simply in equilibrium with the electrical potential: $^{42}K^+/K^+$ exchange, like net uptake, requires concurrent glycolysis; DCCD and other inhibitors of the ATPase block net uptake but not the exchange; and none of the inhibitors elicit efflux of K^+ from the cells unless valinomycin is present as well (Harold and Papineau, 1972a,b; Harold and Altendorf, 1974). The properties of the transport system are quite unlike those of valinomycin or of the proton-linked carriers discussed in Section IV,A. The simplest scheme requires ATP both to generate the electrical imbalance and to confer "mobility" upon the carrier (a channel with appropriate gating would do as well). Na^+/H^+ exchange in these cells seems also to require ATP, but not the ATPase.

What is the teleonomic reason for the existence in the same organism of transport systems that are proton-coupled and others that are ATP-coupled? We do not know, but the fact itself suggests that each mode carries benefits as well as costs. The proton-linked systems have the obvious virtue of versatility and genetic economy. ATP-driven systems can achieve higher concentration gradients and are less subject to leakage when the energy supply becomes limiting. Whatever the reason, bacteria are not as content with proton-linked transport as chemiosmoticists thought they ought to be.

D. GROUP TRANSLOCATION AND OTHER LINKS BETWEEN TRANSPORT AND METABOLISM

Group translocation refers to metabolic sequences so oriented across the membrane as to catalyze transport and chemical transformation concurrently. Vectorial pathways of this kind may be much more common than we realize, but only one has been thoroughly characterized.

Uptake and phosphorylation of sugars by bacteria is often mediated by the phosphotransferase complex of enzymes, with phosphoenolpyruvate as phosphoryl donor. Examples include the uptake of glucose by *E. coli* and *S. faecalis* and that of lactose by *S. aureus*. The evidence supporting the designation of these systems as group translocations has been reviewed more than once (Roseman, 1972; Harold, 1972; Boos, 1974a; Hamilton, 1975) and need not be recapitulated here, but mention must be made of the penetrating studies by Roseman and his colleagues on lactose uptake in staphylococci (Simoni *et al.*, 1973a,b; Hays *et al.*, 1973; Simoni and Roseman, 1973). This work led to the identification of a sequence of cytoplasmic phosphoryl carriers which transfer phosphoryl groups (free energy of hydrolysis near -12 kcal per mole) from phosphoenolpyruvate to factor III. Phosphorylated factor III forms a ternary complex with both the lactose-specific enzyme II that is built into the membrane and with the incoming lactose molecule, and the phosphoryl group is transferred to form lactose 6-phosphate. The large drop in free energy during this reaction reflects the performance of both chemical and osmotic work.

There is no obvious reason why the proton circulation should affect the phosphotransferase system, but a connection clearly exists. Hoffee *et al.* (1964) already noted stimulation of α-methylglucoside uptake by uncouplers; Gilcrist and Konisky (1975) described marked stimulation by colicin K, and del Campo *et al.* (1975) deduced from their experiments that the energized state of the membrane inhibits operation of the phosphotransferase. The mechanism is not known, and one wonders whether the transferase may not after all be a charge-translocating pathway (Mitchell, 1973b).

Two other transport processes in *E. coli* are thought to occur by group translocation. Uptake of long-chain fatty acids such as oleate is very closely linked to their metabolic utilization; kinetic and genetic findings led to the suggestion that uptake is mediated by acyl coenzyme A (CoA) synthetase localized in the cytoplasmic membrane (Klein *et al.*, 1971; Ferman and Bennett, 1973). Ferman (1973) also studied the uptake of butyrate by membrane vesicles and showed that transacetylation with acetyl-CoA led to the accumulation of butyryl-CoA in the vesicular lumen. Uptake of purines and possibly of pyrimidines may be another case of vectorial phosphorylation, with phosphoribosylpyrophosphate as phosphoryl donor. This reaction also has been documented in vesicles (Hochstadt-Ozer, 1974).

Bioenergeticists, including the present author, generally confine themselves to the transport of small metabolites, but bacteria must be more broad minded. The biosynthesis of extracellular macromolecules—cell walls, teichoic acids, lipopolysaccharide, periplasmic proteins, and ex-oenzymes—must all involve transport processes of one kind or another and the performance of work, about which nothing will be said here.

V. Chemical Work: Phosphorylation and Reduction

Transport into cells and out is visibly oriented in space; Curie's principle as well as intuition assure us that its causes must be equally vectorial. This is much less obvious for the performance of chemical work at the membrane level, as in oxidative phosphorylation and transhydrogenation, where there is no net movement of anything across the membrane. The most novel feature of the chemiosmotic theory was the proposition (Mitchell, 1961, 1966) that both the exergonic and the endergonic reaction are in effect transport processes, linked only by a common translocation partner namely the proton.

The rivalry of men and ideas is far from ended, but one can scarcely fail to be impressed by the mass of experimental evidence that now documents the existence of the phenomena predicted by Mitchell, in bacteria as well as in mitochondria and chloroplasts. Aside from the evidence (Section II,B) that a proton-motive force always corresponds to the energized membrane, there is the key observation that ATP synthesis can in fact be supported by an external proton-motive force (Jagendorf and Uribe, 1966, Cockrell et al., 1967; Rossi and Azzone, 1970; Leiser and Gromet-Elhanan, 1974; Maloney et al., 1974; Thayer and Hinkle, 1975a,b), and also by interaction of isolated ATPase with a second proton-translocating pathway incorporated into the same vesicle (Racker and Stoeckenius, 1974; Ryrie, 1975). What remains to be resolved is whether the chemiosmotic coupling mechanism accounts qualitatively and quantitatively for phosphorylation by intact cells and organelles: Is the proton-motive force both sufficient and necessary for phosphorylation? And if so, by what molecular mechanisms is the proton-motive force generated and utilized?

A. PHOSPHORYLATION

The metabolic pathways that support ATP synthesis are diverse (Sections II,A and III) but the mechanism of phosphorylation itself is generally accepted to be unitary and in principle identical with that of mitochondria and chloroplasts (Pedersen, 1975a). This consensus rests on two lines of evidence. All the exergonic reactions can generate that energized state which supports transhydrogenation and transport as well as phosphorylation and is subject to dissipation by ionophores (Section II,A). Furthermore, the coupling factor ATPase, wherever it has been adequately examined, proves to belong to the same family as the mitochondrial one (Table I); this assertion must be qualified in that the ATPases of the strictly anaerobic sulfate reducers (Le Gall and Postgate, 1973), of the anaerobic photosynthetic sulfur bacteria (Gepshtein and Carmeli, 1974) or of the halobacteria are not yet fully characterized, but the trend is unmistakable.

The function of the ATPase complex is undoubtedly to mediate the terminal step, ATP synthesis proper. Mutants in which the ATPase is either absent or defective are "uncoupled"—they continue to respire and to energize membrane functions thereby, but they do not carry out oxidative phosphorylation. Inhibitors of and antibodies against the ATPase block phosphorylation in (inverted) vesicle preparations. Finally, ATPase F_1 is often a coupling factor for oxidative phosphorylation in membrane preparations; its removal stops phosphorylation but not electron transport, and reattachment restores coupled ATP synthesis. In *R. rubrum* which can grow either phototrophically or heterotrophically, the same coupling factor ATPase mediates oxidative and photosynthetic phosphorylation (Cox and Gibson, 1974; Abrams, 1976; Simoni and Postma, 1975; also Lien and Gest, 1973; Gromet-Elhanan, 1974; Kanner *et al.*, 1975; Prasad *et al.*, 1975).

Since the same ATPase also mediates the utilization of ATP as an energy source for transhydrogenase and in some cases transport (Cox and Gibson, 1974; Simoni and Postma, 1975), we can infer that whatever ATPase does, it does it reversibly; but beyond this point consensus crumbles. We shall now turn to the experimental evidence that bears on the mechanism of ATP synthesis in bacterial systems and the nature of its linkage to the ultimate energy donors. The role of ATPase in phosphorylation by mitochondria and chloroplasts has recently been reviewed by Baltscheffsky and Baltscheffsky (1974) and by Pedersen (1975a).

1. Synthesis of ATP by an Artificial Proton-Motive Force

In Section III,D, I summarized the evidence that ATP hydrolysis translocates protons outward across the membrane. It is plausible but hitherto unproved that ATP synthesis is accompanied by influx of protons. What does seem now to be established is that in bacteria, as in mitochondria and chloroplasts, an externally imposed proton-motive force can support the synthesis of ATP.

Particularly instructive are the experiments of Maloney *et al.* (1974) with *Streptococcus lactis*. When grown on glucose these organisms are homofermentative, lacking cytochromes and any known phosphorylation linked to electron transport; the ATPase may be presumed to function physiologically in the hydrolytic direction. Nevertheless, valinomycin-induced K^+ efflux resulted in marked net ATP synthesis to a level comparable to that attained by glycolyzing cells. ATP synthesis was blocked by DCCD and by proton conductors and its magnitude was a function of the K^+ gradient. The formation of ATP was transient, with a time course that parallels the rise and decay of the proton-motive force in experiments of this kind (Kashket and Wilson, 1973).

Analogous results were obtained with *E. coli* depleted of energy reserves; ATP synthesis was abolished by mutations in the ATPase complex but did not require a functional respiratory chain (Maloney *et al.*, 1974. Grinius *et al.* (1975) confirmed ATP synthesis in response to $\Delta\psi$ and found some ATP formation even in response to ΔpH.

It is obviously of great importance to document proton-driven ATP synthesis in membrane vesicles, as Thayer and Hinkle (1975a,b) have recently done for submitochondrial particles; such experiments are technically very difficult because the proton storage capacity of inverted vesicles is limited by their small size. To my knowledge success has so far only been achieved with chromatophores of *R. rubrum* (Leiser and Gromet-Elhanan, 1974); vesicles were subjected to a pH shift of 3 units (acid to alkaline) and in addition valinomycin plus KCl were added during the alkali stage so as to create $\Delta\psi$, interior positive, and enhance the electrochemical potential of the protons. Neither ΔpH alone nor $\Delta\psi$ alone supported good ATP synthesis, apparently because of an insufficient supply of protons. However, a detailed study of the effects of ionophores on postillumination ATP synthesis by chromatophores (Leiser and Gromet-Elhanan, 1975; Gromet-Elhanan and Leiser, 1975) suggested that not only must the total Δp be sufficient but there must also be a pH gradient of some 2.1 units, interior acid. The physiological significance of this requirement for ΔpH is not entirely clear since so large a pH gradient seems unlikely to obtain in living cells. Thayer and Hinkle (1975a) also imposed a pH gradient of this order, but for thermodynamic rather than kinetic reasons.

2. Does Phosphorylation Require a Vesicular Structure?

The general finding that phosphorylating membrane preparations are vesicular and that they are uncoupled by ionophores in a predictable manner buttress the widespread belief that phosphorylation does indeed require a topologically closed structure. Cole and Aleem (1973) have, however, described the isolation of a soluble preparation from *Thiobacillus novellus* which carries out efficient oxidative phosphorylation sensitive to antimycin, HOQNO, CCCP, and dinitrophenol. Centrifugation for 3 hours at 300,000 g failed to sediment any membranous elements, nor could vesicles be detected by electron microscopy. Finally in intact cells, but not in the centrifuged extract, ATP synthesis could be induced by sudden shift of pH from 2 or 3 to 7.5. Cole and Aleem (1973) concluded that vesicles are not required for oxidative phosphorylation in this system. Whether one accepts their results as evidence incompatible with chemiosmotic theory (e.g., Green, 1974) or rejects them on the grounds that small vesicles of low density may fail to sediment and would certainly not respond to a simple pH jump is, at this stage, largely a matter of preconceived beliefs. K^+-conducting ionophores would provide a good test since their mode of action is so very well understood: a vesicular preparation, generating a Δp interior positive, should be uncoupled by valinomycin plus nigericin (Jackson et al., 1968), a nonvesicular one should be unaffected. It is pertinent here that respiratory proton translocation by cells of *Thiobacillus* has been reported (Drozd, 1974).

3. Is the Proton-Motive Force Quantitatively Sufficient to Account for ATP Synthesis?

Perhaps the most serious objection to the chemiosmotic interpretation of oxidative phosphorylation in mitochondria is the discrepancy between the maximal phosphorylation potential and the measured proton-motive force. The phosphorylation potential in state 4 may be as high as 16 kcal/ mole; to support ATP synthesis against so steep a gradient would require a proton-motive force of 350 mV if the ATPase translocates two protons (Slater et al., 1973). Nicholls (1974) has recently confirmed the earlier measurement (Mitchell and Moyle, 1969) of the proton-motive force under these conditions, some 228 mV. Thus chemiosmotic coupling can account for ATP synthesis only if the stoichiometry of charge translocation were greater than two (Nicholls, 1974). In chloroplasts also there is doubt whether the proton-motive force is sufficient to account for the phosphorylation potential, and evidence for the translocation of three charges (Jagendorf, 1975).

In chromatophores from *R. capsulata,* however, Casadio et al. (1974) found no such discrepancy. They estimated $\Delta\psi$ by the carotenoid spectral shift, ΔpH by the quenching of atebrin fluorescence and found a total Δp of some 400 mV, as Crofts and his associates (1974) had done earlier. In these same preparations the phosphorylation potential was 15 to 16 kcal/mole (equivalent to 325–340 mV), well within range for a stoichiometry of two protons per ATP. It is important that phosphorylation and the electrochemical potential of H^+ were monitored concurrently. Nigericin, which abolishes ΔpH but not $\Delta\psi$, and valinomycin plus K^+ which had the opposite effect, reduced the total proton-motive force to 280–300 mV, with a corresponding drop in the maximal phosphorylation potential. It should be mentioned, however, that Schuldiner et al. (1974), using chromatophores of *R. rubrum* and different methods, found the total Δp not to exceed 200 mV; phosphorylation was not measured.

A related question is whether the two components of Δp, ΔpH, and $\Delta\psi$, are interchangeable as the driving force for ATP synthesis as chemiosmotic theory requires. Here again chromatophores provide the only quantitative information for bacterial systems. Thiocyanate is a permeant anion for chromatophores and stimulates H^+ uptake upon illumination. As a result $\Delta\psi$ was reduced and ΔpH enhanced but the total Δp and also photophosphorylation were unchanged (Schuldiner *et al.*, 1974; Leiser and Gromet-Elhanan, 1974; Gromet-Elhanan and Leiser, 1973). Valinomycin and nigericin differentially affect $\Delta\psi$ and ΔpH, respectively, but phosphorylation was a function of the total Δp; for complete uncoupling to occur both components must be collapsed (Schuldiner *et al.*, 1974; Jackson *et al.*, 1968). However, as mentioned above, the studies on postillumination ATP synthesis (Gromet-Elhanan and Leiser, 1975; Leiser and Gromet-Elhanan, 1975) suggest that ΔpH and $\Delta\psi$ are not completely interchangeable in that a threshold ΔpH of about 2 units was required for phosphorylation.

Finally one can inquire whether the rate of formation of the proton-motive force suffices to account for ATP formation. Thayer and Hinkle (1975b) have shown that in submitochondrial particles, phosphorylation in response to an imposed Δp occurs immediately whereas that supported by NADH oxidation is preceded by a lag which may correspond to the time required to build up the necessary Δp. No such experiments have been reported with bacterial systems, but it will be recalled that proton translocation is an integral part of, and thus as rapid as, the redox reactions of photosynthesis (Section III,B).

4. Conformational Change and ATP Synthesis

Synthesis of ATP during oxidative and photosynthetic phosphorylation is apparently accompanied by substantial changes in the configuration of the ATPase (Pedersen, 1975a; Baltscheffsky and Baltscheffsky, 1974). Some evidence of this kind has begun to appear from bacterial systems as well. The ATPase of *R. rubrum* chromatophores, for example, is strongly activated by light and under these conditions becomes sensitive to inactivation by *N*-ethylmaleimide. ADP, uncouplers, or darkness all protect the enzyme (Baccarini-Melandri *et al.*, 1975), suggesting that energization of the enzyme somehow exposes a previously cryptic sulfhydryl group. Conformational changes of this kind may shed light upon the actual mechanism of action of the ATPase; while by no means incompatible with Mitchell's mechanism (Fig. 4a), they are central to the hypothesis of oxidative phosphorylation advanced by Boyer (1975a; Cross and Boyer, 1975, Boyer et al., 1975) and by Slater (1974; Harris and Slater, 1975).

In essence, the proposal is that the energy-requiring step in oxidative phosphorylation is not the synthesis of ATP but the release of tightly bound nucleotide into solution. Formation of ATP from ADP and P_i results simply from the shift in equilibrium brought about by sequestration of one or two molecules of ATP at specific tight binding sites. Their release is effected by an energy-linked conformational change such that the affinity of the site is lowered. The scheme has the merit of accounting for the various exchange reactions catalyzed by ATPase, which have long been recognized as partial reactions of phosphorylation; for the presence of tightly bound nucleotides in ATPase preparations (Table I); and for the synthesis of a small amount of ATP, as well as continued P_i/HOH exchange, in the presence of uncouplers (Boyer et al., 1973, 1975; Cross and Boyer, 1975). Related hypotheses which likewise assign a key role to conformational changes stem from work with bacterial chromatophores, in which tightly bound ATP appears to be the first product of phosphorylation (Yamamoto et al., 1972; Lutz et al., 1974; Beyeler et al., 1975).

The minimal model in which ATP synthesis per se is totally independent of energy input must be modified in light of the work of Harris and Slater (1975) with chloroplast membranes. They verified the existence of bound ATP and its turnover during photosynthesis but, contrary to prediction, incorporation of $^{32}P_i$ even into tightly bound nucleotides required metabolic energy; in chromatophores, also, synthesis of bound ATP is a light-dependent process (Yamamoto et al., 1972). Even in mitochondria it no longer appears that release of ATP is the sole site of energy input (Boyer et al., 1975). Harris and Slater (1975) suggest that energy is needed for a "priming event," perhaps a single turnover of the enzyme to release an inhibitor; subsequent ATP synthesis need require no further energy input though its release would. A rather different scheme is favored by Lutz et al. (1974).

Originally (Boyer, 1974) energy was thought to be transmitted from respiratory chain to ATPase by conformational exchanges via a matrix of adjacent macromolecules. More recent versions, however (Boyer, 1975a; Cross and Boyer, 1975; Boyer et al., 1975), recognize the proton circulation as a possible mode of transmission; its utilization, by whatever mechanism, must be accompanied by return of the protons across the membrane. We arrive then at the sort of thing illustrated in Fig. 4b, in which the proton circulation effects ATP synthesis by inducing cyclic changes in binding affinity rather than by poising the equilibrium across the active site (see also Jagendorf, 1975).

The molecular tactics by which the ATPase actually joins ADP and P_i remain obscure. Aside from the site of energy input, it is not certain whether the bound nucleotides are involved in regulation (Garrett and Penefsky, 1975; Cantley and Hammes, 1975) or are an integral element of the reaction mechanism (Boyer *et al.*, 1975; Harris and Slater, 1975); whether the sites of ATP synthesis and hydrolysis are identical or distinct (Pedersen, 1975a,b); why the kinetics of hydrolysis and phosphorylation are often very different; and precisely what is the role of the basepiece portion of the enzyme. However, if one accepts the thesis developed above (Sections II and III) that what the exergonic pathways employed by bacteria and organelles have in common is that they translocate protons across the membrane, no mechanism of ATP synthesis can be seriously entertained unless it somehow incorporates the return of the protons. If one rejects this thesis in favor of conformational coupling or of anhydrous protons localized within the hydrophobic phase (Williams, 1974, 1975), the task of describing ATP synthesis may be simplified but one is then obliged to devise an alternative explanation for the enormous body of data surveyed elsewhere in this assay. Thus each of us must decide for himself whether the problem of oxidative phosphorylation was solved in principle a decade ago or remains as baffling as ever.

B. Reducing Power: Transhydrogenase and Reversed Electron Transport

Biosynthesis of cell constituents generally requires provision of reducing power as well as energy. This is no problem for anaerobic bacteria which generate electrons of very low potential during fermentation; strict aerobes and photosynthetic bacteria, however, have evolved metabolic devices to generate reduced pyridine nucleotides, some of which depend on energy coupling at the membrane level.

Photosynthetic bacteria (except for the blue-green algae) are unable to oxidize water and require an external reductant such as H_2, H_2S, or (in the nonsulfur purple bacteria) succinate. In many cases the redox potential is too high for direct reduction of NAD^+ and the organisms meet their needs by photoreduction of NAD^+, a subject thoroughly and lucidly reviewed by Gest (1972). Some investigators believe that the mechanism involves photoreduction of a primary acceptor of low potential, such as ferredoxin, which in turn reduces NAD^+. In most cases, however, the evidence favors reduction of NAD^+ by energy-linked reversed electron transport: reduction can be supported in the dark by ATP or PP_i and is always sensitive to uncouplers. Reversed electron flow is also thought to be involved in NADH generation by certain (nonphotosynthetic) chemoautotrophs, and occurs in other bacterial membranes as well (e.g., Poole and Haddock, 1974). The mechanism must be envisaged as a reversal of that by which a proton-motive force is generated between NADH and quinone. Indeed, Shahak *et al.* (1975) have described reversed electron flow in chloroplasts subjected to acid–base transition.

The fraction of NADP in the reduced state is generally greater than that for NAD, even though the redox potentials are much the same (e.g., Lundquist and Olivera, 1971). It is likely that this differential is, at least in part, the work of the energy-linked transhydrogenase first discovered in mitochondria but now known to be widely distributed among bacteria as well. In *E. coli*, transhydrogenase activity of the membranes is repressed by amino acids but not by fermentable carbon sources (Bragg *et al.*, 1972), a finding interpreted as favoring a function in generating reducing power for biosynthesis. Krebs and Veech (1969) have calculated that in liver the differential in pyridine nucleotide ratios can be explained in terms of the equilibria of various cytoplasmic reactions and does not require intervention of energy-linked transhydrogenase. Although the physiological role of the enzyme is still open to doubt, it is a most instructive example of energy coupling all the same.

The transhydrogenase of *R. rubrum* has been much studied. The reaction is catalyzed by a membrane-bound complex that can be dissociated into a soluble factor and a membrane component. Both are needed for activity, perhaps because the dissociable factor bears the NAD(H) binding site, the membrane that for NADP(H) (Konings and Guillory, 1973; Fisher *et al.*, 1975). When the membrane is energized by either light, ATP, or PP_i the equilibrium constant $[NADPH]\cdot[NAD]/[NADP]\cdot[NADH]$ shifts from approximately unity to a value near 28; approximately one ATP is consumed in the dark per NADPH produced (Keister and Yike, 1967). Both in *R. rubrum* and in *E. coli* the transhydrogenase has the earmarks of a process dependent upon the "energized state": The ATPase is required for ATP-driven transhydrogenase but not for that energized by electron transport; both pathways are inhibited by proton conducting uncouplers (Gest, 1972; Konings and Guillory, 1973; Bragg and Hou, 1973; Singh and Bragg, 1974a; Butlin *et al.*, 1973; Cox *et al.*, 1973; Cox and Gibson, 1974; but see also Kay and Bragg, 1975, for studies with a novel mutant that is not easily explained). Evidently the proton-motive force somehow enters into this reaction even though it has no obvious vectorial component. Indeed hydrogen is transferred from the reduced to the oxidized nucleotide directly, without equilibrating with water.

An explanation stems from the discovery that both in mitochondria (Moyle and Mitchell, 1973a; Dontsov *et al.*, 1972) and in bacterial chromatophores (Ostroumov *et al.*, 1973), transhydrogenation is accompanied by the electrogenic translocation of protons across the membrane with the polarity shown in Fig. 6. Thus the oxidation of NADPH "energized" chromatophores and submitochondrial particles with generation of an electrical potential, interior positive, just as respiration and photosynthesis do. Transfer of H in the physiological direction, from NADH to NADP$^+$, generated a negative potential. The stoichiometry was approximately two protons per H transferred (Moyle and Mitchell, 1973a; Dontsov *et al.*, 1972; Skulachev, 1974), and the direction of transfer was a function of the concentrations of the four pyridine nucleotides. We can thus understand how a potential generated by respiration or photosynthesis (interior positive in particles, negative in cells) shifts the equilibrium in the direction of NADP$^+$ reduction (Fig. 6). Under some conditions, however, NADPH oxidation may make a significant contribution to the generation of the proton circulation. Scholes and Mitchell (1970) first noted H$^+$/O ratios near 8 in *Paracoccus denitrificans*, and Jones *et al.* (1975) have since described elevated ratios due to NADPH oxidation in other genera as well.

The molecular mechanism is uncertain. Mitchell (1972a) favors a vectorial pathway so articulated as to produce protons on one side by an arrangement reminiscent of that proposed for ATPase. Rydström's (1974) data may be more easily accommodated by a conformational mechanism, such as the proton translocase invoked by Skulachev (1974). In any event, as in the case of ATPase, the mechanism must include a pathway for proton movement.

C.   Other Kinds of Chemical Work

There is no obvious reason why future research should not reveal additional examples of the performance of chemical work by the proton

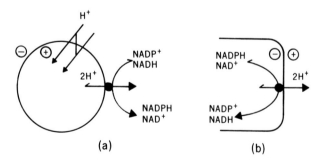

(a)   (b)

Fig. 6. Transhydrogenase as a proton-translocating pathway. (a) Energy-linked reduction of NADP$^+$ in chromatophores or other inverted vesicles. (b) NADPH oxidation as loop 0 of the respiratory chain, in intact cells.

circulation. One possibility is the photoproduction of molecular hydrogen by bacteria, which seems to be an energy-linked process of unknown nature (Gest, 1972).

A hint along quite another line may be contained in the report (Mevel-Ninio and Valentine, 1975) that DNA synthesis in *E. coli* requires the energized state. The basic finding is that, in a mutant deficient in ATPase, DNA synthesis was inhibited under anaerobic conditions but could be stimulated by either oxygen or nitrate; the authors feel that their observations cannot be explained by a primary effect on the transport of adenine. This brings to mind the exceedingly curious findings of Bastos and Mahler (1974; Mahler and Bastos, 1974), which point to involvement of ATPase in the metabolism of mitochondrial DNA in yeast.

VI. The Work of Movement

Many bacteria swim actively and purposefully in response to environmental stimuli, such as specific attractants or repellents, changes in pH or in light intensity. The organs of locomotion are the flagella, long whiplike filaments inserted into the cell envelopes; some bacteria have a single polar flagellum, in others multiple flagella act in concert. The filaments are composed of hundreds of monomers of the protein flagellin, helically arrayed around a central channel. Each filament springs from a basal hook embedded in the cytoplasmic membrane and cell wall by a series of rings—two in the gram-positive bacteria, four in the gram-negatives (Fig. 7) whose envelope is more complex. It has long been recognized that motility depends upon concurrent metabolism, but only recently has it been possible to ask how metabolism generates motion and how information to guide movement is sensed, processed and transmitted to the flagella. The present summary treatment of motility as a form of energy transduction leans on the excellent and recent reviews of the field by some of its premier students (Doetsch, 1972a; Koshland, 1974; Berg, 1975a,b; Adler, 1976).

Until recently it was thought that flagella move by a wave propagated along the filament, as eukaryotic flagella do, but it now seems clear that bacterial flagella are in fact semirigid and rotate around their point of insertion (Berg and Anderson, 1973; Silverman and Simon, 1974). The cell body is thus screwed through the medium; forward movement corresponds to counterclockwise rotation of the flagella (as seen from behind) and a change of direction is achieved by reversing the sense of rotation (Larsen *et al.*, 1974a). The driving force for rotation in both senses now appears to be not ATP, but the proton circulation. Wild-type *E. coli* swim both aerobically and anaerobically but mutants

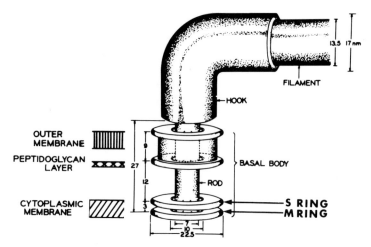

Fig. 7. Model of the basal hook of flagella in *Escherichia coli*. After Adler (1975), with permission.

deficient in the ATPase swim only when allowed to respire. Both aerobic and anaerobic motility was blocked by CCCP at remarkably low levels (10^{-8} M) even though anaerobic ATP generation was unaffected. Conversely, arsenate inhibited ATP synthesis by oxidative phosphorylation but did not paralyze the cells (Larsen *et al.*, 1974b). The role of ATPase in anaerobic motility was confirmed by Thipayathasana and Valentine (1974), who measured, not motility itself but multiplication of a bacteriophage that infects only motile cells. Mutants lacking ATPase were resistant unless provided with either oxygen or nitrate. There is as yet no evidence that an artificial proton-motive force can make bacteria swim in the absence of metabolism, but we may provisionally take the proton circulation to be the vectorial driving force of the flagellar motor.

The workings of the motor are not understood, but speculation is irresistible. In all bacteria (Fig. 7) the base of the flagellar hook terminates in a short rod with two rings associated with the cytoplasmic membrane (DePamphilis and Adler, 1971). Berg (1974) has suggested that this constitutes part of the motor: The M ring rotates freely in the cytoplasmic membrane but is rigidly mounted on the rod so rotation of the ring turns the flagellum; the other rings are bushings and the hook serves as a swivel that links the rod to the filament proper. The rod passes freely through the S ring which is rigidly attached to the wall and torque is generated between the M and S rings. (If the torque is to be applied, some part of the motor must be static. Readers who have as much trouble seeing this as I did may imagine trying to turn the flagellum while floating in the fluid membrane; to do the job one must find footing somewhere!). In eukaryotic flagella rotation involves the successive formation and rupture of cross-links; such a ratchet mechanism is unlikely to apply to bacteria because their rotation is too smooth. Berg (1974) suggests instead that torque may be generated by a flux of ions through the M ring so as to interact with fixed charges on the S ring. Passage of approximately 1000 ions would provide sufficient energy for one turn of the M ring. The fundamental analogy between this idea and proton-coupled transport is plain.

A few years ago Mitchell (1972b) reformulated his earlier proposal that bacteria swim by self-electrophoresis, with flagella serving as giant ionophores while the proton circulation does the work. The recent demonstration that flagella rotate and that the direction of motion depends on the sense of rotation seems to rule out self-electrophoresis. But the idea that the flagellum itself may afford the coupling ions passage into the motor at the base still remains an attractive one.

Let us now consider how environmental stimuli modulate the movement of flagella. It has been clearly established that bacteria possess an array of specific chemoreceptors, many of them the periplasmic binding proteins considered in Section IV,C; for example, the binding proteins for galactose and ribose serve both as chemoreceptors and as elements of the transport machinery. Chemotaxis requires neither transport of the attractant nor its metabolism; apparently the cell somehow monitors the fraction of binding sites occupied at any time and compares this with the occupancy some time earlier to detect the gradient (for documentation of this bare statement, see Adler, 1976; Berg, 1975a,b).

The information so garnered is processed, passed to the flagellar motor, and ultimately regulates the frequency of tumbling. Briefly, the motion of an individual cell consists of straight runs interrupted by brief periods of tumbling, after which the cell sets off in a new direction. Tumbling is brought about by reversal of the sense of rotation of the flagella (monoflagellated bacteria actually back up; in those that have multiple flagella, the flagellar bundle breaks up and the cell tumbles). Tumbling occurs spontaneously, but its frequency may be altered; attractants, for example, suppress tumbling with the result that cells tend to move up the gradient (Berg, 1975a; Koshland, 1974; Taylor and Koshland, 1974).

What input does the motor receive? Larsen et al. (1974b) found that, unlike motility itself, chemotaxis required ATP. It will be recalled that transport systems that include binding proteins also require ATP (Section IV,C), but the ATP may well be needed to make S-adenosylmethionine, which plays a hitherto unexplained role in chemotaxis (Larsen et al., 1974b; Adler, 1976). An alternative that presently seems attractive is the suggestion of Doetsch (1972b) that reversal of the flagella is due to fluctuation of the membrane potential. Ordal and Goldman (1975) noted that uncouplers of oxidative phosphorylation and inhibitors of electron transport act as repellents for *B. subtilis* at concentrations too low to affect motility itself. This reaction was apparently not mediated by chemoreceptors, nor did it involve ATP in any obvious way: repellents were active even though the ATP level was unaltered whereas arsenate lowered the ATP level by two-thirds but did not induce tumbling. Significantly, the bacteria soon ceased tumbling and resumed normal swimming in the presence of the uncouplers, despite persistent effects on the rate of respiration. The authors suggest, therefore, that fluctuation of $\Delta\psi$ induced tumbling. Studies with ionophores, such as valinomycin, should afford further tests of this hypothesis. Fluctuation of $\Delta\psi$ is also a possible interpretation of phototaxis by *Halobacterium halobium*. Hildebrand and Dencher (1975) showed that the light receptor is bacteriorhodopsin itself, which we know to serve directly as a proton pump (Section III,C). Tumbling of *Salmonella* in response to intense light (Macnab and Koshland, 1974; Taylor and Koshland, 1975) may involve flavins and perhaps the potential gradient, though there is no evidence for this. Whether binding of a ligand to its periplasmic receptor protein affects the potential is unknown but may be testable by the use of fluorescent dyes that monitor the potential (Laris and Pershadsingh, 1974).

VII. Coupling and Uncoupling

Links between metabolism and work that involve exchange of covalent bonds are in general dissociated only by reagents that can participate in the reaction mechanism. Uncoupling of glycolysis from phosphorylation by arsenate, at the level of glyceraldehyde phosphate dehydrogenase, is a case in point. Secondary coupling, dependent upon conformational interactions or a vectorial ion circulation is likely to be much more vulnerable. This section collates a somewhat heterogeneous body of data bearing on the tightness of coupling and its dissociation by mutation, sundry reagents, and physiological adjustments.

A. Ionophores and Colicins

Most of the reagents that uncouple metabolism from work at the membrane level conduct ions, usually H^+ or K^+ and uncoupling can be satisfactorily understood as the result of ion conduction (Harold and Altendorf, 1974; Harold *et al.*, 1974; Hamilton, 1975; McLaughlin and Eisenberg, 1975). The mode of action of uncouplers nevertheless remains a perennial issue, particularly among students of mitochondria. Thus, several recent reports reinforce the view that proton conduction across the hydrophobic phase is the heart of the matter (Cunarro and Weiner, 1975; Terada and Van Dam, 1975). On the other hand, Hatefi and his associates (1975) describe experiments that point to stoichiometric binding of certain uncouplers to a particular membrane polypeptide. In the bacterial context, the most burning issue may be the mode of action of colicins which unquestionably react with specific receptors.

Of the many bacteriocins known to disrupt energy coupling, we will consider only colicins El, K, A, and Ia, which have been extensively studied (for review, see Luria, 1973; Holland, 1975). Like other colicins these bind to specific receptors in the cell wall, each colicin to its own receptor, but their target is the cytoplasmic membrane. Disregarding for the present the differences in the effects produced, all block macromolecule synthesis and the uptake of metabolites by sensitive cells; motility ceases and the cellular ATP level declines; and the cells quickly lose K^+ and later Mg^{2+} as well. These observations suggest that colicins uncouple oxidative phosphorylation, and in a general sense this is true: Respiration continues, sometimes at an enhanced rate; so does glycolytic metabolism albeit not without some peculiar changes in the pattern of end products (Luria, 1973).

Some of these physiological sequelae are secondary. Feingold (1970) first showed that the colicin-induced drop in ATP level was prevented when the ATPase was blocked with DCCD. Plate et $al.$ (1974) extended this conclusion by use of the ATPase-deficient mutant $uncA$: in this strain ATP was elevated, not lowered, by colicin K and the inhibition of macromolecule synthesis was much less pronounced. But the uptake of both proline and glutamine was inhibited, a surprising result since the latter is thought to be an ATP-linked process (Section IV,C). Plate et $al.$ (1974) conclude that the primary effect of the colicin is to "deenergize the membrane" in some general sense. Essentially the same conclusion was drawn by other investigators (Jetten and Vogels, 1973; Gilcrist and Konisky, 1975).

In light of the discussion in the preceding sections it seems clear that colicins collapse the membrane potential, a conclusion consistent with the observation that colicins enhance the fluorescence of cell-bound ANS and other fluorescent probes (Jetten and Vogels, 1973; Phillips and Cramer, 1973; Brewer, 1974). But it is not at all clear what ions are enabled to move across the membrane of colicin-killed cells. Several investigators found that proton permeability is not increased (Feingold, 1970; Jetten and Vogels, 1973), in keeping with the fact that proton conductors mimic some but not all the physiological effects of colicins. The rapid loss of K^+ induced by colicins but not by CCCP (Luria, 1973; Feingold, 1970) is suggestive of a cation channel, but the ANS response described by Phillips and Cramer (1973) was unaffected by changes in the external K^+ concentration. It does not seem that colicins simply provide a potassium channel, but one of broader specificity is not yet excluded. Brewer (1976) has suggested that colicins may open an anion channel; in this context the multiple effects of the polyene antibiotics on yeast cells may provide a model.

To compound the complexity, interaction of colicins with the cells depends upon the energized state of the membrane and upon its fluidity as well (Jetten and Jetten, 1975; Okamoto, 1975). There may be an element of "structural uncoupling" due to dislocation of membrane components such as is thought to take place in the preparation of membrane vesicles (Altendorf and Staehelin, 1974).

It will be interesting to see whether the colicin puzzle ultimately yields to a more rigorous application of chemiosmotic principles than it has yet received.

B. GENETIC LESIONS

Of the numerous mutants deficient in energy coupling the majority, like the original *uncA* and *uncB* strains (Butlin *et al.*, 1971, 1973) have a defective ATPase complex. They can therefore neither make ATP by oxidative phosphorylation nor generate a proton circulation by ATP hydrolysis; in some strains there is also a defect in membrane structure that renders it permeable to protons (Section III,D). The genetic lesions have been reviewed by Cox and Gibson (1974) and by Simoni and Postma (1975). Brief mention should, however, be made here of two mutants that do not fit so readily into the general framework advanced here.

Kay and Bragg (1975) described a mutant in which ATP-driven transhydrogenase is defective even though ATP hydrolysis generates a potential gradient (as judged by fluorescence quenching and, in intact cells, by transport); transhydrogenase energized by respiration was normal. These properties are not easily reconciled with chemiosmotic theory. Equally peculiar is a mutant described by Lieberman and Hong (1974) which in some respects recalls the effect of colicins. The mutant is temperature-sensitive; at the restrictive temperature it loses the capacity to accumulate both proton-linked substrates and those that require ATP. Curiously, however, membrane vesicles of the mutant transport normally at 42°C. The defect is due to a double mutation, one in the gene for cystathionase and one in a gene designated *ecf* ("energy coupling factor").

C. GROWTH YIELD AND "ENERGETIC UNCOUPLING"

Despite the great diversity of bacterial metabolic economies, the maximal efficiency of coupling between metabolism and growth is relatively constant. This is formally expressed in terms of Y_{ATP}, the dry weight of cells produced per mole of ATP generated in metabolism. Many data in the literature suggest that for both anaerobic and aerobic growth this value is near 10.5 gm/mole ATP (Payne, 1970; Forrest and Walker, 1971). Recently, however, Stouthamer and Bettenhausen (1973) have questioned the constancy of the growth yield, particularly under continuous culture. They argue cogently that the growth yield should and does vary as a function of the growth rate and of other conditions that affect the proportion of energy used for "maintenance," and under optimal conditions may exceed 20 gm of cells per mole of ATP.

This is an interesting number, for the following reason. Forrest and Walker (1971) estimated the amount of ATP required to support known biosynthetic processes. Less than a third of the ATP requirement (from Y_{ATP}) was thus accounted for, leading them to suggest that as much as two thirds is utilized for the creation of "negative entropy," or order, i.e., for work functions such as transport. Thermodynamic measurements support this conclusion. Stouthamer (1973) has now recalculated the budget with the help of some rough but reasonable assumptions and including energy expenditures for transport. He estimates that during growth on glucose plus inorganic salts a maximum of 28.8 gm of cells might be produced per mole of ATP. With preformed amino acids and nucleic acid bases the yield could exceed 30 gm of cells per mole of ATP; under these conditions 15–20% of the energy budget would be devoted to transport. Thus the maximal growth yields are approaching those that may be theoretically possible. This argument would not be materially affected by substituting the proton-motive force for ATP since these currencies are interconvertible.

The concordance between growth rate and energy production is evidently achieved by regulation of biosynthesis (Nierlich, 1974). Among the controlling elements are the cellular ATP level, the energy charge (ATP + 0.5 ADP/ATP + ADP + AMP), and nucleotides such as NADPH and guanosine-3-diphosphate-5'-diphosphate (ppGpp); we may yet discover that $\Delta\psi$ or ΔpH serve as regulatory signals for some aspect of growth. As a result, bacteria can normally utilize metabolic energy as rapidly as it is produced. The converse, however, is not true: the rate of catabolism is generally maximal and not at all regulated by the demand for precursors or energy. Cells whose growth has slowed continue to catabolize substrate at undiminished rates. Examples include *S. faecalis*, which continues to glycolyze and produce ATP at maximal rate under various conditions suboptimal for growth (Forrest and Walker, 1971); *Zymonas mobilis* behaves likewise when growing in a medium deficient in pantothenic acid (Belaich *et al.*, 1972). In the extreme case, as is well known, washed suspension of bacteria glycolyze or respire furiously to no obvious purpose. This phenomenon, called "energetic uncoupling," raises the question of how cells dispose of their excess energy.

Utilization of relatively inefficient pathways is one device: In slow-growing *E. coli* only one coupling site is believed to be functional (Meyer and Jones, 1973). Another is accumulation of storage polymers, such as glycogen or poly-β-hydroxybutyrate, but microbiologists traditionally invoke an ATPase (e.g., Belaich *et al.*, 1972; Forrest and Walker, 1971). A better appreciation of the mechanisms involved is now possible in terms of the proton circulation.

Washed suspensions of *S. faecalis* glycolyze at a rate corresponding to over 1% of their dry weight per minute, maintaining an ATP pool as large or larger than that of growing cells (Forrest and Walker, 1971; Harold and Baarda, 1968). In glycolysis, substrate utilization is obligatorily linked to ATP synthesis, and the role of the ATPase in maintaining the metabolic rate is easily seen: DCCD reduced the rate of glycolysis to half; arsenate, which dissociates glycolysis from ATP production at the level of glyceraldehyde phosphate dehydrogenase, restored the full rate (Harold *et al.*, 1969). Since the ATPase probably extrudes protons (Harold and Papineau, 1972a) the energy-dissipating step must be the leakage of protons back across the membrane. The rate of ATP hydrolysis is probably limited by the proton-motive force (Mitchell, 1966; Maloney *et al.*, 1974), and this is reflected in the stimulation of glycolysis by proton conductors (Harold and Baarda, 1968). However, the fact that glycolysis continues at a substantial rate even in the presence of DCCD points to the existence of other reactions that hydrolyze ATP and regenerate ADP and P_i.

The pattern is fundamentally the same in respiring cells although the ATPase is not necessarily involved. DCCD has comparatively little effect on the respiratory rate of intact *E. coli* (except when they oxidize anionic substrates; Singh and Bragg, 1974b). Indeed, mutants lacking the ATPase respire as rapidly, or even more so, as the parent cells (Schairer and Haddock, 1972; Kanner and Gutnick, 1972; Simoni and Schallenberger, 1972). Presumably "energy dissipation" is again effected by the leakage of protons through the membrane.

In this connection it may be recalled that bacteria do not usually exhibit respiratory control, at least not in the sense that increased demand for ATP increases the rate of respiration. However, in a number of cases proton conducting uncouplers have been shown to accelerate oxygen uptake by cells or vesicles (Cavari *et al.*, 1967; Jones *et al.*, 1971; John and Hamilton, 1971), in keeping with the presumption that the rate of respiration is limited by the flux of protons back across the membrane.

In bioenergetics, as in other fields of science, problems are not solved so much as transformed. Four years ago (Harold, 1972) the linkage between metabolism and work functions was perceived as the central issue. Today the principles of energy coupling at the cellular level seem to be quite well defined and the questions are posed again at the molecular level: just how do ATPase, redox loops, transport carriers, flagellar motors, and other vectorial systems work?

ACKNOWLEDGMENTS

This article was written during a period of study leave in the Department of Biochemistry, John Curtin School of Medical Research, Canberra, Australia. It is a pleasure to thank Drs. Harry Rosenberg and Frank Gibson for their unstinting hospitality; the Australian National University and the National Science Foundation for financial support under the U.S.–Australia Cooperative Science Program: and Drs. Graeme Cox, Ian Young, and Simon Silver (as well as the above) for questioning almost everything I regarded as self-evident.

Thanks are due to all who sent preprints and helped resolve difficulties, particularly to Drs. A. Abrams, H. Berg, A. R. Crofts, H. Gest, B. A. Haddock, P. C. Hinkle, P. Mitchell, W. Stoeckenius, B. Taylor, and T. H. Wilson; to Dr. K. R. Popper and the Clarendon Press for permission to quote from *Objective Knowledge: An Evolutionary Approach*; to Dr. R. C. Prince, A. R. Crofts and Elsevier Scientific Publishing Co. for permission to adapt Fig. 3; to Dr. Peter Mitchell and North-Holland Publishing Co. for Fig. 4a; and to Dr. J. Adler and the *Journal of Bacteriology* for Fig. 7.

Last, but far from least, I would like to thank Mrs. Diane Grimshaw, Mrs. Kay Ward, and Mrs. Susan Walker for patiently typing an unending stream of words.

ADDENDUM (April 1976)

Nearly a hundred relevant papers have come to hand since the preceding text was completed in September 1975; only a fraction can be cited here. Nothing has arisen to call the general thesis into question, but some of the puzzles noted above seem closer to resolution.

1. *Generation of pH Gradient and Membrane Potential*

Several quantitative studies on ΔpH and $\Delta\psi$ in respiring *E. coli* cells and vesicles have been published. Padan *et al.* (1976) found that intact cells (treated with EDTA and studied at low concentrations of external K^+) maintain a constant cytoplasmic pH near 7.7 and a proton-motive force near -130 mV. The proportion of $\Delta\psi$ and ΔpH varies with the external pH and K^+ level; for example, at an external pH of 6 the pH gradient was almost two units. Schuldiner and Kaback (1975) confirmed and extended earlier reports on proton extrusion and generation of an electrical potential, interior negative, by respiring membrane vesicles. Subsequently, Ramos *et al.* (1976) found that at an external pH below 7 the vesicles also generate a pH gradient which may be as large as two units, interior alkaline. Internal pH was estimated from the distribution of weak acids, measured with the aid of a flow dialysis apparatus; assay by the usual filtration procedure was shown to be inadequate for this purpose. According to Ramos *et al.* (1976) the total proton-motive force may be as high as -180 mV, sufficient to account for the transport capacities of the vesicles.

In the strict anaerobe *Clostridium pasteurianum* the proton-motive force is involved in the accumulation of galactose and gluconic acid. A DCCD-sensitive ATPase presumably mediates proton extrusion (Booth and Morris, 1975; Clarke and Morris, 1976).

2. *Proton-Translocating Redox Chains*

The gaps in our knowledge of bacterial respiratory chains are beginning to shrink. A finding of particular interest is that *E. coli* grown on sulfate-limited medium appears to be deficient in coupling functions at site I (Poole and Haddock, 1975b). Coenzyme Q is usually thought of as a mobile hydrogen carrier, but a study by Stroobant and Kaback (1975) suggests that it may in fact be relatively fixed in position. Downs and Jones (1975) analyze the various redox loops encountered in strains of *Bacillus megaterium*.

Considerable progress has been made on anaerobic respiration of *E. coli* with nitrate as electron acceptor. Respiratory nitrate reduction translocates two or four protons, depending on the substrate. The nitrate reductase itself is thought to span the membrane, catalyzing a vectorial redox reaction in which nitrate at the exterior surface accepts reducing equivalents from the interior. The molecular characteristics of the enzyme appear to be consistent with this hypothesis (Garland *et al.*, 1975; Boxer and Clegg, 1975).

Mitchell (1975c) has presented a generalized version of the proton-motive coenzyme Q cycle which avoids some of the difficulties in the original version. Mention should also be made of the alternative proposal by Skulachev (1975) which attributes proton translocation in sites I and II to functionally specialized proton translocases rather than to redox loops.

3. *Photosynthesis*

There is not space to do justice to an important series of papers on H^+ translocation and phosphorylation in chromatophores of *Rhodopseudomonas spheroides* (Saphon *et al.*, 1975a,b; Jackson *et al.*, 1975). Among their findings are that as little as a single molecule of valinomycin per chromatophore has a noticeable effect on both $\Delta\psi$ and ATP synthesis, strong evidence for chemiosmotic coupling. Synthesis of ATP is accompanied by outward movement of protons through the ATPase, with a probable stoichiometry of two. The rate of electron transport controls the activity of the ATPase complex (see also Edwards and Jackson, 1976).

4. *Oxidative Phosphorylation and ATPase*

Maloney and Wilson (1975) have described in detail their studies on ATP synthesis by *Streptococcus lactis* in response to artificial gradients of pH and of electrical potential. Tsuchiya and Rosen (1976a) successfully applied essentially the same procedure to membrane vesicles of *E. coli*: vesicles preloaded with ADP and P_i synthesized ATP when subjected to an artificial proton-motive force. Yoshida *et al.* (1975) report ATP synthesis by phospholipid vesicles inlaid with bacteriorhodopsin plus a highly purified ATPase complex from a thermophilic bacterium. While all these observations lend further support to the principle that respiration and ATPase are coupled via the proton circulation, the operation of the ATPase complex itself appears more sophisticated than ever (see, for example, Ferguson *et al.*, 1976; Edwards and Jackson, 1976; Pedersen, 1976).

DCCD-sensitive ATPase has been purified from *E. coli* (Hare, 1975) and from a thermophilic bacterium (Sone *et al.*, 1975). A total of 12 polypeptides was found in the former preparation, eight in the latter. One of the polypeptides of the basepiece is altered in a mutant defective in ATP-coupled functions (Simoni and Shandell, 1975). Another component of the basepiece, the proteolipid that binds DCCD, has been isolated and characterized (Altendorf and Zitzman, 1975; Fillingame, 1975). Chemical, genetic, and physiological manipulations that alter the proton permeability of the membrane affect this proteolipid (Boonstra et al., 1975; Patel and Kaback, 1976); it is possible but far from certain that it is part of the proton-conducting channel within the basepiece.

Several metal ions participate in the structure of the ATPase complex. Abrams et al. (1976) suggest that magnesium may anchor the δ subunit to the core of the ATPase headpiece, while δ in turn links it to the basepiece. Sun and Crane (1975) found zinc to be present and perhaps nonheme iron as well.

Boyer (1975) has presented a fairly detailed model for coupling of proton translocation to ATP synthesis via conformational transitions in the ATPase. This may presumably be taken to mark his acceptance of the principle of chemiosmotic coupling in oxidative phosphorylation, a historic end point of some significance. However, studies on phosphorylation by purified ATPase localized at the interface between water and octanol were interpreted to mean that a proton-motive force is not required (Yaguzhinsky et al., 1976).

5. Coupling of Transport to Metabolism

Burnell et al. (1975) reported that accumulation of inorganic phosphate and sulfate by membrane vesicles of Paracoccus denitrificans occurs by electroneutral symport with protons, with ΔpH as the driving force. In E. coli, Ca^{2+} extrusion is a clear case of antiport with protons, but there is still some doubt that movement is electroneutral (Tsuchiya and Rosen, 1976b).

K. H. Altendorf (personal communication) finds that valinomycin allows the accumulation of K^+ by respiring membrane vesicles from mutants deficient in K^+ transport, thus demonstrating that the valinomycin effect has nothing to do with physiological K^+ transport (Section IV,B,1).

In Section IV,B,3 an account is given of experiments by Kaback and his associates which suggest that in membrane vesicles the binding of galactosides to the lac carrier, quite apart from transport, requires coupling to metabolism. Recent experiments (Schuldiner et al., 1975c, 1976) lend strong support to this iconoclastic claim and are consistent with the interpretation that the carrier bears a net negative charge and therefore becomes available at the external surface only when a potential has been established across the membrane. The observation that energy-dependent binding to the carrier is reversed by proton conductors negates my hint that respiration may be needed to expel protons that enter by symport with the substrate. The conflict between these vesicle experiments and those of Cecchini and Koch (1975) on intact cells is unresolved.

Gutowski and Rosenberg (1976b) confirmed with E. coli grown under strictly anaerobic conditions that two classes of transport systems exist, dependent respectively upon the "energized state" and upon "ATP" (Section IV,C). However, papers by Lieberman and Hong (1976) and by Plate (1976) suggest that these two classes may have at least one protein in common and that colicin K may act at the level of this protein. Thus the plot thickens and the eventual outcome will be awaited with interest by the swelling hordes of bacterial bioenergeticists.

REFERENCES

Abrams, A. (1976). In "Membrane-Bound Enzymes" (A. Martonosi, ed.), pp. 57–73. Plenum, New York.

Abrams, A., and Smith, J. B. (1974). In "The Enzymes" (P. D. Boyer, ed.), 3rd ed., Vol. 10, pp. 395–429. Academic Press, New York.

Abrams, A., Jensen, C., and Morris, D. (1975). *J. Supramol. Struct.* **3**, 261–274.

Abrams, A., Jensen, C., and Morris, D. H. (1976). *Biochem. Biophys. Res. Commun.* **69**, 804–811.

Adler, J. (1975). *Annu. Rev. Biochem.* **44**, 341–356.

Adolfsen, R., McClung, J. A., and Moudrianakis, E. N. (1975). *Biochemistry* **14**, 1727–1735.

Altendorf, K. H., and Staehelin, L. A. (1974). *J. Bacteriol.* **117**, 888–899.

Altendorf, K. A., and Zitzman, W. (1975). *FEBS Lett.* **59**, 268–272.

Altendorf, K., Harold, F. M., and Simoni, R. D. (1974). *J. Biol. Chem.* **249**, 4587–4593.

Altendorf, K., Hirata, H., and Harold, F. M. (1975). *J. Biol. Chem.* **250**, 1405–1412.

Andreu, J. M., and Muñoz, E. (1975). *Biochim. Biophys. Acta* **387**, 228–233.

Asghar, S. S., Levin, E., and Harold, F. M. (1973). *J. Biol. Chem.* **248**, 5225–5233.

Ashcroft, J. R., and Haddock, B. A. (1975). *Biochem. J.* **148**, 349–352.

Baccarini-Melandri, A., Zannoni, D., and Melandri, B. A. (1973). *Biochim. Biophys. Acta* **314**, 298–311.

Baccarini-Melandri, A., Fabri, E., Firstater, E., and Melandri, B. A. (1975). *Biochim. Biophys. Acta* **376**, 72–81.

Baltscheffsky, H., and Baltscheffsky, M. (1974). *Annu. Rev. Biochem.* **43**, 871–897.

Baltscheffsky, H., Baltscheffsky, M., and Thore, A. (1971). *Curr. Top. Bioenerg.* **4**, 273–325.

Barker, H. A. (1972). *In* ''Horizons of Bioenergetics'' (A. San Pietro and H. Gest, eds.), pp. 7–32. Academic Press, New York.

Barsky, E. L., Bonch-Osmolovskaya, E. A., Ostroumov, S. A., Samuilov, V. D., and Skulachev, V. P. (1975). *Biochim. Biophys. Acta* **387**, 388–396.

Bastos, R. N., and Mahler, H. R. (1974). *J. Biol. Chem.* **249**, 6617–6627.

Belaich, J. P., Belaich, A., and Simonipietri, P. (1972). *J. Gen. Microbiol.* **70**, 179–185.

Berg, H. C. (1974). *Nature (London)* **249**, 77–79.

Berg, H. C. (1975a). *Nature (London)* **254**, 389–392.

Berg, H. C. (1975b). *Annu. Rev. Biophys. Bioeng.* **4**, 119–136.

Berg, H. C., and Anderson, R. A. (1973). *Nature (London)* **245**, 380–382.

Berger, E. A. (1973). *Proc. Natl. Acad. Sci. U.S.A.* **70**, 1514–1518.

Berger, E. A., and Heppel, L. A. (1974). *J. Biol. Chem.* **249**, 7747–7755.

Beyeler, W., Lutz, H. U., and Bachofen, R. (1975). *J. Bioenerg.* **6**, 233–242.

Bhattacharyya, P. (1975). *J. Bacteriol.* **123**, 123–127.

Bhattacharyya, P., Epstein, W., and Silver, S. (1971). *Proc. Natl. Acad. Sci. U.S.A.* **68**, 1488–1492.

Blaurock, A. E. (1975). *J. Mol. Biol.* **93**, 139–158.

Boguslavsky, L. I., Kondrashin, A. A., Kozlov, I. A., Metelsky, S. T., Skulachev, V. P., and Vokov, A. G. (1975). *FEBS Lett.* **50**, 223–226.

Boonstra, J., Gutnick, D. L., and Kaback, H. R. (1975). *J. Bacteriol.* **124**, 1248–1255.

Boos, W. (1974a). *Annu. Rev. Biochem.* **43**, 123–146.

Boos, W. (1974b). *Curr. Top. Membr. Transp.* **5**, 52–136.

Booth, I. R., and Morris, J. G. (1975). *FEBS Lett.* **59**, 153–157.

Boxer, D. H., and Clegg, R. A. (1975). *FEBS Lett.* **60**, 54–57.

Boyer, P. D. (1974). *In* ''Dynamics of Energy-Transducing Membranes'' (L. Ernster, R. W. Estabrook, and E. C. Slater, eds.), pp. 289–301. Elsevier, Amsterdam.

Boyer, P. D. (1975a). *FEBS Lett.* **50**, 91–94.

Boyer, P. D. (1975b). *FEBS Lett.* **58**, 1–6.

Boyer, P. D., Cross, R. L., and Momsen, W. (1973). *Proc. Natl. Acad. Sci. U.S.A.* **70**, 2837–2839.

Boyer, P. D., Stokes, B. O., Wolcott, R. G., and Degani, C. (1975). *Fed. Proc., Fed. Am. Soc. Exp. Biol.* **34**, 1711–1717.

Bragg, P. D., and Hou, C. (1973). *Biochem. Biophys. Res. Commun.* **50**, 729–736.

Bragg, P. D., and Hou, C. (1974). *Arch. Biochem. Biophys.* **163**, 614–616.

Bragg, P. D., and Hou, C. (1975). *Arch. Biochem. Biophys.* **167**, 311–321.

Bragg, P. D., Davies, P. L., and Hou, C. (1972). *Biochem. Biophys. Res. Commun.* **47**, 1248–1255.

Bragg, P. D., Davies, P. L., and Hou, C. (1973). *Arch. Biochem. Biophys.* **159**, 664–670.

Brewer, G. J. (1974). *Biochemistry* **13**, 5038–5045.

Brewer, G. J. (1976). *Biochemistry* **15**, 1387–1392.

Burnell, J. N., John, P., and Whatley, F. R. (1975). *Biochem. J.* **150**, 527–536.

Butlin, J. D., Cox, G. B., and Gibson, F. (1971). *Biochem. J.* **124**, 75–81.

Butlin, J. D., Cox, G. B., and Gibson, F. (1973). *Biochim. Biophys. Acta* **292**, 366–375.

Cantley, L. C., and Hammes, G. G. (1975). *Biochemistry* **14**, 2968–2975.

Casadio, R., Baccarini-Melandri, A., Zannoni, A., and Melandri, B. A. (1974). *FEBS Lett.* **49**, 203–207.

Caserta, G., and Cerrigni, T. (1973). *J. Theor. Biol.* **41**, 127–142.

Cavari, B. Z., Avi-Dor, Y., and Grossowicz, N. (1967). *Biochem. J.* **103**, 601–608.

Cecchini, G., and Koch, A. L. (1975). *J. Bacteriol.* **123**, 187–195.

Clarke, D. J., and Morris, J. G. (1976). *Biochem. J.* **154**, 725–729.

Cockburn, M., Earnshaw, P., and Eddy, A. A. (1975). *Biochem. J.* **146**, 705–712.

Cockrell, R. S., Harris, E. J., and Pressman, B. C. (1967). *Nature (London)* **215**, 1487–1488.

Cogdell, R. J., and Crofts, A. R. (1974). *Biochim. Biophys. Acta* **347**, 264–272.

Cogdell, R. J., Jackson, J. B., and Crofts, A. R. (1973). *J. Bioenerg.* **4**, 211–227.

Cole, J. S., and Aleem, M. I. (1973). *Proc. Natl. Acad. Sci. U.S.A.* **70**, 3571–3575.

Connelly, J. L., Jones, O. T. G., Saunders, V. A., and Yates, D. W. (1973). *Biochim. Biophys. Acta* **242**, 644–653.

Cowell, J. L. (1974). *J. Bacteriol.* **120**, 139–146.

Cox, G. B., and Gibson, F. (1974). *Biochim. Biophys. Acta* **346**, 1–25.

Cox, G. B., Gibson, F., and McCann, L. (1973). *Biochem. J.* **134**, 1015–1021.

Cox, G. B., Gibson, F., and McCann, L. (1974). *Biochem. J.* **138**, 211–215.

Crofts, A. R., Evans, E. H., and Cogdell, R. J. (1974). *Ann. N.Y. Acad. Sci.* **227**, 227–242.

Cross, R. L., and Boyer, P. D. (1975). *Biochemistry* **14**, 392–398.

Cunarro, J., and Weiner, M. W. (1975). *Biochim. Biophys. Acta* **387**, 234–240.

Curtis, S. J. (1974). *J. Bacteriol.* **120**, 295–303.

Daniel, J., Roisin, M.-P., Burstein, C., and Kepes, A. (1975). *Biochim. Biophys. Acta* **376**, 195–209.

Danon, A., and Stoeckenius, W. (1974). *Proc. Natl. Acad. Sci. U.S.A.* **71**, 1234–1238.

Dekker, K., Jungermann, K., and Thauer, R. K. (1970). *Angew. Chem., Int. Ed. Engl.* **9**, 138–158.

del Campo, F. F., Hernandez-Asensio, M., and Ramirez, J. M. (1975). *Biochem. Biophys. Res. Commun.* **63**, 1099–1105.

DePamphilis, M. L., and Adler, J. (1971). *J. Bacteriol.* **105**, 384–395.

Dietz, G. W. (1972). *J. Biol. Chem.* **247**, 4561–4565.

Doetsch, R. N. (1972a). *Crit. Rev. Microbiol.* **1**, 73–103.

Doetsch, R. N. (1972b). *J. Theor. Biol.* **35**, 55–66.

Dontsov, A. E., Grinius, L. L., Jasaitis, A. A., Severina, I. I., and Skulachev, V. P. (1972). *J. Bioenerg.* **3**, 277–303.

Downs, A. J. and Jones, C. W. (1975). *Arch. Microbiol.* **105**, 159–167.

Drachev, L. A., Jasaitis, A. A., Kaulen, A. D., Kondrashin, A. A., Liberman, E. A., Nemecek, I. B., Ostroumov, S. A., Semenov, A. Yu., and Skulachev, V. P. (1974). *Nature (London)* **249**, 321–324.

Drachev, L. A., Kondrashin, A. A., Samuilov, V. D., and Skulachev, V. P. (1975). *FEBS Lett.* **50**, 219–222.

Drozd, J. W. (1974). *FEBS Lett.* **49**, 103–105.

Dutton, P. L., and Leigh, J. S. (1973). *Biochim. Biophys. Acta* **314**, 178–190.

Dutton, P. L., and Wilson, D. W. (1974). *Biochim. Biophys. Acta* **346**, 165–212.

Dutton, P. L., Petty, K. M., Bonner, M. S., and Morse, S. D. (1975). *Biochim. Biophys. Acta* **387**, 536–556.

Eagon, R. G., and Wilkerson, L. S. (1972). *Biochem. Biophys. Res. Commun.* **46**, 1944–1950.

Edwards, P. A., and Jackson, J. B. (1976). *Eur. J. Biochem.* **62**, 7–14.

Enoch, H. G., and Lester, R. L. (1975). *J. Biol. Chem.* **250**, 6693–6705.

Ernster, L., and Lee, C.-P. (1964). *Annu. Rev. Biochem.* **33**, 729–788.

Essenberg, R. C., and Kornberg, H. L. (1975). *J. Biol. Chem.* **256**, 939–945.

Feingold, D. S. (1970). *J. Membr. Biol.* **3**, 372–386.

Ferguson, S. J., John, P., Lloyd, W. J., Radda, G. K., and Whatley, F. R. (1976). *FEBS Lett.* **62**, 272–275.

Ferman, F. E. (1973). *Arch. Biochem. Biophys.* **159**, 444–452.

Ferman, F. E., and Bennett, W. (1973). *Arch. Biochem. Biophys.* **159**, 434–443.

Fillingame, R. H. (1975). *J. Bacteriol.* **124**, 870–883.

Fisher, R. R., Rampey, S. A., Sadighi, A., and Fisher, K. (1975). *J. Biol. Chem.* **250**, 810–825.

Forrest, W. W., and Walker, D. J. (1971). *Adv. Microb. Physiol.* **5**, 213–274.

Fournier, R. E., and Pardee, A. B. (1974). *J. Biol. Chem.* **249**, 5948–5954.

Futai, M. (1974a). *J. Bacteriol.* **120**, 861–865.

Futai, M. (1974b). *Biochemistry* **13**, 2327–2333.

Futai, M., Sternweis, P. C., and Heppel, L. A. (1974). *Proc. Natl. Acad. Sci. U.S.A.* **71**, 2725–2729.

Gale, E. F., and Llewellin, J. M. (1972). *Biochim. Biophys. Acta* **266**, 182–205.

Garland, P. B., Downie, J. A., and Haddock, B. A. (1975). *Biochem. J.* **152**, 547–559.

Garrett, N. E., and Penefsky, H. S. (1975). *J. Biol. Chem.* **250**, 6640–6647.

Gepshtein, A., and Carmeli, C. (1974). *Eur. J. Biochem.* **44**, 593–602.

Gest, H. (1972). *Adv. Microb. Physiol.* **7**, 243–282.

Gilcrist, M. J. R., and Konisky, J. (1975). *J. Biol. Chem.* **250**, 2457–2462.

Gorneva, G. A., and Ryabova, I. D. (1974). *FEBS Lett.* **42**, 271–274.

Green, D. E. (1974). *Biochim. Biophys. Acta* **346**, 27–78.

Green, D. E., and Reible, S. (1974). *Proc. Natl. Acad. Sci. U.S.A.* **71**, 4850–4854.

Green, D. E., and Reible, S. (1975). *Proc. Natl. Sci. U.S.A.* **72**, 253–257.

Green, D. E., Blondin, G., Kessler, R., and Southard, J. H. (1975). *Proc. Natl. Acad. Sci. U.S.A.* **72**, 896–900.

Greville, G. D. (1969). *Curr. Top. Bioenerg.* **3**, 1–78.

Grinius, L., Slušnyte, R., and Griniuviene, B. (1975). *FEBS Lett.* **57**, 290–293.

Griniuviene, B., Chmieliauskaite, V., and Grinius, L. (1974). *Biochem. Biophys. Res. Commun.* **56**, 206–213.

Griniuviene, B., Dzheia, P., and Grinius, L. (1975). *Biochem. Biophys. Res. Commun.* **64**, 790–796.

Gromet-Elhanan, Z. (1974). *J. Biol. Chem.* **249**, 2522–2527.

Gromet-Elhanan, Z., and Leiser, M. (1973). *Arch. Biochem. Biophys.* **159**, 583–589.

Gromet-Elhanan, Z., and Leiser, M. (1975). *J. Biol. Chem.* **250**, 84–89.
Gutowski, S. J., and Rosenberg, H. (1976a). *Biochem. J.* **152**, 647–654.
Gutowski, S. J., and Rosenberg, H. (1976b). *Biochem. J.* **154**, 731–734.
Haddock, B. A., and Jones, C. W. (1976). *Bacteriol. Rev.* (in press).
Hamilton, W. A. (1975). *Adv. Microb. Physiol.* **12**, 1–53.
Hampton, M. L., and Freese, E. (1974). *J. Bacteriol.* **118**, 497–504.
Hanson, R. L., and Kennedy, E. P. (1973). *J. Bacteriol.* **114**, 772–781.
Hare, J. F. (1975). *Biochem. Biophys. Res. Commun.* **66**, 1329–1337.
Harmon, H. J., Hall, J. D., and Crane, F. L. (1974). *Biochim. Biophys. Acta* **344**, 119–155.
Harold, F. M. (1972). *Bacteriol. Rev.* **36**, 172–230.
Harold, F. M. (1974). *Ann. N.Y. Acad. Sci.* **227**, 297–311.
Harold, F. M., and Altendorf, K. H. (1974). *Curr. Top. Membr. Transp.* **5**, 2–50.
Harold, F. M., and Baarda, J. R. (1968). *J. Bacteriol.* **96**, 2025–2034.
Harold, F. M., and Levin, E. (1974). *J. Bacteriol.* **117**, 1141–1148.
Harold, F. M., and Papineau, D. (1972a). *J. Membr. Biol.* **8**, 27–44.
Harold, F. M., and Papineau, D. (1972b). *J. Membr. Biol.* **8**, 45–62.
Harold, F. M., and Spitz, E. (1975). *J. Bacteriol.* **122**, 266–277.
Harold, F. M., Baarda, J. R., Baron, C., and Abrams, A. (1969). *J. Biol. Chem.* **244**, 2261–2268.
Harold, F. M., Altendorf, K. H., and Hirata, H. (1974). *Ann. N.Y. Acad. Sci.* **235**, 149–160.
Harris, D. A., and Slater, E. C. (1975). *Biochim. Biophys. Acta* **387**, 335–348.
Hatefi, Y., Hanstein, W. G., Galante, Y., and Stiggall, D. L. (1975). *Fed. Proc., Fed. Am. Soc. Exp. Biol.* **34**, 1699–1706.
Hays, J. B., Simoni, R. D., and Roseman, S. (1973). *J. Biol. Chem.* **248**, 941–956.
Hellingwerf, K. J., Michels, P. A. M., Dorpema, J. W., and Konings, W. N. (1975). *Eur. J. Biochem.* **55**, 397–406.
Henderson, P. J. F. (1971). *Annu. Rev. Microbiol.* **25**, 394–428.
Henderson, P. J. F., and Skinner, A. (1974). *Biochem. Soc. Trans.* **2**, 543–545.
Henderson, R. (1975). *J. Mol. Biol.* **93**, 123–138.
Henderson, R., and Unwin, P. N. T. (1975). *Nature (London)* **257**, 28–32.
Hendler, R. W., Towne, D. W., and Shrager, R. I. (1975). *Biochim. Biophys. Acta* **376**, 42–62.
Hertzberg, E. L., and Hinkle, P. C. (1974). *Biochem. Biophys. Res. Commun.* **58**, 178–184.
Hildebrand, E., and Dencher, N. (1975). *Nature (London)* **257**, 46–48.
Hinkle, P. C. (1973). *Fed. Proc., Fed. Am. Soc. Exp. Biol.* **32**, 1988–1992.
Hirata, H., Altendorf, K., and Harold, F. M. (1973). *Proc. Natl. Acad. Sci. U.S.A.* **70**, 1804–1808.
Hirata, H., Altendorf, K., and Harold, F. M. (1974a). *J. Biol. Chem.* **249**, 2939–2945.
Hirata, H., Kosmakos, F. C., and Brodie, A. F. (1974b). *J. Biol. Chem.* **249**, 6465–6970.
Hirata, H., Sone, N., Yoshida, M., and Kagawa, Y. (1976). *J. Biochem. (Tokyo)* (in press).
Hochstadt-Ozer, J. (1974). *Crit. Rev. Microbiol.* **2**, 259–310.
Hoffee, P., Englesberg, E., and Lamy, F. (1964). *Biochim. Biophys. Acta* **79**, 337–350.
Holland, I. B. (1975). *Adv. Microb. Physiol.* **12**, 55–139.
Hunter, D. R., and Capaldi, R. A. (1974). *Biochem. Biophys. Res. Commun.* **56**, 623–628.
Hunter, D. R., Komai, H., and Haworth, R. A. (1974). *Biochem. Biophys. Res. Commun.* **56**, 647–653.
Jackson, J. B., and Dutton, P. L. (1973). *Biochim. Biophys. Acta* **325**, 102–113.

Jackson, J. B., Crofts, A. R., and von Stedingk, L. V. (1968). *Eur. J. Biochem.* **6**, 41–54.
Jackson, J. B., Saphon, S., and Witt, T. H. (1975). *Biochim. Biophys. Acta* **408**, 83–92.
Jagendorf, A. T. (1975). *Fed. Proc., Fed. Am. Soc. Exp. Biol.* **34**, 1718–1721.
Jagendorf, A. T., and Uribe, E. (1966). *Proc. Natl. Acad. Sci. U.S.A.* **55**, 170–177.
Jetten, A. M., and Jetten, M. E. R. (1975). *Biochim. Biophys. Acta* **387**, 12–22.
Jetten, A. M., and Vogels, G. D. (1973). *Biochim. Biophys. Acta* **311**, 483–495.
Johansson, B. C., and Baltscheffsky, M. (1975). *FEBS Lett.* **53**, 221–224.
John, P., and Hamilton, W. A. (1971). *Eur. J. Biochem.* **23**, 529–532.
John, P., and Whatley, F. R. (1975). *Nature (London)* **254**, 495–498.
Johnson, C. L., Cha, Y.-A., and Stern, J. R. (1975). *J. Bacteriol.* **121**, 682–687.
Jones, C. W., Ackrell, B. A. C., and Erickson, S. K. (1971). *Biochim. Biophys. Acta* **245**, 54–62.
Jones, C. W., Brice, J. M., Downs, A. J., and Drozd, J. W. (1975). *Eur. J. Biochem.* **52**, 265–271.
Jones, O. T. G., and Plewis, K. M. (1974). *Biochim. Biophys. Acta* **357**, 204–214.
Jurtshuk, P., Mueller, T. J., and Acord, W. C. (1975). *Crit. Rev. Microbiol.* **3**, 399–468.
Kaback, H. R. (1972). *Biochim. Biophys. Acta* **265**, 367–416.
Kaback, H. R. (1974). *Science* **186**, 882–892.
Kaback, H. R., and Hong, J.-S. (1973). *Crit. Rev. Microbiol.* **2**, 333–376.
Kaback, H. R., and Stadtman, E. R. (1966). *Proc. Natl. Acad. Sci. U.S.A.* **55**, 920–927.
Kadner, R. J., and Winkler, H. H. (1975). *J. Bacteriol.* **123**, 985–991.
Kagawa, Y., Kandrach, A., and Racker, E. (1973). *J. Biol. Chem.* **248**, 676–684.
Kahane, S., Marcus, M., Barash, H., Halpern, Y. S., and Kaback, H. R. (1975). *FEBS Lett.* **56**, 235–239.
Kanner, B. I., and Gutnick, D. L. (1972). *J. Bacteriol.* **111**, 287–289.
Kanner, B. I., and Racker, E. (1975). *Biochem. Biophys. Res. Commun.* **64**, 1054–1061.
Kanner, B. I., Nelson, N., and Gutnick, D. L. (1975). *Biochim. Biophys. Acta* **396**, 347–359.
Kasahara, M., and Anraku, Y. (1974). *J. Biochem. (Tokyo)* **76**, 977–983.
Kashket, E. R., and Wilson, T. H. (1973). *Proc. Natl. Acad. Sci. U.S.A.* **70**, 2866–2869.
Kashket, E. R., and Wilson, T. H. (1974). *Biochem. Biophys. Res. Commun.* **59**, 879–886.
Kay, W. W., and Bragg, P. D. (1975). *Biochem. J.* **150**, 21–30.
Kayushin, L. P., and Skulachev, V. P. (1974). *FEBS Lett.* **39**, 39–42.
Keister, D. L., and Raveed, N. J. (1974). *J. Biol. Chem.* **249**, 6454–6458.
Keister, D. L., and Yike, N. J. (1967). *Biochemistry* **6**, 3847–3857.
Kemp, M. B., Haddock, B. A., and Garland, P. B. (1975). *Biochem. J.* **148**, 329–333.
King, M. T., and Drews, G. (1975). *Arch. Microbiol.* **102**, 219–232.
Klein, K., Steinberg, B., Fiethen, B., and Overath, P. (1971). *Eur. J. Biochem.* **19**, 442–450.
Knaff, D. B., and Buchanan, B. B. (1975). *Biochim. Biophys. Acta* **376**, 549–560.
Kobayashi, H., and Anraku, Y. (1974). *J. Biochem. (Tokyo)* **76**, 1175–1182.
Kobayashi, H., Kin, E., and Anraku, Y. (1974). *J. Biochem. (Tokyo)* **76**, 251–261.
Koch, A. L. (1971). *J. Mol. Biol.* **59**, 447–459.
Konings, A. W. T., and Guillory, R. J. (1973). *J. Biol. Chem.* **248**, 1045–1050.
Konings, W. N., and Boonstra, J. (1976). *Curr. Top. Membr. Transp.* (in press).
Konings, W. N., Boonstra, J., and de Vries, W. (1975). *J. Bacteriol.* **122**, 245–249.
Koshland, D. E. (1974). *FEBS Lett.* **40**, S3–S4.
Krebs, H. A., and Veech, R. L. (1969). *In* "The Energy Level and Metabolic Control in Mitochondria" (S. Papa *et al.*, eds.), pp. 329–381. Adriatica Editrice, Bari.
Kuhn, T. S. (1970). "The Structure of Scientific Revolutions," 2nd ed. Univ. of Chicago Press, Chicago, Illinois.

Kustu, S. G., and Ames, G. F. (1974). *J. Biol. Chem.* **249**, 6976–6983.

Laris, P. C., and Pershadsingh, H. A. (1974). *Biochem. Biophys. Res. Commun.* **57**, 620–626.

Larsen, S. H., Reader, R. W., Kort, E. N., Tso, W.-W., and Adler, J. (1974a). *Nature (London)* **249**, 75–77.

Larsen, S. H., Adler, J., Gargus, J. J., and Hogg, R. W. (1974b). *Proc. Natl. Acad. Sci. U.S.A.* **71**, 1239–1243.

Lawford, H. G., and Haddock, B. A. (1973). *Biochem. J.* **136**, 217–220.

LeGall, J., and Postgate, J. R. (1973). *Adv. Microb. Physiol.* **10**, 82–135.

Leiser, M., and Gromet-Elhanan, Z. (1974). *FEBS Lett.* **43**, 267–270.

Leiser, M., and Gromet-Elhanan, Z. (1975). *J. Biol. Chem.* **250**, 40–93.

Lewis, A. J., Spoonhower, R. A., Bogomolni, R. A., Lozier, R. H., and Stoeckenius, W. (1974). *Proc. Natl. Acad. Sci. U.S.A.* **71**, 4462–4466.

Lieberman, M. A., and Hong, J.-S. (1974). *Proc. Natl. Acad. Sci. U.S.A.* **81**, 4395–4399.

Lieberman, M. A., and Hong, J. S. (1976). *Arch. Biochem. Biophys.* **172**, 312–315.

Lien, S., and Gest, H. (1973). *Arch. Biochem. Biophys.* **159**, 730–737.

Lipmann, F. (1941). *Adv. Enzymol.* **1**, 99–162.

Lo, T. C. Y., and Sanwal, B. D. (1975). *Biochem. Biophys. Res. Commun.* **63**, 278–285.

Lombardi, F. J., and Kaback, H. R. (1972). *J. Biol. Chem.* **247**, 7844–7857.

Lombardi, F. J., Reeves, J. P., and Kaback, H. R. (1973). *J. Biol. Chem.* **248**, 3551–3565.

Lombardi, F. J., Reeves, J. P., Short, S. A., and Kaback, H. R. (1974). *Ann. N.Y. Acad. Sci.* **227**, 312–327.

Lozier, R. H., Bogomolni, R. A., and Stoeckenius, W. (1975). *Biophys. J.* **15**, 955–962.

Lundquist, R., and Olivera, B. M. (1971). *J. Biol. Chem.* **246**, 1107–1116.

Luria, S. L. (1973). *In* "Bacterial Membranes and Walls" (L. Leive, ed.), p. 243–320. Dekker, New York.

Lutz, H. U., Dahl, J. S., and Bachofen, R. (1974). *Biochim. Biophys. Acta* **347**, 359–370.

MacDonald, R. E., and Lanyi, J. K. (1975). *Biochemistry* **14**, 2882–2889.

MacGregor, C. H. (1975). *J. Bacteriol.* **121**, 1111–1116.

McLaughlin, S., and Eisenberg, M. (1975). *Annu. Rev. Biophys. Bioeng.* **4**, 335–366.

Macnab, R., and Koshland, D. E. (1974). *J. Mol. Biol.* **84**, 399–406.

Mahler, H. R., and Bastos, R. N. (1974). *Proc. Natl. Acad. Sci. U.S.A.* **71**, 2241–2245.

Maloney, P. C., and Wilson, T. H. (1975). *J. Membr. Biol.* **25**, 285–310.

Maloney, P. C., Kashket, E. R., and Wilson, T. H. (1974). *Proc. Natl. Acad. Sci. U.S.A.* **71**, 3896–3900.

Mevel-Ninio, M. T., and Valentine, R. C. (1975). *Biochim. Biophys. Acta* **376**, 485–491.

Meyer, D. J., and Jones, C. W. (1973). *Eur. J. Biochem.* **36**, 144–151.

Miner, K. M., and Franck, L. (1974). *J. Bacteriol.* **117**, 1093–1098.

Mitchell, P. (1957). *Nature (London)* **180**, 134–136.

Mitchell, P. (1961). *Nature (London)* **191**, 144–148.

Mitchell, P. (1962a). *Biochem. Soc. Symp.* **22**, 142–168.

Mitchell, P. (1962b). *J. Gen. Microbiol.* **24**, 25–37.

Mitchell, P. (1966). *Biol. Rev. Cambridge Philos. Soc.* **41**, 445–502.

Mitchell, P. (1967). *Adv. Enzymol.* **29**, 33–87.

Mitchell, P. (1968). "Chemiosmotic Coupling and Energy Transduction." Glynn Res., Bodmin, Cornwall, England.

Mitchell, P. (1970a). *In* "Membranes and Ion Transport" (E. E. Bittar, ed.), Vol. 1, pp. 192–256. Wiley (Interscience), New York.

Mitchell, P. (1970b). *Soc. Gen. Microbiol.* **20**, 121–166.

Mitchell, P. (1972a). *J. Bioenerg.* **3**, 5–24.

Mitchell, P. (1972b). *FEBS Lett.* **28**, 1–4.

Mitchell, P. (1973a). *FEBS Lett.* **33**, 267–274.

Mitchell, P. (1973b). *J. Bioenerg.* **4**, 63–91.

Mitchell, P. (1974). *FEBS Lett.* **43**, 189–194.

Mitchell, P. (1975a). *FEBS Lett.* **50**, 95–97.

Mitchell, P. (1975b). *FEBS Lett.* **56**, 1–6.

Mitchell, P. (1975c). *FEBS Lett.* **59**, 137–139.

Mitchell, P., and Moyle, J. (1969). *Eur. J. Biochem.* **1**, 471–489.

Moyle, J., and Mitchell, P. (1973a). *Biochem. J.* **132**, 571–585.

Moyle, J., and Mitchell, P. (1973b). *FEBS Lett.* **30**, 317–320.

Moyle, J., Mitchell, R., and Mitchell, P. (1972). *FEBS Lett.* **23**, 233–235.

Nelson, N., Kanner, B. I., and Gutnick, D. L. (1974). *Proc. Natl. Acad. Sci. U.S.A.* **71**, 2720–2724.

Nicholls, D. G. (1974). *Eur. J. Biochem.* **50**, 305–315.

Nierlich, D. P. (1974). *Science* **184**, 1043–1050.

Niven, D. F., and Hamilton, W. A. (1974). *Eur. J. Biochem.* **44**, 517–522.

Oehr, P., and Willecke, K. (1974). *J. Biol. Chem.* **249**, 2037–2042.

Oelze, J., and Kamen, M. D. (1975). *Biochim. Biophys. Acta* **387**, 1–11.

Oesterhelt, D., and Hess, B. (1974). *Eur. J. Biochem.* **37**, 316–326.

Oesterhelt, D., and Stoeckenius, W. (1973). *Proc. Natl. Acad. Sci. U.S.A.* **70**, 2853–2857.

Oesterhelt, D., Meentzen, M., and Schuhmann, L. (1973). *Eur. J. Biochem.* **40**, 453–463.

Okamoto, K. (1975). *Biochim. Biophys. Acta* **389**, 370–379.

Ordal, G. W., and Goldman, D. J. (1975). *Science* **189**, 802–805.

Ostroumov, S. A., Samuilov, V. D., and Skulachev, V. P. (1973). *FEBS Lett.* **31**, 27–30.

Oxender, D. L. (1974). *Biomembranes* **5**, 25–79.

Oxender, D. L., and Quay, S. C. (1976). *In* "Methods in Membrane Biology" (E. D. Korn, ed.). Plenum, New York **6**, 183–242.

Padan, E., Zilberstein, D., and Rottenberg, H. (1976). *Eur. J. Biochem.* **63**, 533–541.

Papa, S., Guerrieri, F., and Lorusso, M. (1974). *Biochim. Biophys. Acta* **357**, 181–192.

Papa, S., Lorusso, M., and Guerrieri, F. (1975). *Biochim. Biophys. Acta* **387**, 425–440.

Parnes, J. R., and Boos, W. (1973). *J. Biol. Chem.* **248**, 4436–4445.

Parson, W. W. (1974). *Annu. Rev. Microbiol.* **28**, 41–59.

Parson, W. W., and Cogdell, R. J. (1975). *Biochim. Biophys. Acta* **416**, 105–149.

Patel, L., and Kaback, H. R. (1976). *Biochemistry* (in press).

Patel, L., Schuldiner, S., and Kaback, H. R. (1975). *Proc. Natl. Acad. Sci. U.S.A.* **72**, 3387–3391.

Payne, W. J. (1970). *Annu. Rev. Microbiol.* **24**, 17–52.

Pedersen, P. L. (1975a). *J. Bioenerg.* **6**, 243–275.

Pedersen, P. L. (1975b). *Biochem. Biophys. Res. Commun.* **64**, 610–616.

Pedersen, P. L. (1976). *J. Biol. Chem.* **251**, 934–940.

Phillips, S. K., and Cramer, W. A. (1973). *Biochemistry* **12**, 1170–1176.

Plate, C. A. (1976). *J. Bacteriol.* **125**, 467–474.

Plate, C. A., Suit, J. L., Jetten, A. M., and Luria, S. L. (1974). *J. Biol. Chem.* **249**, 6138–6143.

Poole, R. K., and Haddock, B. A. (1974). *Biochem. J.* **144**, 77–85.

Poole, R. K., and Haddock, B. A. (1975a). *FEBS Lett.* **52**, 13–16.

Poole, R. K., and Haddock, B. A. (1975b). *Biochem. J.* **152**, 537–546.

Pouyssegur, J. M., Faik, P., and Kornberg, H. L. (1974). *Biochem. J.* **140**, 193–203.

Prasad, R., Kalra, V. K., and Brodie, A. F. (1975). *J. Biol. Chem.* **250**, 3640–3698.

Prince, R. C., Baccarini-Melandri, A., Hauska, G. A., Melandri, B. A., and Crofts, R. A. (1975). *Biochim. Biophys. Acta* **387**, 212–227.

Pudek, M. R., and Bragg, P. D. (1974). *Arch. Biochem. Biophys.* **164**, 682–693.

Racker, E., and Hinkle, P. C. (1974). *J. Membr. Biol.* **17**, 181–188.
Racker, E., and Stoeckenius, W. (1974). *J. Biol. Chem.* **249**, 662–663.
Ramos, S., Schuldiner, S., and Kaback, H. R. (1976). *Proc. Natl. Acad. Sci. U.S.A.* **73**, 1892–1896.
Rayman, M. K., Lo, T. C. Y., and Sanwal, B. D. (1972). *J. Biol. Chem.* **248**, 6332–6339.
Reeves, J. P., Lombardi, F. J., and Kaback, H. R. (1972). *J. Biol. Chem.* **247**, 6204–6211.
Richey, D. P., and Lin, E. C. C. (1972). *J. Bacteriol.* **112**, 784–790.
Riebling, V., Thauer, R. K., and Jungermann, K. (1975). *Eur. J. Biochem.* **55**, 445–454.
Ritchey, T. W., and Seeley, H. W., Jr. (1975). *J. Gen. Microbiol.* **85**, 220–228.
Robbins, A. R., and Rotman, B. (1975). *Proc. Natl. Acad. Sci. U.S.A.* **72**, 423–427.
Robertson, R. N. (1968). "Protons, Electrons, Phosphorylation and Active Transport." Cambridge Univ. Press, London and New York.
Robertson, R. N., and Boardman, N. K. (1975). *FEBS Lett.* **60**, 1–6.
Robin, A., and Kepes, A. (1973). *FEBS Lett.* **36**, 133–136.
Robin, A., and Kepes, A. (1975). *Biochim. Biophys. Acta* **406**, 50–59.
Roseman, S. (1972). *Metab. Pathways, 3rd Ed.* **6**, 42–91.
Rosen, B. P. (1973). *Biochem. Biophys. Res. Commun.* **53**, 1289–1296.
Rosen, B. P., and Adler, L. W. (1975). *Biochim. Biophys. Acta* **387**, 23–36.
Rosen, B. P., and Heppel, L. A. (1973). *In* "Bacterial Membranes and Walls" (L. Leive, ed.), pp. 204–239. Dekker, New York.
Rosen, B. P., and McClees, J. S. (1974). *Proc. Natl. Acad. Sci. U.S.A.* **71**, 5042–5046.
Rosenberg, H., Cox, G. B., Butlin, J. D., and Gutowski, S. J. (1975). *Biochem. J.* **146**, 417–423.
Rossi, E., and Azzone, G. F. (1970). *Eur. J. Biochem.* **12**, 319–327.
Rottenberg, H. (1975). *J. Bioenerg.* **7**, 63–74.
Rudnick, G., Kaback, H. R., and Weil, R. (1975). *J. Biol. Chem.* **250**, 6847–6851.
Rydström, J. (1974). *Eur. J. Biochem.* **45**, 67–76.
Ryrie, I. J. (1975). *Arch. Biochem. Biophys.* **168**, 704–711.
Saphon, S., Jackson, J. B., and Witt, T. H. (1975a). *Biochim. Biophys. Acta* **408**, 58–66.
Saphon, S., Jackson, J. B., and Witt, T. H. (1975b). *Biochim. Biophys. Acta* **408**, 67–82.
Schairer, H. U., and Haddock, B. A. (1972). *Biochem. Biophys. Res. Commun.* **48**, 544–551.
Scholes, P., and Mitchell, P. (1970). *J. Bioenerg.* **1**, 309–323.
Scholes, P., Mitchell, P., and Moyle, J. (1969). *Eur. J. Biochem.* **8**, 450–454.
Schuldiner, S., and Kaback, H. R. (1975). *Biochemistry* **14**, 5451–5461.
Schuldiner, S., Padan, E., Rottenberg, H., Gromet-Elhanan, Z., and Avron, M. (1974). *FEBS Lett.* **49**, 174–177.
Schuldiner, S., Kerwar, G. K., Kaback, H. R., and Weil, R. (1975a). *J. Biol. Chem.* **250**, 1361–1370.
Schuldiner, S., Kung, H.-F., Kaback, H. R., and Weil, R. (1975b). *J. Biol. Chem.* **250**, 3679–3682.
Schuldiner, S., Spencer, R. D., Weber, G., Weil, R., and Kaback, H. R. (1975c). *J. Biol. Chem.* **250**, 8893–8896.
Schuldiner, S., Weil, R., and Kaback, H. R. (1976). *Proc. Natl. Acad. Sci. U.S.A.* **73**, 109–112.
Shahak, Y., Hardt, H., and Avron, M. (1975). *FEBS Lett.* **54**, 151–154.
Short, S. A., Kaback, H. R., and Kohn, L. D. (1974). *Proc. Natl. Acad. Sci. U.S.A.* **71**, 1461–1465.
Short, S. A., Kaback, H. R., and Kohn, L. D. (1975). *J. Biol. Chem.* **250**, 4291–4296.
Silverman, M., and Simon, M. (1974). *Nature (London)* **249**, 73–74.
Simoni, R. D., and Postma, P. W. (1975). *Annu. Rev. Biochem.* **43**, 523–554.

Simoni, R. D., and Roseman, S. (1973). *J. Biol. Chem.* **248**, 966–976.

Simoni, R. D., and Schallenberger, M. K. (1972). *Proc. Natl. Acad. Sci. U.S.A.* **69**, 2663–2667.

Simoni, R. D., and Shandell, A. (1975). *J. Biol. Chem.* **250**, 9421–9427.

Simoni, R. D., Nakagawa, T., Hays, J. B., and Roseman, S. (1973a). *J. Biol. Chem.* **248**, 932–940.

Simoni, R. D., Hays, J. B., Nakagawa, T., and Roseman, S. (1973b). *J. Biol. Chem.* **248**, 957–965.

Singh, A. P., and Bragg, P. D. (1974a). *Biochem. Biophys. Res. Commun.* **57**, 1200–1206.

Singh, A. P., and Bragg, P. D. (1974b). *J. Bacteriol.* **119**, 129–137.

Singh, A. P., and Bragg, P. D. (1975). *Biochim. Biophys. Acta* **396**, 229–241.

Skulachev, V. P. (1974). *Ann. N.Y. Acad. Sci.* **227**, 188–202.

Skulachev, V. P. (1975). *In* MTP International Review of Science, Biochemistry Series One, Vol. 3, "Energy Transducing Mechanisms" (E. Racker, ed.), pp. 31–73. Univ. Park Press, Baltimore, Maryland.

Slater, E. C. (1971). *Q. Rev. Biophys.* **4**, 35–72.

Slater, E. C. (1974). *In* "Dynamics of Energy-Transducing Membranes" (L. Ernster, R. W. Estabrook, and E. C. Slater, eds.), pp. 1–20. Elsevier, Amsterdam.

Slater, E. C., Rosing, J., and Mol, A. (1973). *Biochim. Biophys. Acta* **292**, 534–553.

Smith, J., and Sternweis, P. C. (1975). *Biochem. Biophys. Res. Commun.* **62**, 764–771.

Sone, N., Yoshida, M., Hirata, H., and Kagawa, Y. (1975). *J. Biol. Chem.* **250**, 7917–7923.

Sprott, G. D., Drozdowski, J. P., Martin, E. L., and MacLeod, R. A. (1975). *Can. J. Microbiol.* **21**, 43–50.

Stouthamer, A. H. (1973). *Antonie van Leeuwenhoek* **39**, 545–565.

Stouthamer, A. H., and Bettenhausen, B. (1973). *Biochim. Biophys. Acta* **301**, 53–70.

Straub, K. D. (1974). *J. Theor. Biol.* **44**, 191–206.

Stroobant, P., and Kaback, H. R. (1975). *Proc. Natl. Acad. Sci. U.S.A.* **72**, 3970–3974.

Sun, I. L., and Crane, F. L. (1975). *Biochem. Biophys. Res. Commun.* **65**, 1334–1342.

Suzuki, I. (1974). *Annu. Rev. Microbiol.* **28**, 85–102.

Taylor, B. L., and Koshland, D. E. (1974). *J. Bacteriol.* **119**, 640–642.

Taylor, B. L., and Koshland, D. E. (1975). *J. Bacteriol.* **123**, 557–569.

Terada, H., and Van Dam, K. (1975). *Biochim. Biophys. Acta* **387**, 507–518.

Thayer, W. S., and Hinkle, P. C. (1973). *J. Biol. Chem.* **248**, 5395–5402.

Thayer, W. S., and Hinkle, P. C. (1975a). *J. Biol. Chem.* **250**, 5330–5335.

Thayer, W. S., and Hinkle, P. C. (1975b). *J. Biol. Chem.* **250**, 5336–5342.

Thipayathasana, P., and Valentine, R. C. (1974). *Biochim. Biophys. Acta* **347**, 464–468.

Thompson, J., and MacLeod, R. A. (1973). *J. Biol. Chem.* **248**, 7106–7111.

Thompson, J., and MacLeod, R. A. (1974). *J. Bacteriol.* **120**, 598–603.

Tsuchiya, T., and Rosen, B. P. (1976a). *Biochem. Biophys. Res. Commun.* **68**, 497–502.

Tsuchiya, T., and Rosen, B. P. (1976b). *J. Biol. Chem.* **251**, 962–967.

Weiss, D. E. (1973). *Sub-Cell. Biochem.* **2**, 201–235.

West, I. C., and Mitchell, P. (1972). *J. Bioenerg.* **3**, 445–462.

West, I. C., and Mitchell, P. (1973). *Biochem. J.* **132**, 587–592.

West, I. C., and Mitchell, P. (1974a). *FEBS Lett.* **40**, 1–4.

West, I. C., and Mitchell, P. (1974b). *Biochem. J.* **144**, 87–90.

West, I. C., and Wilson, T. H. (1973). *Biochem. Biophys. Res. Commun.* **50**, 551–558.

Wikström, M. K. F. (1973). *Biochim. Biophys. Acta* **301**, 155–193.

Willecke, K., Gries, E. M., and Dehr, P. (1973). *J. Biol. Chem.* **248**, 807–814.

Williams, R. J. P. (1974). *Ann. N.Y. Acad. Sci.* **227**, 98–107.

Williams, R. J. P. (1975). *FEBS Lett.* **53**, 123–125.

Wilson, D. B. (1974). *J. Bacteriol.* **120**, 866–871.

Wong, P. T. S., and MacLennan, D. H. (1973). *Can. J. Biochem.* **51**, 538–549.

Wood, J. M. (1975). *J. Biol. Chem.* **250**, 4477–4485.

Yaguzhinsky, L. S., Boguslavsky, L. I., Volkov, A. G., and Rakhmaninova, A. B. (1976). *Nature (London)* **259**, 494–495.

Yamamoto, N., Yoshimura, S., Higuti, T., Nishikawa, K., and Horio, T. (1972). *J. Biochem. (Tokyo)* **72**, 1397–1406.

Yoshida, M., Sone, N., Hirata, H., and Kagawa. Y. (1975). *Biochem. Biophys. Res. Commun.* **67**, 1295–1300.

Proton Translocation in Chloroplasts [1]

G. HAUSKA AND A. TREBST
Lehrstuhl für Biochemie der Pflanzen,
Ruhr Universität Bochum,
West Germany

---

[1] Abbreviations used in this article: DPIP and DPIPH₂, oxidized and reduced form of 2,6-dichlorophenolindophenol; DAD, 2,3,5,6-tetramethyl-*p*-phenylenediamine (diaminodurene); TMPD, *N,N,N',N'*-tetramethyl-*p*-phenylenediamine; DMPD, *N,N*-dimethyl-*p*-phenylenediamine; PMS, *N*-methyl-phenazonium methosulfate; MV, methyl viologen (*N,N'*-dimethyl-4,4'-dipyridylium dichloride); AQ, anthraquinone-2-sulfonate; FCCP, carbonylcyanide-*p*-trifluoromethoxy-phenylhydrazone; DNP, 2,4-dinitrophenol; DCCD, dicyclohexyl-carbodiimide; EDAC, 1-ethyl-3-(3-dimethylaminopropyl)-carbodiimide; CF_1, coupling factor 1 of chloroplasts (site of ATP synthesis); CF_0, a membrane component to which CF_1 is attached. For further abbreviations, see legends.

I. Introduction

Proton translocation linked to electron transport was first discovered in chloroplasts (Jagendorf and Hind, 1963) two years after its anticipation in Mitchell's "Chemiosmotic Hypothesis" (Mitchell, 1961), which states that an electrochemical proton potential functions as energy transmitter between electron transport and ATP formation. This concept, like hardly anything else, stimulated bioenergetic research in the years following. The subject has been repeatedly reviewed for chloroplasts with individually differing emphasis (see Hind and McCarty, 1973; Trebst, 1974; the articles by Jagendorf, 1975; Witt, 1975; Avron, 1975a; Dilley, and Giaquinta, 1975; Rottenberg, 1975; Heber, 1976; Hall, 1976; McCarty, 1976). For other electron transport systems, see Crofts *et al.* (1975a) for bacterial photosynthesis, Harold and Altendorf (1974) for bacteria, and Papa (1976) for mitochondria. As to the present state of knowledge in photosynthesis, the reader is also referred to the proceedings of the international congresses on photosynthesis (Metzner, 1969; Forti *et al.*, 1972; Avron, 1975b) as well as to the forthcoming new edition of the "Encyclopedia of Plant Physiology" (Pirson and Zimmermann, 1976).

Our article should be regarded as an attempt to complement the reviews of Trebst (1974) and of Jagendorf (1975). We have tried to incorporate results from biophysical work, as far as we felt competent to do so. On the other hand, we have largely left out the aspect of morphological organization of the chloroplast membrane. The reader should consult the comprehensive reviews by Park and Sane (1971), by Anderson (1975), and by Arntzen and Briantais (1975). Being attracted by the universality of bioenergetics, particularly under a chemiosmotic heading, we sometimes have gone beyond our objective. The recent productivity of pertinent bioenergetic research expresses itself in numerous scientific meetings, to which we refer the unsatisfied reader (see Ernster *et al.*, 1974; Estrada-O. and Gitler 1974; Green 1974; Hatefi, 1975; Quagliarello *et al.*, 1975).

II. Photosynthetic Electron Transport, Photophosphorylation, and the Topography of the Chloroplast Membrane

A cross-sectional view of chloroplast compartmentation *in vivo* is shown at the top of Fig. 1, with the localization of the functions indicated. Light-induced electron transport is bound to the lamellar membrane system and yields O_2, ATP, and NADPH; the later two are consumed in CO_2-assimilation in the Calvin cycle, localized in the matrix. Assimilated carbon leaves the chloroplast, mainly in the form of triosephosphate in exchange for P_i (see Heber, 1974). Only carefully isolated chloroplasts retain the envelope and the stroma (type A chloroplasts, see Hall, 1972). Most experiments on electron transport and phosphorylation, to which we address ourselves, are carried out with stripped lamellar systems (type C chloroplasts). The photosynthetic electron transport chain from water to $NADP^+$, containing two light reactions together with the corresponding reaction centers plus pigment systems, connected in series by several electron carriers, is depicted in three different forms in Fig. 1, a–c. The first shows a linear scheme, with four distinct sites for specific inhibition (KCN, DBMIB, DCMU, NH_2OH treatment) and two main regions for entry (D_1/D_2) as well as exit (A_1/A_2) of electrons from or to artificial electron donors and acceptors, respectively. By proper combination of an inhibitor and redox compounds, partial reactions of the overall chain can be functionally separated (Trebst, 1974). If a redox compound can simultaneously act as D_1 and A_1, it catalyzes cyclic electron transport around photosystem I. Figure 1a, in addition, contains some kinetic constants, the oxidation of plastoquinone being the rate-limiting step for the rate of electron transport from water to X (see Witt, 1975).

The second drawing, Fig. 1b, represents the "Z scheme" of photosynthetic electron transport, the carriers approximately placed on the redox potential scale. Present knowledge has been reveiwed lately, on the whole system (see Trebst, 1974; Witt, 1975; Avron, 1975c; Hauska, 1975), as well as on individual components [see Joliot and Kok (1975) for the water-splitting complex; Radmer and Kok (1975), Warden *et al.* (1976), and van Gorkom *et al.* (1976) for photosystem II; Amesz (1973) for Q and plastoquinone; and Ke (1973) for P_{700} and X].

A good deal of experimental evidence supports the notion of vectorial electron transport in the chloroplast membrane, resulting from an asymmetric topography, as put together in Fig. 1c. This was scrutinized in detail by Trebst (1974; see also Junge, 1975; Hauska, 1975), and only a few facets will be repeated here.

The two light reactions lead to a charge separation across the

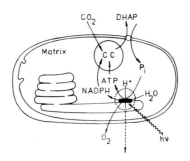

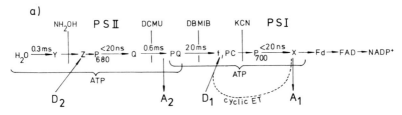

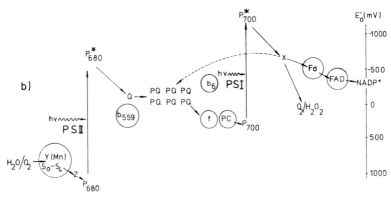

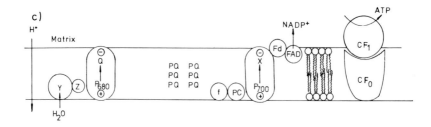

membrane, with the negative side facing the stromal surface, i.e., the suspending medium, in isolated lamellar systems. This is concluded for both photosystems from certain absorption changes (see Witt, 1975, and Section V), for photosystem II from chlorophyll luminescence measurements (see Lavorel, 1975, and Section VI,B), and for photosystem I by the observation that artificial redox compounds have to be lipid soluble in order to donate electrons to it but may be lipid insoluble to accept electrons from it (see Trebst, 1974; Hauska, 1975). For reaction with photosystem II, both donors and acceptors have to be lipophilic. By immunological studies, ferredoxin and ferredoxin-$NADP^+$-reductase could be located on the stromal surface, while cytochrome f and plastocyanine were inaccessible from that side of the membrane. [More recent experiments with antibodies (Schmid et $al.$, 1975) and with chemical labels (Selman et $al.$, 1975) produced evidence, however, that plastocyanine might be partially accessible.] The location of the water-oxidizing site in complex Y on the inner surface of the chloroplast membrane (Fig. 1c) has been contested, but is now gaining support from new data. The appearance of protons from water oxidation in the external medium seems to be delayed by a lipid barrier which is overcome by addition of uncouplers (see Section IV,A).

   Proton liberation linked to water oxidation was recently found to exhibit a periodicity similar to oxygen evolution (Fowler and Kok, 1974a). The dependence of a delayed chlorophyll fluorescence transient on the high-energy state in illuminated chloroplasts can be explained by an effect of internal protons coming from water oxidation (Kraan et $al.$, 1970; see Lavorel, 1975, and Section VI,B). The intimate relation of this transient

---

FIG. 1. Localization, reaction sequence, and topography of photosynthetic electron transport in chloroplasts. The compartmentation of photosynthetic reactions in the chloroplast is shown at the top; CC stands for Calvin cycle. (a) Linear scheme of photosynthetic electron transport from water to $NADP^+$, including sites for inhibition, as well as for donation and acceptance of electrons by artificial redox compounds. PS I and II, photosystems I and II, respectively; D_1 and D_2, electron donors for photosystems I and II, respectively; A_1 and A_2, corresponding electron acceptors; DCMU, N-dichloro-phenyl-N'-dimethylurea; DBMIB, dibromomethyl-isopropyl-p-benzoquinone; Y, the water-splitting complex; Z, the primary electron donor, and Q, the primary electron acceptor in photosystem II; P_{680}, the reaction center chlorophyll in photosystem II; PQ, plastoquinone; f, cytochrome f; PC, plastocyanine; P_{700}, the reaction center chlorophyll in photosystem I; X, the primary acceptor in photosystem I; Fd, ferredoxin, FAD, ferredoxin-$NADP^+$ reductase; ET, electron transport. (b) Z scheme of photosynthetic electron transport placed into relation to the redox potential scale; S_0–S_4, the different oxidation states of Y; b_{559} and b_6, cytochromes b_{559} and b_6, respectively. (c) Topography of photosynthetic electron transport and the ATP-forming complex, including the direction of proton translocation.

to the water-splitting reaction is suggested by the observation that both show a periodicity of four in flashing light (Malkin and Hardt, 1972). Third, the water-splitting reaction can be inactivated by high external pH only in the light and under conditions when internal and external pH can equilibrate (Reimer and Trebst, 1975; Trebst et al., 1975). This seems to indicate an exposure of the water-splitting reaction to the internal aqueous space. Similarly light dependent was the inactivation of oxygen evolution by the lipid-insoluble chemical diazobenzene sulfonic acid, which suggests, that Y, after a conformational change, might just as well be reached from the external aqueous phase, and might extend through the membrane (Giaquinta et al., 1975). Conformational changes, complicating the static picture in Fig. 1c, will be discussed in Section IX,B. A location for the active center of Y beyond a lipid barrier is also supported by the finding that the lifetime of the consecutively accumulated four positive charges (S_0–S_4 in Fig. 1b) is decreased by lipophilic, weakly acidic agents (Renger, 1973).

Photosynthetic electron transport is coupled to ATP formation. This holds for the whole chain, as well as for certain partial reactions with artificial redox compounds (see Trebst, 1974, and Section III). In "noncyclic photophosphorylation" the stoichiometry of electron transport to ATP formation can be measured, whereas in "cyclic photophosphorylation" electron transport escapes measurement in continuous light. After a long controversy in the past, the existence of two independent "coupling sites" along the overall sequence from water to NADP$^+$ is now established. This was possible after introduction of the inhibitors DBMIB and KCN, which allowed a study of ATP formation dependent on photosystem II alone (Trebst and Reimer, 1973a; Izawa et al., 1973; Ouitrakul and Izawa, 1973) (Fig. 1a). Photosystem I-dependent phosphorylation can be isolated in the presence of DCMU by addition of D_1 plus A_1 (Fig. 1a) for the noncyclic type of the reaction, or by addition of a suitable mediator such as PMS or pyocyanine, for cyclic electron flow.

Considering these two partial reactions, each involving a protolytic step and a photocenter, together with a concept of vectorial electron transport, one naturally arrives at Mitchell's chemiosmotic hypothesis for energy conservation (1961, 1966, 1967, 1968, 1970). Some differences between coupling site I and coupling site II have been found, however, which can be interpreted as incompatible with the chemiosmotic concept in its pure form (see Section III).

Figure 1c includes, in addition to the topography of electron transport, the vectorial organization of the ATP-forming complex, which consists of the peripheral coupling factor 1 (CF_1) facing the stroma (Racker et al., 1972) and of a hydrophobic part (CF_0) integrated into the membrane (see Section VII,A). The complex undergoes light-dependent conformational changes (see Section IX,C) and was found to be laterally mobile in the membrane (Berzborn *et al.*, 1974). Similar dual complexes with analogous orientation have been found in mitochondrial and bacterial membranes. Together with vectorial electron transport, which results in proton translocation always directed away from CF_1 (Figs. 1c and 3), this can be taken as indicative for an universal mechanism of energy conservation.

III.   Native and Artificial Energy Conservation (P/e_2 Ratios)

The chemiosmotic hypothesis for the mechanism of energy coupling postulates that the electrochemical proton potential built up by vectorial electron flow drives phosphorylation (Mitchell, 1961, 1966). Coupling sites are specified as electron transport loops through the membrane, comprising electrogenic steps in one direction and electroneutral hydrogen translocation in the other. No spatial proximity of the loops to the ATP-forming complex is needed because the proton potential delocalizes over the whole compartment bounded by the membrane. Two such loops can be formulated for electron transport from water to $NADP^+$ (Fig. 2a) (Mitchell, 1966, 1967; also Witt, 1975; Trebst, 1974) in accordance with membrane topography (Fig. 1c). Native energy-conserving site I (EC I) is composed of the charge separation in photosystem I plus proton translocation by plastoquinone, and native energy-conserving site II (EC II) of the charge separation in photosystem II plus proton liberation from water. These two native sites can be functionally separated from each other. EC II can be measured by the addition of a suitable electron acceptor for photosystem II (A_2) in the

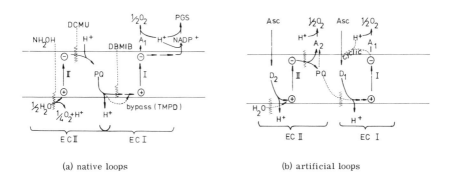

(a) native loops   (b) artificial loops

FIG. 2. Native (a) and artificial (b) loops for energy conservation in photosynthetic electron transport in chloroplasts. EC I and EC II, for energy conservation linked to photosystems I and II, respectively; I and II, photosystem I and II; TMPD, N,N,N',N'-tetramethyl-*p*-phenylenediamine; Asc, ascorbate; other abbreviations as in Fig. 1.

presence of DBMIB, which blocks electron flow to photosystem I (Figs. 1a and 2b) (Trebst and Reimer, 1973a; Izawa *et al.*, 1973), and EC I by addition of a suitable electron donor (D_1) in the presence of DCMU, which blocks photosystem II (see Trebst, 1974). The loop in such a functionally isolated EC II remains essentially unchanged. This is not the case for isolated EC I, because it was also found to be largely insensitive to DBMIB (Böhme *et al.*, 1971) Hauska *et al.*, 1974, 1975b; see Trebst, 1974), which inhibits oxidation of plastohydroquinone eliminating its proton-translocating function.

The conclusion was that proton translocation by plastoquinone in the native loop of EC I, is replaced by the artificial electron donor D_1 (Fig. 2b). The term artificial energy conservation was coined for such an artificial transmembrane, proton-translocating loop, with the knowledge that the electrogenic part of the native loop was still operative. The conclusion is supported by the observation that compounds acting as D_1, or mediators of cyclic electron transport, have to be lipophilic (Hauska, 1972; Hauska *et al.*, 1973), as mentioned in Section II, and, in order to catalyze photophosphorylation, they have to be protolytic upon oxidation (Trebst and Hauska, 1974; Hauska *et al.*, 1975b). The latter point is strikingly demonstrated by the old finding that electron transport via photosystem I at the expense of external ascorbate with *N, N, N',N'*-tetramethyl-*p*-phenylenediamine (TMPD) as D_1 is not coupled, whereas with 2,3,5,6-tetramethyl-*p*-phenylenediamine (DAD) it is (see Table I). TMPD forms a radical cation upon oxidation without loss of protons, while DAD behaves as a quinoid system, giving two electrons and two protons. A similar pair of electron donors for photosystem I is *N*-pentamethylindamine/indamine (Table I) (Oettmeier *et al.*, 1974). The reaction of the first compound is not coupled as against the reaction of the second. Similarly, artificial energy conservation was also found for EC II when water oxidation was blocked by NH_2OH treatment (Fig. 2b). D_2 also has to be lipophilic and has to liberate protons when oxidized in order to catalyze phosphorylation (Harth *et al.*, 1974; Izawa and Ort, 1974). In this case *N*-tetramethylbenzidine/benzidine proved to be a suitable pair of compounds. Mn complexes, ferrocyanide, and I^- seem to act like the former (Table I); i.e., these donor systems lead to half the P/e_2-ratio compared with benzidine.

So far, artificial energy conservation in photosystem II could not be measured independent of electron flow through photosystem I because of direct chemical interaction of D_2 and A_2. Therefore, it is seen on top of native EC I only.

Inhibition of electron flow from water to $NADP^+$ by DBMIB is released by addition of TMPD (no ascorbate added). This function of TMPD is explained by an internal bypass, linking plastoquinone to plastocyanine, because the system is coupled to phosphorylation almost as efficiently as the control without the inhibitor (Trebst and Reimer, 1973b) (see Fig. 2a and Table I). In this case, both regions of native energy conservation operate, and are linked by the TMPD bypass. The release of antimycin inhibition of cyclic phosphorylation in bacterial chromatophores by TMPD can be explained by a similar internal bypass (Trebst, 1976). Transmembrane bypass cannot be assumed, since with TMPD this would not be coupled.

The concept of artificial energy conservation for photosynthetic phosphorylation originates from Hinkle's system of vectorial electron flow in liposomes, mediated by lipophilic redox compounds from external ascorbate to internally trapped ferricyanide (Hinkle, 1970; see also Deamer et al., 1972; Hauska and Prince, 1974), and might be extended to mitochondrial and bacterial membranes (Trebst, 1976). Transmembrane proton translocation, shuttled by artificial quinoid compounds, has been observed in this liposomal system. The position of plastoquinone in the chloroplast membrane in Fig. 2 implies a similar diffusional mechanism for proton translocation in vivo. However, more sophisticated mechanisms are discussed (see Section X).

Our view of native and artificial energy conservation is not unanimously shared among photosynthesists (see Gould and Izawa, 1973 ; Bradeen and Winget, 1974; Gould, 1975a,b; Izawa et al., 1975; Hall, 1976). It is maintained that D_1 compounds, when catalyzing photophosphorylation, donate electrons to the native "coupling site I," somewhere before cytochrome f in the chain and after the site of inhibition by DBMIB. Noncyclic electron flow with $DPIPH_2$ as D_1 is only partially inhibited by KCN, which blocks plastocyanine, close to P_{700} (Fig. 1a) (Ouitrakul and Izawa, 1973). The KCN-insensitive reaction, which is rather slow, is not coupled to ATP formation, which seems to support the location of the coupling site before the KCN block (Gould, 1975b). However, this is not a compelling argument, since a minimal proton potential is required to observe ATP synthesis (see Section VIII,B), which might not be attained by the slow reaction. Cyclic phosphorylation with PMS as mediator is also partially insensitive to KCN (Ouitrakul and Izawa, 1973), a fact that had to be explained by the assumption that PMS exerts a double function, bridging electron transport from the reductant in photosystem I (X^-) to the coupling site, and from cytochrome f to P_{700}. This requires the additional assumption that PMS acts in two isolated pools, possibly on opposite sides of the chloroplast membrane; otherwise the redox potential energy available in the coupling site should be attenuated to the extent that PMS can equilibrate through the membrane. Since PMS is perfectly lipid permeable, our concept of artificial energy conservation, i.e., the PMS catalyz-

TABLE I

STOICHIOMETRIES OF ATP FORMATION AND NONCYCLIC ELECTRON TRANSPORT (P/e$_2$ RATIO)[a]

Electron donor	Electron acceptor	Photosystems participating	Inhibitor present	P/e$_2$ ratio	Number of native/artificial energy-conserving sites (according to Hauska and Trebst)	Involved coupling sites (according to Izawa et al., 1975)	References
I. Type C chloroplasts							
A. Hill Reaction							
H$_2$O	A$_1$: NADP, MV, AQ, ferricyanide	I + II	—	1.0–1.3	2/—	I + II	Arnon et al. (1957), Izawa and Good (1968), Saha et al. (1971), Hauska et al. (1973), Izawa et al. (1975)
H$_2$O	A$_2$: Ferricyanide	II	DBMIB	0.2–0.4	1/—	II	Trebst and Reimer (1973a,b), Gould and Izawa (1973), Izawa et al. (1973, 1975)
H$_2$O	Silicomolybdate	II	DCMU	0	—/—	—	Giaquinta and Dilley (1975)
H$_2$O	Phenylenediamines and benzoquinones	II	DBMIB, KCN, polylysine	0.3–0.7	1/—	II	Trebst and Reimer (1973a,b,c), Gould and Izawa (1973), Izawa et al. (1973), Gould and Ort (1973), Ouitrakul and Izawa (1973), Trebst (1974), Izawa et al. (1975), Ort et al. (1973)

B. TRANSMEMBRANE BYPASS OF AN INHIBITION SITE

1. Donor systems for photosystem I

Donor	Acceptor						References
D₁: Phenylenediamines, DPIP indamine	A₁: NADP, MV, I, AQ		DCMU	0.6–1.0	—/1	I	Losada et al. (1961), Trebst and Pistorius (1965), Izawa et al. (1966), Ort and Izawa (1974), Gould (1975a), Ort (1975), Hauska et al. (1975b), Oettmeier et al. (1974)
TMPD, DMPD	NADP	I	DCMU	0	—/—	—	Trebst (1964), Wessels (1964), Trebst and Pistorius (1965), Hauska et al. (1975b)
Pentamethylindamine	NADP	I	DCMU	0	—/—	—	Oettmeier et al. (1974)

2. Donor systems for photosystem II

Donor	Acceptor						References
D₂: benzidine catechol	NADP, MV	I + II	NH₂OH	1.0–1.1	1/1	I + II	Yamashita and Butler (1969), Izawa et al. (1975), Harth et al. (1974)
tetramethylbenzidine	NADP	I + II	NH₂OH	0.6	1/—	I	Harth et al. (1974), Trebst (1974)
I₂, ferrocyanide, Mn complex	MV	I + II	NH₂OH	0.35–0.61	1/—	I	Izawa and Ort (1974), Izawa et al. 1975

C. INTERNAL BYPASS OF THE INHIBITION SITE

Restored Hill Reaction

Donor	Acceptor						References
H₂O	NADP, MV	I + II	DBMIB (TMPD)	0.8	2/—	I + II	Trebst and Reimer (1973b), Selman, 1976

(Continued)

TABLE I (*Continued*)

Electron donor	Electron acceptor	Photo-systems partic-ipating	Inhibitor present	P/e_2 ratio	Number of *native/artificial* energy-conserving sites (according to Hauska and Trebst)	Involved coupling sites (according to Izawa et al., 1975)	References
II. Type B chloroplasts							
H_2O	NADP, MV ferricyanide	I + II	—	1.6–2.1	2/—	I + II	Hall *et al.* (1971), West and Wiskich (1973), Heathcote and Hall (1975), Hall (1976)
H_2O	DAD, quinones	II	DBMIB	0.6–0.9	1/—	II	Heathcote and Hall (1974, 1975)
DPIP	MV	I	DCMU	0.9	—/1	I	Heathcote and Hall (1974, 1975), Hall (1976)

[a] Type B and type C chloroplasts denote isolated whole chloroplasts (type A), put into the hypotonic reaction medium, and isolated chloroplast lamellar systems, osmotically shocked, respectively (Hall, 1972) (see Fig. 3). A_1 and A_2 and D_1 and D_2 stand for electron acceptors and donors for photosystems I and II, as depicted in Fig. 1a.

ing external proton uptake by reduction from X^-, and internal release being oxidized directly by $P_{700}{}^+$, seems preferable.

Additional difficulties arise from the differential behavior of EC I and EC II. If these turn out to be genuine mechanistic differences, domains in the membrane for EC I and EC II have to be assumed, which are incompatible with a delocalized proton potential as the energy transmitter. First of all, a different dependence of phosphorylation efficiency (P/e_2 ratio) on external pH was found for EC II and EC I (Gould and Izawa, 1973). Furthermore, in contrast to EC I and the overall reaction, electron transport control, i.e., stimulation by phosphorylating conditions or uncouplers, was not found for EC II (Gould and Ort, 1973). Actually, even inhibition by uncouplers is observed (Trebst and Reimer, 1973c) (see Section IX,A). The energy transfer inhibition $HgCl_2$ inhibited EC I at about 50 times lower concentration compared to EC II (Bradeen and Winget, 1974; Gould, 1975a), while p-hydroxymercuribenzoate, a more lipophilic mercurial, was about equally effective in both systems. Finally, based on experiments with silicomolybdate, Giaquinta *et al.* (1975) conclude that protons resulting from water oxidation are released into a different compartment than protons resulting from a photosystem I reaction.

The first two arguments are not conclusive against our concept because it is feasible that the rate limit in EC I and in the overall reaction is controlled by proton concentration and the high energy state in the membrane, differently from the rate limit in EC II (see Section IX,A). The third argument poses a more serious problem. A way around might be the consideration of secondary effects. For instance, $HgCl_2$ has been reported to be an electron transport inhibitor as well, at higher concentrations (Kimimura and Katoh, 1972).

Table I contains a collection of P/e_2 ratios reported for the overall reaction involving both photosystems, as well as for partial reactions. Besides the specification of the electron transport system and a selection of references, the number of coupling sites according to the designation of Izawa *et al.* (1975), or of native/artificial electron transport loops involved according to Trebst and Hauska (1974), are indicated. A more complete summary of P/e_2 ratios is presented by Hall (1976). In spite of a long history, the argument as to the P/e_2 ratio in the overall reaction is still not settled (see Trebst, 1974; Hall, 1976; Heber, 1976), but will not be repeated here. It seems to be accepted by now that the P/e_2 ratio for a Hill reaction is above 1.0, but there is still reluctance to accept a value of 2.0 [which has been found in type B chloroplasts (Hall, 1976)], not the least because of energetic reasons (see Section VIII,B). It should be pointed out that the mechanistic P/e_2 ratio need not be a whole number for a chemiosmotic mechanism. If the H^+/e ratio were 2 for the two loops involved, as in Figs. 2a and 4 (see Section IV,A), and the H^+/ATP ratio were 3, as reported by several investigators (see Section VII,D), a theoretical P/e_2 ratio of 1.33 should result, which indeed is favored by some authors (see Trebst, 1974; Heber, 1976; McCarty, 1976). A P/e_2 ratio of 2 would result from an H^+/ATP ratio of 2 (Gräber and Witt, 1976; Hall, 1976). It is interesting to note that indications for a flexible P/e_2 ratio, oriented on the physiological need for ATP, have been found (Heber and Kirk, 1975; Heber, 1976). This could be explained by a controlled change of proton permeability of the chloroplast membrane (see Section XI,C). For a comprehensive treatment of energy coupling in photosynthesis by application of the "thermodynamics of irreversible processes," see Rottenberg (1976). Although there is still controversy as to the correct P/e_2 ratio, there is no disagreement that, in photophosphorylation involving just one photosystem, ATP is formed with half the stoichiometry (Table I). If the mechanistic stoichiometry of the overall reaction were 1.33, it would be 0.66 for a single loop. Values close to that number have been obtained.

Some partial reactions are not coupled to ATP-formation. One is the action of TMPD or N-pentamethylindamine as D_1, which have been discussed above. Another is the action of silicomolybdate as A_2 (Giaquinta et al., 1975). This reaction is interesting too, since it is less sensitive to DCMU. The DCMU-insensitive part is not coupled.

IV. Light-Driven Proton Uptake

Proton uptake by illuminated chloroplasts was discovered by Jagendorf and Hind (1963) and since then has been intensively studied. The studies have been reviewed in detail by Jagendorf (1975; see also Hind and McCarty, 1973; Dilley and Giaquinta, 1975). Proton uptake is reversed in the dark and is sensitive to uncouplers and detergents (Neumann and Jagendorf, 1964). As implied in Section III, it can also be catalyzed by partial reactions of electron transport in the presence of inhibitors and artificial redox compounds (see Fig. 1), mediators of cyclic electron transport being the most efficient (Dilley and Vernon, 1967). Electron flow through photosystem I with TMPD as D_1, however, does not catalyze proton uptake (Hauska and Prince, 1974). It is significant that this reaction is also not coupled to ATP formation, as discussed in Section III (see Table I). Proton uptake is dependent on the proper ionic environment and is lost at low ionic strength (Gross et al., 1969), probably by structural changes of the membrane. It is more specifically abolished by removal of CF_1 by EDTA treatment, and is restored by reconstitution with CF_1 (McCarty and Racker, 1966) or treatment with DCCD (McCarty and Racker, 1967), which is discussed in Section VII,A.

The extent of proton uptake is optimal at an external pH of 6.5, and is dependent on the buffering capacity of chloroplasts. It can be increased severalfold by addition of weak permeant bases (Crofts, 1968; Lynn, 1968; Nelson *et al.*, 1971; Avron, 1972). The increase is dependent on the pK of the base and most likely reflects additional buffering of the intrathylakoid space. This suggests that protons are translocated across, not merely bound to, the membrane. The quantitative substitution of protons by ammonium ions (Crofts, 1968) actually indicates that all protons taken up are released into the internal aqueous space, where they combine with ammonia to ammonium ions (see Fig. 7e).

Mitochondria or bacteria extrude protons during electron transport (Mitchell and Moyle, 1965a; Scholes *et al.*, 1969; Harold and Altendorf, 1974), but membrane vesicles obtained by fragmentation exhibit proton uptake (Mitchell and Moyle, 1965b; Hinkle and Horstman, 1971; von Stedingk and Baltscheffsky, 1966) as depicted in Fig. 3. Such a change in polarity with respect to the suspending medium cannot be observed with chloroplasts because the lamellar system, which is differentiated from the inner envelope during chloroplast development, is not in free spatial continuum with the interenvelope space (dotted lines in Fig. 3).

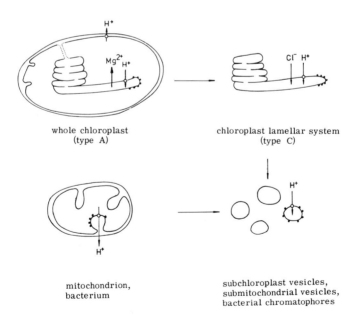

whole chloroplast
(type A)

chloroplast lamellar system
(type C)

mitochondrion,
bacterium

subchloroplast vesicles,
submitochondrial vesicles,
bacterial chromatophores

FIG. 3. Direction of proton transport in chloroplast, mitochondrial, and bacterial membrane systems. The black "knobs" indicate the location of coupling factor 1, i.e., the ATPase, on the membrane. Type A and C denote chloroplast preparations according to the nomenclature of Hall (1972).

This was established by Heldt *et al.* (1973), when they showed that, in intact chloroplasts that retained the stromal compartment (type A chloroplasts), the pH of the intrathylakoid space is not in equilibrium with, but drops more than 2 units below, that of the external medium. A small and sluggish acidification by proton translocation through the envelope of type A chloroplasts has been reported (Heber and Krause, 1972; Heldt *et al.*, 1973; Gimmler *et al.*, 1975); this is superimposed on alkalinization by the process in the lamellar system (Fig. 3). The pH of the stroma rises from 7.5 to about 8.5 in the light (Heldt *et al.*, 1973; Werdan *et al.*, 1975). Complex proton movements have also been reported for chloroplasts from *Euglena* (Kahn, 1971).

Both the glass electrode and pH-indicating dyes have been employed for quantitation of proton uptake, under continuous as well as flashing-light regimes. The limiting slow response time of the glass electrode has been largely overcome by using a flow system (Izawa and Hind, 1967) or by bringing the chloroplasts in very close contact with the electrode glass (Schwartz, 1968; Fowler and Kok, 1974a). Izawa and Hind (1967) in addition developed a mathematical method to correct the slow response of normal glass electrodes.

pH indicators respond fast, but often exhibit side effects, e.g., spectral shifts due to binding to the membrane. These can be largely eliminated by subtracting changes that are insensitive to pH buffering (see Heath and Hind, 1972; Junge and Ausländer, 1974, 1975). Redox reactions possibly resulting in irreversible bleaching must also be considered, since most of the pH indicating dyes are quinoid redox systems (Fiolet and van de Vlugt, 1975). Table II presents some of the indicators used, together with the pertinent pK values. Bromothymol blue was first introduced to measure pH changes in mitochondria (Chance and Mela, 1966) or chromatophores from *Rhodospirillum rubrum* (Chance *et al.*, 1966). It has been suggested that it measures the pH in the internal aqueous compartment (pH_i), but its responses have been found to be complex and ambiguous (Cost and Frenkel, 1967; Mitchell *et al.*, 1968; Jackson and Crofts, 1969b). Bromocresol purple, phenol red, and cresol red are most suitable for measuring changes of external pH (pH_e), since they show very little residual response in suspensions buffered externally. Little binding to the membrane in comparison to bromothymol blue might reflect decreased lipid solubility when the thymol substituents are replaced by protons or methyl groups (formulas in Table II).

Grünhagen and Witt (1970) introduced umbelliferone, a fluorescent indicator for external pH, fluorescence being quenched upon protonation. Fluorescence indicators, emitting in the blue, have the advantage of avoiding background changes of the chloroplast pigments. Binding of

TABLE II

pH INDICATORS USED TO MEASURE PROTON TRANSLOCATION[a]

Compound	Formula	pK_a	Indication	References
Bromothymol blue		7.0	complex (pH_i)	Chance and Mela (1966)
Bromocresol purple	Same as Bromothymol blue, except —CH_3 instead of —$CH(CH_3)_2$	6.3	pH_e	Jackson and Crofts (1969b), Heath and Hind (1972)
Cresol red	Same as Bromothymol blue, but minus —Br, and —CH_3 instead of —$CH(CH_3)_2$.	8.3	pH_e	Junge and Ausländer (1974)
Phenol red	Same as Bromothymol blue, but minus —Br and —$CH(CH_3)_2$	7.8	pH_e	Schröder et al. (1972), Crofts et al. (1972)
Umbelliferone		8.0	pH_e	Grünhagen and Witt (1970)
Neutral red		6.7	pH_i	Junge and Ausländer (1975)

[a] pH_e and pH_i = external and internal pH, respectively.

umbelliferone to the membrane, however, has not been fully excluded, although the fluorescence changes decreased linearly with the buffering capacity of the external medium.

Following Lynn (1968), Junge and Ausländer (1975) succeeded in measuring the pH of the internal space of chloroplasts with neutral red as a permeable indicator. The change was calibrated by the permeable buffering substance imidazole. In combination with the impermeable indicator cresol red and the impermeable buffer bovine serum albumin, they managed to measure the disappearance of protons from the external medium and their appearance in the internal aqueous space separately— a remarkable achievement. More indirect measurements of internal proton release are described in Section IV,A.

A. H$^+$/e Ratios

The difficulties arising in the estimation of H$^+$/e ratios have again been summarized in detail by Jagendorf (1975). They result from the problem of how to measure electron transport and proton movement accurately at the same time. Incorrect estimates resulted from inappropriate matching of rates under continuous-light regimes. Table III presents a selection of values reported in the literature for a pH of the chloroplast suspension around 8.0. Initial rates of electron transport and proton uptake have been compared by Izawa and Hind (1967) in measurements with their glass electrode flow system. Actually, they measured the amounts of proton uptake and ferricyanide reduction after brief illumination periods of increasing length, similar to the O$_2$ pulse-relaxation technique first applied to mitochondria (Mitchell and Moyle, 1965a). With reasonable corrections they arrived at a H$^+$/e ratio of 2 for ferricyanide reduction, which involves photosystems I and II. A value of 3 was reported from measurements of initial rates of NH$_4^+$ uptake (Crofts, 1968). Schwartz (1968), with his fast glass electrode, compared the steady-state rate of ferricyanide or NADP$^+$ reduction with the initial rate of proton release after the light period, assuming that the latter matches the rate of proton efflux in the steady state, which equals the rate of uptake. He again arrived at a value of 2 for H$^+$/e for the whole electron transport chain. However, with the same rationale, lower values around 1 have consistently been found by other investigators (Dilley, 1970; Telfer and Evans, 1972). Schröder et al. (1972) have criticized the assumption that the observed initial proton efflux rate in the dark resembles the flux in the light because an opposing diffusion potential might form if the counterion fluxes are comparatively slow (see Section V,B and Fig. 5). Indeed, increasing the flux of K$^+$ as a counterion by the addition of valinomycin increased the H$^+$/e from about

1 to 2. This was also found by Karlish and Avron (1971), but a different interpretation was given.

A low H^+/e value of 0.4 for proton uptake dependent on photosystem II alone, measured in the presence of DBMIB, has recently been reported by Gould and Izawa (1974; see also de Kouchkovsky, 1974). The authors followed initial rates, using the glass electrode method of Izawa and Hind (1967).

An H^+/e ratio of 1, on the other hand, has been found for photosystem I-dependent electron transport, in the presence of DCMU, with ascorbate-DPIP as the artificial electron donor system (Strotmann and von Gösseln, 1972). The value was obtained from the initial rate of proton efflux and the steady-state rate of electron transport, without further corrections.

Surprisingly high values, up to 7, were obtained for cyclic electron transport around photosystem I in continuous light (Dilley and Vernon, 1967; Heath, 1972), which are not consistent with a simple translocation of protons in redox loops. The values have been calculated from quantum efficiencies of proton uptake, because cyclic electron transport escapes measurements in continuous light. They are at variance with the results obtained by flash photometry.

The first report for chloroplasts employing repetitive flash spectrophotometry was by Schliephake et al. (1968; see Witt, 1971, 1975). They used the buffer-sensitive change of bromothymol blue as a measure for external pH and calculated the rate of electron transport from the absorption changes of P_{700}. The later has to be regarded as an underestimate in the light of the correct extinction coefficient for this pigment (Hiyama and Ke, 1972). With a number of electron acceptors, a H^+/e ratio of 2 for the whole electron transport chain, and, in the presence of DCMU and indophenol as D_1, a ratio of 1 for photosystem I-dependent electron transport was found. The later agrees with the value of Strotmann and van Gösseln (1972).

These early reports have been extended and improved by Junge and Ausländer (1974), using cresol red as pH indicator and oxygen evolution as a measure for electron transport. In addition to proton uptake, they also quantitated the relaxation of the change, which represents the leak of the protons back out of the thylakoids and was accelerated by the uncoupler FCCP. Their results are summarized in Fig. 4 (solid lines). With benzyl viologen as electron acceptor A_1, 2 protons are taken up and leak back out per turnover of the system. With low concentrations of ferricyanide, 1 proton seemed to be taken up and 2 to be leaking out, and with high concentrations of ferricyanide, or a combination of ferricyanide and DPIP, both acting as A_2, no uptake and 1 proton leaking out could be observed. The excess of 1 proton leaking out under

TABLE III
H$^+$/e RATIOS^a

Electron transport system involved	Light conditions	H$^+$/e	References	Comments
H$_2$O–A$_1$ (both photosystems)	Continuous	2	Izawa and Hind (1967)	Glass electrode (flow system); initial rates of H$^+$ uptake and electron transport.
		3	Crofts (1968)	Ammonium uptake; initial rates of NH$_4^+$ uptake and electron flow
		2	Schwartz (1968)	Rapidly responding glass electrode; H$^+$ efflux in the dark and steady-state electron transport
		ca. 1	Telfer and Evans (1972)	Glass electrode (slow response corrected); rates as above; energy transfer inhibitors stimulate
		2	Schröder et al. (1972)	Phenol red; rates as above; corrected for diffusion potential in the dark
		3	Fowler and Kok (1976)	Rapidly responding glass electrode; rates as above; low light intensity; FeCy as A$_1$
		4	Fowler and Kok (1976)	As above, but MV as A$_1$
		2	Fowler and Kok (1976)	As above, but high light intensity; FeCy or MV as A$_1$
	Flash	2	Schliephake et al. (1968)	Bromothymol blue; H$^+$ uptake and P$_{700}$ turnover
			Junge and Ausländer (1974)	Cresol red; H$^+$ uptake and back efflux, O$_2$ evolution

System	Light	H^+/e	Reference	Comments
H_2O–A_2 (photosystem II)	Continuous	2	Junge and Ausländer (1975)	Neutral red; internal H^+ release, O_2 evolution
		2	Gräber and Witt (1975a)	Cresol red and 9-aminoacridine; uptake and internal release of H^+, P_{700} turnover
		3	Fowler and Kok (1976)	Rapidly responding glass electrode; H^+ uptake; FeCy as A_1
		4	Fowler and Kok (1976)	As above, but MV as A_1
		0.4	Gould and Izawa (1974)	Glass electrode (corrected for slow response); DBMIB present
	Flash	1	Junge and Ausländer (1974)	Cresol red; uptake and back efflux of H^+; high FeCy or DPIP/FeCy as A_2
D_1–A_1 (photosystem I)	Continuous	1	Ausländer et al. (1974)	As above, but FeCy as A_2 in the presence of DBMIB
		1	Strotmann and von Gösseln (1972)	Glass electrode
	Flash	1	Schliephake et al. (1968)	Bromothymol blue; H^+ uptake, and P_{700} turnover
Cyclic electron transport (photosystem I)	Continuous	3–7	Dilley and Vernon (1967), Heath (1972)	Glass electrode; quantum efficiency of H^+ uptake and efflux
	Flash	1	Gräber and Witt (1975a)	Cresol red and 9-aminoacridine; uptake and internal release of H^+, P_{700} turnover

[a] D_1, A_1, and A_2: electron donor for photosystem I, and electron acceptor for photosystems I or II, respectively; FeCy, ferricyanide; MV, methylviologen. Comments include the system used to measure pH changes, and which measurements of H^+ movement and electron transport were matched to obtain the H^+/e ratio.

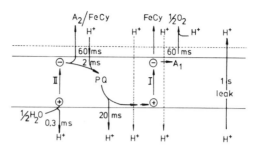

FIG. 4. Kinetics and stoichiometry of proton translocation linked to photosynthetic electron flow in the chloroplast membrane. FeCy, ferricyanide; for other abbreviations, see the legends for Figs. 1 and 2.

the latter two conditions represent the protons coming from water oxidation according to:

$$\tfrac{1}{2}\,H_2O + Fe(CN)_6^{3-} \rightarrow \tfrac{1}{4}\,O_2 + H^+ + Fe(CN)_6^{4-}$$

and must be formed beyond a permeability barrier (see Section II). Corroborating results have been obtained by isolation of photosystem II in the presence of DBMIB (Ausländer *et al.*, 1974). The ratio of 1 proton released per electron in photosystem II disagrees with the low ratio of 0.4 found for the corresponding proton uptake in continuous light (Gould and Izawa, 1974). In the overall chain the second proton is presumably translocated by the redox cycle of plastoquinone. The internal release of 2 protons with the expected different kinetics (compare Fig. 1) has been measured more directly with the indicator neutral red (Junge and Ausländer, 1975). In a similar study, but using 9-NH$_2$-acridine as an indicator for internal pH (see Section IV,C) and estimating electron transport from absorption changes of P$_{700}$, Gräber and Witt (1975a) also found 2 protons taken up outside and 2 released on the inside when electron transport involved both photosystems, and about half the amount for each event for cyclic electron transport in photosystem I with pyocyanine. The latter value stands in contradiction to the abnormally high quantum efficiencies in continuous light (see above) and might suggest that additional binding of protons needs continuous turnover. In summary, the impressive results of the group in Berlin show H$^+$/e ratios quite close to those postulated by Mitchell (1966, 1967), and expected from vectorial electron flow.

However, more complicated possibilities are discussed (see Section X), and indeed Fowler and Kok (1976) most recently arrived at different values, employing flashing light and the rapidly responding glass electrode system developed by Schwartz (1968). Using ferricyanide at low concentrations, they quantitated electron flow by the release of protons according the above equation for water oxidation. This proton release was also taken to calibrate the other pH changes. At low flash frequencies, stoichiometries of 4 and 3 H^+/e were calculated from the increments of the pH changes per flash, for ferricyanide and methyl viologen as A_1, respectively (see Fig. 4, including the dashed arrows). They found the same values by calculating from the steady-state rate of electron transport and the initial rate of proton release in the dark. However, at higher light intensities, i.e., higher flash frequencies (which were beyond the resolution of the individual flash increments) a value of 2 was found for both acceptors, in agreement with Schwartz (1968). According to the authors, proton uptake, symbolized by the dashed arrows in Fig. 4, does not operate in high light, possibly reflecting the back pressure of a high electrochemical proton potential. However, no care has been taken to account for diffusion potentials during dark efflux of protons (Schröder et al., 1972) (see Fig. 5) which should also be higher at higher proton potential.

B. KINETICS OF PROTON UPTAKE AND INTERNAL RELEASE

The rates of proton uptake and efflux have half-times in the range of seconds and increase with temperature and pH of the suspending medium, proton uptake being 2–3 times faster and less temperature-dependent (see Nishizaki and Jagendorf, 1971). The rate of efflux is much more variable, depending on the conditions of the isolated chloroplasts, and is drastically increased by the addition of uncouplers, as well as by the addition of valinomycin plus K^+, as mentioned above. Under nonphosphorylating conditions, H^+ efflux depends with first order on the electrochemical proton potential across the membrane (Gräber and Witt, 1976; Schröder et al., 1975). The acceleration of proton efflux under phosphorylating conditions is discussed in Section VII,B.

During their careful investigation Izawa and Hind (1967) found a fast initial phase of proton uptake with a half-time below 50 msec. This phenomenon had a pool size of 1 proton per 30–40 chlorophylls and was termed "pH gush." It could be correlated with the initial reduction of plastoquinone (and also the rise of the membrane potential, see Section V,B) during flash illumination up to 20 msec flash duration (Reinwald et al., 1968), which corresponds closely to the half-time of plastoquinone oxidation (see Fig. 1a). No pH gush was found in proton uptake during electron transport involving photosystem II alone (Gould and Izawa, 1974). This is surprising in view of the inhibition site of DBMIB after the plastoquinone pool in the chain (see Trebst, 1974) and suggests that the phenomenon is not related to plastoquinone reduction in a simple manner. However, the DBMIB concentration used was relatively high and probably eliminated the plastoquinone pool as indicated from the induction of chlorophyll fluorescence (Bauer and Wijnands, 1974; de Kouchkovsky and de Kouchkovsky, 1974).

In their flash experiments with cresol red, Ausländer and Junge (1974) found that both protons from the external medium are taken up rather slowly, with a half-time of 60 msec (Fig. 4), which is slower than the rate limiting oxidation of plastoquinone in overall electron transport (see Fig. 1a). They explained their finding by the assumption that plastoquinone and the reducing end of photosystem I are shielded from the suspending medium, symbolized by the dashed line in Fig. 4. Similar slow rates of uptake have been obtained by Grünhagen and Witt (1970), and Fowler and Kok (1976). The nature of the shield remains to be established. It is possible that it is related to the stacked structure of chloroplasts, since fragmentation of the lamellar system accelerates proton uptake (Ausländer and Junge, 1974). It is not found in chromatophores (Saphon *et al.*, 1975b). This barrier for proton flux can also be largely overcome by uncoupling agents. The binding of protons to plastoquinone from the local environment can be estimated from a pH-dependent lag of P_{700} rereduction after a saturating flash under special light regimes (Haehnel, 1976). Its half-time is less than 2 msec (Fig. 4).

The half-time of the internal proton release during water and plasto-quinone oxidation have been found to be 0.3 and 20 msec, respectively (Fig. 4), by Junge and Ausländer (1975) in their experiments with neutral red, which agrees well with the corresponding half-times of electron transport (Fig. 1a).

For rapid measurements of proton uptake in chromatophores of photosynthetic bacteria, consult Chance *et al.* (1970), Crofts *et al.* (1972), Cogdell and Crofts (1974), and Saphon *et al.* (1975b).

C.   The pH Difference across the Thylakoid Membrane

Proton translocating, vectorial electron transport primarily results in a transmembrane electric potential (Mitchell, 1968). The extent of internal acidification thus is dependent on secondary counterion fluxes. As depicted in Fig. 3 for chloroplasts, both cation flux out of and anion flux into the thyalkoids have been observed. The arguments as to which of the two processes prevails (see Jagendorf, 1975) has been largely settled by Hind *et al.* (1974), who showed that in isolated chloroplasts, at about equimolar concentrations, release of Mg^{2+} and uptake of chloride are the predominant processes, Na^+ and K^+ movements being negligible. At low concentration of Mg^{2+}, K^+ and, if this is absent, also Na^+ (Schröder *et al.*, 1972) can substitute. In the absence of permeant cations, Cl^- might fully account for counterion flux in chloroplasts (Gaensslen and McCarty, 1971). If permeant ions are excluded from the medium, the extent of proton uptake is drastically decreased (Cohen and Jagendorf, 1972). Recently, Telfer *et al.* (1975), employing cation-specific ionophores with intact chloroplasts, provided independent evidence that *in vivo* Mg^{2+} is the major counterion during proton uptake into the thylakoids. An extrusion of Mg^{2+} from the lamellar system into the matrix during illumination (see Bassham, 1971), together with alkalinization (Werdan *et al.*, 1975), might regulate CO_2 fixation in chloroplasts (Figs. 1 and 3).

The sum of the counterions balances proton flux, and the membrane potential during the steady state of illumination is rather low in chloroplasts (Schröder *et al.*, 1972). Little limitation by counterion flux is also suggested by the fact that proton uptake is only slightly stimulated by addition of valinomycin/K^+ (Karlish and Avron, 1971; Rumberg and Muhle, 1976). In subchloroplast vesicles (McCarty, 1969) and in chromatophores (von Stedingk and Baltscheffsky, 1966; Jackson *et al.*, 1968; Thore *et al.*, 1968) proton uptake is stimulated much more.

Uptake and release of counterions are associated with water flow, resulting in swelling and shrinking, respectively, of the chloroplasts and possibly in additional conformational changes (for pertinent reviews, see Dilley, 1971; Murakami *et al.*, 1975). The structural changes express themselves as changes in light scattering and in slow fluorescence transients of chlorophyll (see Section VI,A).

Rumberg and Siggel (1969), by an ingenious rationale, were the first to estimate the pH difference across the thylakoid membrane. They measured the rate of rereduction of P_{700} in the dark after illumination, varying external pH. With the assumptions that electron transport is controlled by internal pH and that the pH inside fully equilibrates with the one outside in the presence of gramicidin, they were able to assess the pH difference in the absence of gramicidin. A value of 3 pH units was obtained.

Several other methods have been developed, useful also to study mitochondrial and bacterial H^+ transport. Rottenberg (1975) has reviewed them in detail, together with the methods applied to estimate transmembrane electric potentials (see also Hind and McCarty, 1973). This need not be comprehensively repeated here.

Most accurate results have been obtained by measuring the distribution of a weak base or acid, which follows a pH difference, if the neutral form is permeant but the corresponding ion is not (see Fig. 7a,b). All forms of amines were used in chloroplasts for that purpose, after Crofts (1967, 1968) had established the mechanism of light-induced amine uptake. In proton-extruding systems, like mitochondria and bacteria, weak acids, like radioactive dimethyloxazolidinedione (DMO) have been used with success (see Rottenberg, 1975). From the distribution and an independent measurement of the internal osmotic space, the pH difference can be derived. Values between 2.5 and 4.0 have been obtained for chloroplasts measuring uptake of ammonium ions with a specific electrode (Rottenberg and Grunwald, 1972), measuring the distribution of ^{14}C-labeled amines (Gaensslen and McCarty, 1971; Rottenberg *et al.*, 1971, 1972; Portis and McCarty, 1973), and measuring the quenching of 9-aminoacridine fluorescence (Schuldiner *et al.*, 1972a). The second method seems to be the most reliable, but the most elaborate as well, because it affords rapid centrifugation of illuminated chloroplasts from the reaction medium, preferentially through a silicon fluid layer into a quenching medium (Gaensslen and McCarty, 1971; Portis and McCarty, 1973). The measurement of fluorescence quenching of 9-aminoacridine, first observed by Kraayenhof (1970), is a very convenient method, which has been questioned (Fiolet *et al.*, 1974; Kraayenhof and Slater, 1975; Buchholz *et al.*, 1975) as well as defended (Deamer *et al.*, 1972; Casadio *et al.*, 1974; Rottenberg and Lee, 1975; Avron, 1975a; Gräber and Witt, 1976). Aminoacridines seem to bind to the membrane surface and might indicate pH changes at the inner interphase rather than in the inner bulk phase of chloroplasts. The method probably arrives at overestimates.

In flashing light, with the external pH at 7.0, a drop of internal pH of 0.33 per flash, indicated by neutral red, has been estimated (Junge and Ausländer, 1975).

The pH difference was found to be optimal at external pH values between 8.0 and 9.0, and the rather drastic decrease at lower pH has been explained to reflect strong internal buffering with a pK around 5.0 (Rottenberg *et al.*, 1972), which can be correlated to the minimum of light-induced light scattering observed around pH 5.0 (Dilley, 1966, 1971). However, Portis and McCarty (1973) could show that the sharp decrease of the pH difference, at least in part, reflects insufficient equilibration of amines with high pK at lower external pH. Distribution of [^{14}C]aniline, an amine with low pK, indicated that a pH difference of 3 units could be maintained between external pH values of 8.0 and 6.5.

The extent of the pH difference seems to be little dependent on temperature in the physiological range (Kraayenhof *et al.*, 1971), although the rates of proton uptake, and especially of proton release, are temperature dependent as mentioned above.

For small subchloroplast vesicles the pH differences has been estimated to be about one unit lower than in chloroplasts (Rottenberg and Grunwald, 1972; Samoray and Hauska, 1975), and the membrane potential was reported to be correspondingly higher (Rottenberg, 1975), a fact that might explain their decreased sensitivity toward uncoupling by amines (Section VI.C).

V. Light-Driven Membrane Potential

As stated above, vectorial electron transport leads to a membrane potential. The extent of it should be proportional to the driving force of electron transport and inversely related to secondary ion fluxes (Mitchell, 1968). Methods for the estimation of it have been reviewed (Rottenberg, 1975).

Qualitative results have recently been obtained for the membrane potential in illuminated chloroplasts with the help of ion-specific electrodes, in two ways. One way was to keep two electrodes immersed in an illuminated chloroplast suspension at different depths. The light gradient in the chloroplast suspension resulted in a polarization gradient which could be correlated with the transmembrane potential (Fowler and Kok, 1974a,b; Witt and Zickler, 1973, 1974). The other way was to insert an electrode into the chloroplast of a living cell (Bulychev et al., 1971; Vredenberg and Tonk, 1975).

It has been attempted to obtain quantitative results from the distribution of permeant ions, either by using radioactive ions and rapid separation techniques (Rottenberg et al., 1972; Schröder et al., 1972) or by measuring the response of a diffusion potential across a black lipid membrane to the redistribution of permeant ions in energized chloroplasts, mitochondria or bacteria (see Skulachev, 1971, 1974). These methods are largely limited to measurements in the steady state.

The approach most extensively used is via field-indicating absorption changes of endogenous pigments in the membranes of chloroplasts (see Witt, 1971, 1975) and chromatophores (see Crofts et al., 1975a). The absorption changes are found throughout the whole spectrum of the chloroplast pigments (Emrich et al., 1969), but are large in the region of carotenoid absorption and are therefore often referred to as the carotenoid shift, or 515 shift. This light-induced change slightly above 500 nm was discovered by Duysens (1954) and was correlated with the high-energy state, the precursor for photophosphorylation, by Witt et al. (1966). It has been attributed to the effect of an electric field on the transition moment of individual pigment molecules leading to an electrochromic shift in the absorption spectrum (Junge and Witt, 1968). This view is not supported by recent experiments (Crofts et al., 1975a), which suggest, rather, an effect on two different states of pigment organization in the membrane.

In chloroplasts, because of large, but slow light-scattering changes, only rapid measurements give reliable results on the carotenoid shift. This is often neglected in the interpretation of experiments in continuous light. The observed changes in continuous light are much larger in type A chloroplasts than in type C chloroplasts (Larkum and Bonner, 1972), and are still smaller in subchloroplast vesicles (Hauska et al., 1970; Neumann et al., 1970). It is not clear at the moment whether this difference reflects different amounts of responding pigment or different membrane potentials, provided light scattering can be excluded to interfere—a safe assumption for subchloroplast vesicles only. For recent detailed studies of the change in green algae, consult Joliot and Delosme (1974) and Kulandaivelu and Senger (1976). Electrochromic responses of artificial dyes, added to the membrane system, may also serve to indicate membrane potentials (see Chance et al., 1974; Pick and Avron, 1976; Emrich et al., 1969).

A.   KINETICS OF RISE AND DECAY

The half-time of the absorption increase at 515 nm, following a saturating flash, is extremely fast, i.e., less than 20 nsec (Witt, 1967). This corresponds to the rates of the photochemical reactions in photosystems I and II (see Fig. 1), each of them contributing about one half to the total change (Schliephake et al., 1968). In chromatophores the rate of the charge separation in the photochemical reaction center, indicated by the carotenoid shift, has recently been found to be in the picosecond range (Leigh et al., 1974). Jackson and Crofts (1971) in addition reported on a second, slower, antimycin-sensitive phase in the kinetics of the rise after one-turnover flashes for chromatophores. Only one time-constant has been found in chloroplasts. During prolonged illumination the 515 shift exhibits a transient maximum before reaching a steady-state value (see Section V,B and Fig. 5).

The time of field decay in the dark varies a great deal with the condition of the chloroplast preparation and can be taken as a measure of the membrane conductivity. It is accelerated by uncouplers and ionophores (Junge and Witt, 1968; see Witt, 1971, 1975; Schmid and Junge, 1975). Titration with gramicidin showed that 50% of the maximal acceleration of the decay time after a flash is obtained at extremely low concentrations. This indicates that compartments of the dimension of a thylakoid or larger represent functional units of the chloroplast membrane (Junge and Witt, 1968). More recently, a correspondingly smaller functional unit has also been estimated for chromatophores (Saphon et al., 1975a). The decay in the dark is also characteristically accelerated by phosphorylating conditions, which has been attributed to a proton conducting channel through the ATP-forming complex in the membrane and will be discussed in Section VII,B. Its temperature dependence shows a break at 18°C (Gräber and Witt, 1975b), which corresponds to a similar break found for the return of aminoacridine fluorescence to the dark level (Kraayenhof *et al.*, 1971). The later is related to proton efflux, and both studies seem to indicate a change of membrane conductance, reflecting a change of state in the membrane around 20°C.

B. EXTENT OF THE ELECTRIC FIELD AND ITS RELATION TO THE pH DIFFERENCE

From the extent of the absorption change at 515 nm per saturating flash, a membrane potential of 50 mV across the thylakoid membrane has been assessed. For the calculation, it was necessary to assume reasonable values for the number of electron transport chains per membrane area, for the dielectric constant, and for the thickness of the membrane dielectric (Junge and Witt, 1968). With increasing flash length, up to 20 msec, the extent of the change is increased 4-fold and then drops again (Reinwald *et al.*, 1968). This is shown in Fig. 5, on the short initial part of the time scale (taken from Rumberg and Muhle, 1976).

In bacterial chromatophores, ion diffusion potentials across the membrane were found to induce carotenoid shifts in the dark. Moreover, the direction of the shift depended on the direction of the membrane potential (Jackson and Crofts, 1969a). From the exerted Nernst potentials, the carotenoid shift could be calibrated and values up to 400 mV have been estimated. A similar approach was attempted for chloroplasts (Stricharz and Chance, 1972).

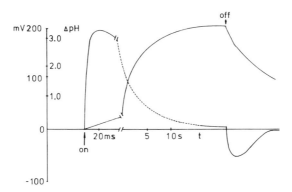

FIG. 5. Induction of the membrane potential and the pH difference across the illuminated chloroplast membrane. The faster-responding trace reflects the transient of the membrane potential; the slower trace shows the pH difference. After Rumberg and Muhle (1976).

Approaching the steady state of illumination, the membrane potential should fall, and the pH difference should rise, with the counterion fluxes (Mitchell, 1968), as shown in Fig. 5. Corresponding transients of the carotenoid shift have been repeatedly observed in algae (see, e.g., Joliot and Delosme, 1974), in chloroplasts (see, e.g., Larkum and Bonner, 1972), in subchloroplast vesicles (Hauska et al., 1970; Neumann et al., 1970), as well as in bacterial chromatophores (Jackson and Crofts, 1969b, 1971). The steady-state value of the membrane potential has been estimated from the carotenoid shift in Chlorella cells (Gräber and Witt, 1974) to be 100 mV. This corresponds well with an estimate from the stimulation of delayed chlorophyll fluorescence by membrane potential in type C chloroplasts (Barber, 1972) (Section VI,B). In studies of the distribution of radioactive ions, much lower values, between 5 and 10 mV, have been calculated for type C chloroplasts (Schröder et al., 1972; Rottenberg et al., 1972). Stricharz and Chance (1972) arrived at a value of 30 mV. There is obviously disagreement that calls for reconciliation and might reflect the different membrane conductances of different preparations. More satisfactorily, the discrepancy is explained by considering the profile of the electric potential difference from one aqueous bulk phase to the other, across the membrane shown in Fig. 6 (Mitchell, 1968; Rumberg and Muhle, 1976), and where the different probes might measure along this profile. It is feasible that the 515 nm absorption changes and delayed fluorescence indicate electric potentials across the

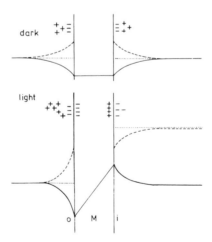

FIG. 6. Profiles of the electric field and the pH difference across the chloroplast membrane in the dark and in the light. $\Delta\psi$ (——), the electric field; sum (. . . . .), the total electrochemical proton potential, $\Delta\psi$ + $Z\Delta$pH (– – –); Z, RT/F; o, the matrix side (outside); i, the intrathylakoid space (inside); M, membrane. After Rumberg and Muhle (1976).

membrane core, while ions might distribute more into the aqueous surfaces. It would be of importance to know where, along such a profile, the site of ATP synthesis is located. A decrease of the carotenoid shift by phosphorylating conditions in the steady state of continuous illumination has been reported for carefully isolated chloroplasts (Baltscheffsky and Hall, 1974). For illuminated chromatophores 90–200 mV (Jackson and Crofts, 1969a; Jackson *et al.*, 1968; Casadio *et al.*, 1974; Schuldiner *et al.*, 1974) and for subchloroplast vesicles, 60 mV (Rottenberg, 1975) have been reported for the steady-state value of the membrane potential. In accordance with a correspondingly higher value in these systems, compared to type C chloroplasts, is the fact that the pH difference can be substantially increased by increasing the membrane conductance— e.g., with valinomycin plus K^+—in chromatophores and subchloroplast vesicles (von Stedingk and Baltscheffsky, 1966; Jackson *et al.*, 1968; Thore *et al.*, 1968; McCarty, 1970)—and only to a small extent in type C chloroplasts (Karlish and Avron, 1971; Rumberg and Muhle, 1976).

The curve for the off-response in Fig. 5 allows for the argument of Schröder *et al.* (1972) that an opposite diffusion potential is set up in the dark, provided the permeability for protons is much higher than for the counterions. Thereby the efflux of protons is retarded, which complicates the calculation of H^+/e ratios as discussed in Section IV,A. Even more likely, this might be the case under phosphorylation conditions (see Section VII,B).

VI.   Phenomena Related to the Electrochemical Proton Potential

A.   INDUCTION OF CHLOROPHYLL FLUORESCENCE

Chlorophyll fluorescence of illuminated chloroplasts exhibits complex induction phenomena responding to the presteady state of electron transport and coupled proton accumulation. A slow quenching of fluorescence, i.e., the transition from P to S, in the terminology used (see Papageorgiou, 1975a), could be correlated to the rise of the pH difference across the membrane by its sensitivity to uncouplers and ionophores (Wraight and Crofts, 1970; Evans and Crofts, 1973). It can be separately observed in DCMU-poisoned chloroplasts, when cyclic electron transport with PMS as mediator drives proton uptake and induction phenomena reflecting the redox state of photosystem II are excluded (Murata and Sugahara, 1969; see Papageorgiou, 1975b). This transient is lost in chloroplasts treated with EDTA, which have lost their capacity to maintain a pH difference, and can be restored by addition of DCCD (Cohen and Sherman, 1971). However, it appears to be linked not directly to proton translocation, but rather to secondary structural changes in the chloroplast membrane. Accordingly, the fluorescence transient is paralleled by chloroplast shrinkage (Heber, 1969) and is lost in glutaraldehyde-fixed chloroplasts, which have retained about half the capacity for proton uptake (West and Packer, 1970). It has been shown to depend on the presence of Mg^{2+} (Krause, 1974; Barber and Telfer, 1974), which specifies its relation to ultrastructural changes resulting from release of bound Mg^{2+} in response to proton accumulation. In a more recent view, the structural change responsible for the fluorescence transient is seen as a consequence not of counterion movement, but of conformational changes of the ATP-forming complex induced by the proton potential (Jennings et al., 1975) (see Section IX,C).

B.   Chlorophyll Luminescence and Delayed Fluorescence

Delayed fluorescence and luminescence of chlorophyll in the chloroplast membrane is thought to indicate the recombination of metastable electrons and holes, left in the quasi-crystalline matrix of pigments after illumination. The effect of an electrochemical proton potential on these processes has been extensively reviewed by Lavorel (1975).

pH jumps (Mayne and Clayton, 1966) as well as salt jumps (Miles and Jagendorf, 1969; Barber and Kraan, 1970) lead to luminescence bursts of preilluminated chloroplasts in the dark. Mechanisms as to how a pH difference (Kraan et al., 1970) or a membrane potential (Barber and Kraan, 1970, Crofts et al., 1971) would lower the activation energy for the recombination of trapped electrons and holes have been suggested (see Lavorel, 1975). The former is particularly interesting, since it supports the notion of a vectorial organization of the reaction center in photosystem II (see Section II), which is connected to a protolytic step on each side of the membrane (see Figs. 2 and 4). Delayed fluorescence of chlorophyll, when followed throughout the whole presteady state of chloroplasts after onset of illumination, shows a characteristic biphasic induction corresponding to the induction of the electrochemical proton potential shown in Fig. 5 (Wraight and Crofts, 1971; Itoh et al., 1971). Valinomycin/K^+ specifically inhibits the fast initial rise, which therefore indicates the effect of the membrane potential. The slower second rise corresponds to the rise of the pH difference. Similar induction phenomena of delayed fluorescence have been observed in vivo (Bauer and Wijnands, 1974). Luminescence can also be induced by application of external electric fields to chloroplast suspensions (see Ellenson and Sauer, 1976).

In bacterial chromatophores delayed light emission is stimulated by the membrane potential only (Evans and Crofts, 1974). This is a significant difference to the chloroplast system, since chromatophores lack the water-splitting reaction. Therefore in chloroplasts the pH difference stimulates delayed light, like luminescence, via the intimate link between protolytic reactions and photosystem II.

Barber (1972) succeeded in measuring the membrane potential during the steady state of illuminated chloroplasts, by comparing the steady-state level of delayed fluorescence with the emission bursts by transient diffusion potentials, resulting from K^+ pulses in the presence of valinomycin. He arrived at a value of 80 mV (see Section V,B).

C. Synergistic Uncoupling by Ionophores

According to the chemiosmotic hypothesis, efficient uncoupling affords a cyclic process of dissipating both the membrane potential and the pH difference, as depicted in Fig. 7 (Mitchell, 1970; Chance and Montal, 1971; Jagendorf, 1975). Classic uncouplers, which are lipophilic weak acids or bases and are lipophilic also in the charged form, like nitrophenols (DNP) or phenylhydrazones (FCCP) and higher aliphatic amines, are thought to act as in Fig. 7a and b, fulfilling both roles in a cyclic fashion [but see Hatefi et al. (1975) for a different view]. The action of nigericin/K^+ or ammonia, K^+ and NH_4^+ being impermeable, results in a cation/proton exchange (Fig. 7c,d), while valinomycin/K^+, valinomycin/NH_4^+, or permeant anions, like thiocyanate, neutralize the

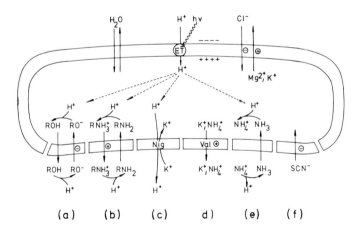

Fig. 7. Chemiosmotic uncoupling mechanisms in chloroplasts. ET, electron transport; Nig, nigericin; Val, valinomycin. For other abbreviations, see Figs. 1 and 2 legends. (a) Uncoupling proton shuttle by a weak, permeable acid; (b) uncoupling proton shuttle by a weak, permeable base; (c) ionophoretic exchange of protons for potassium ions by nigericin; (d) ionophoretic transport of potassium or ammonium ions by valinomycin; (e) substitution of ammonium ions for protons via amine uptake; (f) permeation of lipophilic anions.

electric field by countercharge transport (Fig. 7e,f). Synergistic uncoupling by nigericin/K^+ or ammonia, and by valinomycin/K^+ or lipophilic anions, is expected, since these combinations would result in complete dissipation of the electrochemical proton potential. The combinations with valinomycin act in a cyclic way, while those with lipophilic anions result in uptake of potassium or ammonium salt with osmotic swelling caused by accompanying water uptake (see Fig. 7).

The fact that chloroplasts are fully uncoupled by ammonium salts (see Good et al., 1966) or by nigericin/K^+ (Thore et al., 1968) is in accordance with efficient counterion flux of Cl^-, Mg^{2+}, or K^+ and with little contribution of membrane potential in the steady state. However, synergism between valinomycin and a low concentration of ammonium chloride (McCarty, 1969), as well as between valinomycin/K^+ and suboptimal concentrations of nigericin (Shavit et al., 1970) and of FCCP or DNP (Karlish et al., 1969), has been observed. The latter represents a combination of processes a and d in Fig. 7; its synergism is not plausible at first sight, because of the question of how valinomycin/K^+ facilitates the cycling of the weak acid and its anion. The effect can be explained, though, by the assumption that the rate of ion transport through a lipid membrane is increased by the presence of a lipophilic counterion, in this case valinomycin/K^+ raising the dielectric constant of the barrier (see Hinkle, 1970).

A relatively higher membrane potential in subchloroplast vesicles compared to chloroplasts is suggested by lower sensitivity of phosphorylation to ammonium salts, or nigericin/K^+, and by more expressed synergistic uncoupling with the combinations valinomycin–NH_4^+ or valinomycin–nigericin/K^+ (McCarty, 1969), as well as by the more effective stimulation of H^+ uptake by valinomycin/K^+, as discussed before. Corresponding synergism has also been found in bacterial chromatophores (Montal et al., 1970) and submitochondrial vesicles (Cockrell and Racker, 1969; Montal et al., 1969). Also the unexpected findings that in subchloroplast vesicles phosphorylation uncoupled by valinomycin–NH_4^+ is partially restored by amines (McCarty, 1969; Hauska et al., 1970) and that phosphorylation accompanying electron transport from ascorbate/DPIP through photosystem I is stimulated, not inhibited, by ammonium chloride (Hauska et al., 1975b; see Neumann et al., 1971) are readily explained by the relatively high contribution of a membrane potential in the steady state of energy transduction. The loss of Cl^--permeability during fragmentation of chloroplasts has been suggested to account for this fact (McCarty, 1969; Arntzen et al., 1971). Alternatively, it has been pointed out that fluctuations of membrane conductivity, if they occur statistically with time and membrane area, might discharge the electric field more efficiently in chloroplasts, with large membrane areas per compartment, than in small vesicles (Hauska and Sane, 1972).

However, the decreased sensitivity of subchloroplast vesicles to nigericin/K^+ or to ammonium salts as uncouplers can also be explained by a decreased capacity for osmotic swelling, and therefore a lower limit for salt uptake (Gaensslen and McCarty, 1971; Samoray and Hauska, 1975; Walker, 1975).

VII. Proton Translocation by the ATP-Forming Complex

In the preceding sections we have summarized the evidence for the formation of an electrochemical proton potential in illuminated chloroplasts. In the following, we collect experimental proof for a proton-conducting channel in the ATP-forming complex. The term "channel" signifies a function without anticipation of any mechanism.

A. Increased Proton Efflux and Membrane Conductivity by Removal of CF₁-ATPase

Coupling factor 1 (CF_1), the photophosphorylating enzyme, is localized on the thylakoid membrane facing the matrix, as indicated in Figs. 1 and 3. If it is removed by treatment with EDTA at low ionic strength, the capacity for the chloroplasts to accumulate protons in the light is lost, but it is restored upon addition of solubilized CF_1 (McCarty and Racker, 1966). Similar results have been obtained with submitochondrial vesicles (Hinkle and Horstman, 1971). In accordance, it could be demonstrated recently, that the membrane electric conductance in chloroplasts, which is thought to reflect proton permeability and is measured by the decay of the field indicating absorbance change at 515 nm, is drastically increased by removal of CF_1, which is partially reversed after reconstitution with the soluble protein (Schmid and Junge, 1975; Girault *et al.*, 1975). DCCD, an inhibitor of energy transfer from electron transport to ATP synthesis, significantly also restores H^+ accumulation (McCarty and Racker, 1968) and membrane electric resistance (Schmid and Junge, 1975) in CF_1-deficient chloroplasts. Together, these observations clearly indicate the existence of a channel, conducting protons to the active site for ATP synthesis. At higher pH, DCCD also increases the extent of H^+ uptake in control chloroplasts by way of a decreased proton efflux, which is accompanied by inhibition of electron transport even in the absence of phosphorylation (Uribe, 1972; Orlich, 1974). It seems, therefore, that basal electron flow, in the absence of phosphorylation substrates, is correlated to the leak of protons through the ATP-forming complex. The action of DCCD exhibits a cooperative induction phenomenon, i.e., it progressively increases with the time of incubation (Uribe, 1972; Orlich, 1974; Hauska *et al.*, 1975a).

To review the biochemistry of the ATP-forming complex is beyond the scope of this article. It apparently is constituted by a proton conducting part, called CF_0, integrated into the membrane core, to which CF_1 is bound on one surface of the membrane (see Fig. 1). This duality, as well as the action of energy-transfer inhibitors, like DCCD, on the proton conductance, are not confined to the chloroplast system, but seem to be universal features of energy-transducing biomembranes established for the chloroplast and the mitochondrial and bacterial systems (see Postma and van Dam, 1976; Racker, 1975; Senior, 1973). The whole complex, with the proton conducting moiety, has been purified from mitochondria (Kagawa and Racker, 1966; see Kagawa, 1972), from chloroplasts (Carmeli and Racker, 1973), from membranes of *Escherichia coli* (Nieuwenhuis *et al.*, 1974; Hare, 1975), and from membranes of a thermophilic bacterium (Sone *et al.*, 1975).

In chromatophores from photosynthetic bacteria, removal of CF_1 does not likewise result in a comparable increase of proton conductivity (Melandri *et al.*, 1970, 1972; Gromet-Elhanan, 1974).

B. INCREASED PROTON EFFLUX AND MEMBRANE CONDUCTIVITY BY
      PHOSPHORYLATING CONDITIONS

The extent of the electrochemical proton potential in the steady state is expected to be deminished under phosphorylating conditions if this potential is an intermediate or is in equilibrium with an intermediate driving ATP synthesis. However, the expected decrease has been found to be masked by interference of a conformational change of CF_1 induced by minute amounts of ATP or ADP, which decreases H^+ permeability (McCarty *et al.*, 1971) and is dependent on high light intensities (Portis *et al.*, 1975) (see Section IX,C). The reason why other investigators had no difficulty in observing the expected decrease might be sought in the different dependence on light of the masking effect in different chloroplast preparations (see Jagendorf, 1975, p. 448). The observed decrease was 0.4 pH unit (Portis and McCarty, 1974; Pick *et al.*, 1973; Schröder *et al.*, 1972).

The decrease in amount of proton uptake should be caused by a faster proton efflux during phosphorylation. To observe this, another complication discussed before has to be considered. Increased proton efflux even more likely should lead to a braking diffusion potential after light has been switched off, as discussed in Section IV,A and for Fig. 5 (Schröder *et al.*, 1972). Actual acceleration of proton efflux, therefore, can be observed only if the diffusion potential is abolished by valinomycin plus K^+. In addition the rates of proton efflux under phosphorylating and nonphosphorylating conditions must be compared at the same driving force, i.e., at equal proton gradients (Schröder et al., 1972) (see Section VII,D).

The dark-decay of the absorption change at 515 nm, indicating the electric field in illuminated chloroplasts, is accelerated under phosphorylating conditions; this has been taken as evidence for an increased conductance, specific for protons (Rumberg and Siggel, 1969; Junge et al., 1970; Gräber and Witt, 1976; see Witt, 1975). For this acceleration a threshold value for a minimal membrane potential was originally reported (Junge et al., 1970), and from this the hypothesis for the function of the electric field, triggering the ATP-forming complex via a conformational change, was elaborated (Junge, 1970). However, Gräber and Witt (1976) could show that it is not merely the membrane potential, but rather the total of the electrochemical proton potential, that is forcing protons through the ATP-forming complex and that the apparent threshold is caused by unspecific proton conductance of the membrane. This conductance outruns the specific pathway at low light intensity because it depends at lower power on the electrochemical H^+ gradient (Gräber and Witt, 1976); it is discussed in detail in Section VII,D.

In chromatophores from *Rhodopseudomonas spheroides*, only a small portion of the carotenoid change exhibits accelerated decay in the dark under phosphorylating conditions (Jackson et al., 1975); this finding suggests that only a small fraction of the vesicle population is responding, which is surprising in view of the high rates of phosphorylation usually observed. The finding, however, might in turn relate to the fact that removal of CF_1 from chromatophores does not substantially decrease the ability to accumulate protons (Melandri et al., 1970).

C. ATP-DRIVEN PROTON UPTAKE

Proton accumulation within the thylakoids can also be catalyzed by ATP-hydrolysis after activation of ATPase activity (see Section IX,C), in reverse to proton efflux during ATP formation. This could be directly observed with a glass electrode, after proton liberation at pH 8.0 in the ATP hydrolysis reaction itself had been canceled by an ATP-regenerating system (Carmeli, 1970; Carmeli et al., 1975). Indirect evidence already had been provided by an earlier measurement of ATP-driven ammonium uptake (Crofts, 1966). The pH difference across the chloroplast membrane, attained by ATP-hydrolysis, was found to be not much below that formed in the light. Values up to 3 pH units have been calculated in a study of the distribution of the fluorescent 9-aminoacridine (Bakker-Grunwald and van Dam, 1973; see also Gaensslen and McCarty, 1971).

ATP-dependent proton uptake has similarly been demonstrated in submitochondrial vesicles (Thayer and Hinkle, 1973; see also Mitchell and Moyle, 1965b) and in chromatophores from *Rhodospirillum rubrum* (Scholes *et al.*, 1969) and *Rhodopseudomonas capsulata* (Melandri *et al.*, 1972). Further evidence for a H$^+$-translocating ATPase in bacteria and its role in active transport has been reviewed (see Harold and Altendorf, 1974; Simoni and Postma, 1975).

It is of considerable interest that the ATP-forming complex from mitochondria can be incorporated into lipid vesicles (see Kagawa, 1972) and there catalyzes the formation of an ATP-dependent membrane potential, inside positive (see Skulachev, 1974). Furthermore, it has been shown that coupling factor 1 alone, i.e., the water-soluble part of the complex, induces an ATP-dependent electric field across water–octane interphases, positive in the octane phase, provided a lipophilic anion is present in the octane phase to accept protons (Boguslavsky *et al.*, 1975). These experiments perfectly fit the concept that protons are forced from the active site of ATP hydrolysis into the hydrophobic part of the complex.

D. H$^+$/ATP RATIOS

Much experimental effort has been put into resolving the question of how many protons are mechanistically used per ATP formed (see Jagendorf, 1975), not the least because of the energetic consequences. A selection of reported values, with emphasis on more recent measurements, is presented in Table IV, together with the expected P/e$_2$ ratios for electron flow from water to NADP$^+$, if H$^+$/e is assumed to be 2.

Measurement of the back reaction, i.e., ATP-driven H$^+$ uptake, might be favorable because of less proton leak compared to the forward reaction, but it is complicated by the difficulty of measuring true initial rates. The reported values, somewhat below 2 for H$^+$/ATP, therefore might represent underestimates (Carmeli, 1970; Carmeli *et al.*, 1975; see also Gaensslen and McCarty, 1971). A rough estimate for H$^+$/ATP was provided by comparison of the decay of the pH gradient and of the phosphorylation capacity in the dark (Izawa, 1970) (see Section VIII,A).

After Schwartz (1968), Rumberg and collaborators have continuously addressed themselves to this problem, with technical elegance and sophisticated reasoning, by measuring the forward reaction, i.e., the extra proton efflux under phosphorylating conditions in continuous light (Schröder *et al.*, 1972, 1975). According to their rationale, as discussed

TABLE IV

H$^+$/ATP Ratios and Corresponding P/e$_2$ Ratios for Electron Transport from Water to NADP$^+$ [a]

Reaction measured	H$^+$/ATP	P/e$_2$	References	Comments
pH changes during ATP-hydrolysis	2	2.0	Carmeli (1970), Carmeli et al. (1975)	Glass electrode, not corrected for slow response
Decay of pH difference and of X$_e$ in the dark	2–3	1.33–2.0	Izawa (1970)	Assessment of H$^+$ leak
ATP-driven amine uptake	2	2.0	Gaensslen and McCarty (1971)	Admitted underestimate
Extra H$^+$ efflux under phosphorylating conditions	2	2.0	Schwartz (1968)	Glass electrode
	3	1.33	Schröder et al. (1972)	Phenol red; correction for H$^+$ leak and diffusion potential in the dark
	4	1.0	Schröder et al. (1975)	As above
	3	1.33	Junge et al. (1970)	515 nm shift
Extra membrane conductance under phosphorylating conditions	2.4	1.66	Gräber and Witt (1976)	515 nm shift correction for H$^+$ leak
Functional dependence of the rate of ATP formation on internal H$^+$ concentration	3	1.33	Portis and McCarty (1974)	

[a] X$_e$ stands for the phosphorylation capacity of chloroplasts after illumination (see Section VIII,A). For the P/e$_2$ ratios presented, an H$^+$/e ratio of 2 has been assumed, a value that prevails in Table III.

in Section IV,A and VII,B, the formation of a diffusion potential has to be avoided by addition of valinomycin plus K^+, to be safe in the assumption that the observed initial proton efflux rates in the dark represent efflux in the light. This has been overlooked by many investigators (see Dilley and Giaquinta, 1975, for a complete list of references). For instance, the effect of energy-transfer inhibitors, such as DCCD or Dio-9, in apparently increasing the H^+/e ratios is simply explained by their inhibition of proton efflux, resulting in a lower diffusion potential in the dark and less masking of the true proton efflux rates (Telfer and Evans, 1972; see Dilley and Giaquinta, 1975).

Furthermore, for subtraction of the proper unspecific H^+ leak, Rumberg and collaborators considered its dependence on internal proton concentration. The membrane potential was found to be low under their conditions, and its interference was neglected. With all these corrections they arrived at values of 3–4 for H^+/ATP.

Pulse-spectrophotometric measurements of the electric field across the chloroplast membrane, reflected by the light-induced absorbance change at 515 nm, showed that its decay is accelerated under phosphorylating conditions (see Section VII,B). By assuming that the extra current through the membrane resembles proton translocation, Junge *et al.* (1970) arrived at a H^+/ATP ratio of 3. An important extension of this approach was recently published in a paper by Gräber and Witt (1976), also relating to Rumberg's measurements in continuous light. The technique allows variation of the membrane potential (50–125 mV) and the pH difference (1.8–2.7 units) independently in a pseudosteady state, and measurement of their influence on the rate of the field decay, resembling proton efflux, and on the rate of photophosphorylation. Although the quantitative results are open to criticism because of a number of assumptions, the wealth of condensed information in this paper on the qualitative behavior of this energy-coupling system has not previously been reached; it will be further discussed in Section VIII. The key finding is that H^+ leak and H^+ flux through the phosphorylating pathway depend with different exponential power on both the pH difference and the electric potential across the membrane.

At constant electric potential, the exponent for the dependence on the pH difference is 1.0 for the H^+ leak, and 2.2–2.6 for the flux through the ATP-forming complex. Similar exponents, 1.0 and 2.0, respectively, for the dependence of the two fluxes on internal proton concentration have been published by Schröder *et al.* (1975). This means that at high electrochemical potential most of the protons are forced through the phosphorylating channel whereas at low energy pressure the leak predominates, simulating an energy threshold for phosphorylation (see

Section VIII,B). The value obtained for H^+/ATP from these measurements, either by correcting for the leak or from data at the highest light intensities, is 2.4, which is considered to represent 2. A value of 2 is consistent with Mitchell's chemiosmotic hypothesis (see Mitchell, 1974) and is in accordance with the value reported for submitochondrial vesicles (Thayer and Hinkle, 1973) and chromatophores from *Rhodopseudomonas spheroides* (Jackson *et al.*, 1975), but might be energetically insufficient for the chloroplast system (see Section VIII,B).

Portis and McCarty (1974) directly relate the exponent of the dependence of photophosphorylation on internal H^+ concentration to the H^+/ATP ratio, which is justified only if all the protons functioning in ATP formation are translocated in the rate-limiting step of the reaction. Their value of 3.0 compares with the exponents 2.2–2.6 (Gräber and Witt, 1976) and 2.0 (Schröder *et al.*, 1975), mentioned above.

VIII. The Competence of the Electrochemical Proton Potential for Energy Transmission

At the present stage, besides Mitchell's "proton motive force," conformational energy is seriously discussed as the link between electron transport and phosphorylation (see Boyer *et al.*, 1975; Harris and Slater, 1975; Dilley and Giaquinta, 1975). The functional requirement of both conformational changes and proton movements can no longer be ignored, but the question of the linkage pattern of the different energy forms is not settled. Free interchangeability of conformational energy and proton potential, without any hierarchy, might provide advantages in terms of versatility, might settle arguments, but is against a minimum-assumption hypothesis. The puristic chemiosmotic view considers conformational changes of secondary, possibly regulatory, importance (see Wikström, 1975, for this view). The puristic conformational alternative puts the proton potential on the side, possibly functioning as energy buffer, or in regulating the system (see Section IX). Threefold linked sequences, with both energy forms as obligatory intermediates, also are feasible.

A trivial but not sufficient criterion for the function of an intermediate in a reaction sequence is the ability to form the product. Other criteria are that (1) the free energy of the intermediate during the reaction flow should exceed the free energy of the product, and (2) the intermediate should be formed and used faster and more efficiently than the product is formed in the overall reaction. All these criteria have so far been applied to the electrochemical proton potential only.

A.   ATP Formation Driven by Proton Potentials in the Dark

A high-energy intermediate between electron transport and ATP formation, called X_e, was experimentally proved by separation of its formation in the light and its utilization in the dark (Shen and Shen, 1962; Hind and Jagendorf, 1963), and could be convincingly identified as the pH difference across the chloroplast membrane (see Jagendorf, 1975). Its extent is dependent on the amount of internal protons stored in the light; it shows a pH optimum at 6.5 (external pH) and is increased severalfold by addition of permeant amines with low pK, which function as additional internal buffers (Nelson et al., 1971; Avron, 1972). Accordingly, the yield of ATP is increased in subchloroplast vesicles and bacterial chromatophores by addition of valinomycin plus K^+ (McCarty, 1970) or of permeant anions (Leiser and Gromet-Elhanan, 1975a) to the light stage, which increases the uptake of protons by lowering the membrane potential in the steady state (see Sections IV,C and V,B). Apparently, the membrane potential, built up during illumination, does not contribute to phosphorylation in the dark, presumably because it relaxes too fast. On the other hand, phosphorylation is stimulated if a diffusion potential, positive inside, is maintained by including valinomycin plus K^+ in the dark stage in chloroplasts (Schuldiner et al., 1972b, 1973) and in chromatophores (Leiser and Gromet-Elhanan, 1975b).

In a recent paper it was shown that X_e can be formed at temperatures down to $-13°C$ and can be stored for weeks below $-30°C$ (Tyszkiewics and Roux, 1975).

A milestone in bioenergetic research was the discovery of Jagendorf and Uribe (1966) that ATP was formed in the dark in chloroplasts by a pH gradient, artificially imposed by transition from acid to alkaline pH. The amount of ATP formation was dependent on a minimum of a pH difference of about 3 and again on the amount of stored protons. This could be increased by the presence of a dicarboxylic acid, such as succinate, which would equilibrate with the inside aqueous space in the acid stage (see Jagendorf, 1975, for a summary). The participation of redox reactions could be excluded. Stop-flow studies of the proton efflux after the pH jump showed biphasic kinetics (Nishizaki and Jagendorf, 1971).

Like X_e phosphorylation, acid-base phosphorylation also is stimulated by a diffusion potential set up in the second stage (Schuldiner et al., 1972b, 1973; Uribe and Li, 1973).

Acid-base-phosphorylation and its stimulation by a diffusion potential has also been demonstrated in bacterial chromatophores (Leiser and Gromet-Elhanan, 1974). Similarly, ATP synthesis driven by artificially imposed electrochemical proton gradients has been observed in mito-chondria (Reid *et al.*, 1966; Cockrell *et al.*, 1967), in submitochondrial vesicles (Thayer and Hinkle, 1975a,b), and in membrane systems from *Streptococcus lactis* or *Escherichia coli* (Maloney *et al.*, 1974; Grinius *et al.*, 1975). Also the reversal of the ATP-driven Na/K pump in erythrocytes (Lew *et al.*, 1970) and of the Ca pump in sarcoplasmic reticulum (Makinose and Hasselbach, 1971) should be mentioned here.

By these two-stage phosphorylation experiments, it has been estab-lished that an electrochemical proton potential is able to drive ATP synthesis, and the joint contribution of an electric potential and a pH difference was demonstrated. The interchangeability of the two energy forms for ATP formation during illumination has recently been investi-gated under a flashing-light regime (Gräber and Witt, 1976; see below).

It is worth mentioning in this context that ATP formation in the dark can be obtained via the artificial, transmembrane redox reaction of external ascorbate with ferricyanide, trapped inside the chloroplasts, provided the reaction is mediated by a hydrogen-carrying redox com-pound—yet another type of two-stage phosphorylation (Selman and Psczolla, 1976). This system is an extension of the work with lipophilic electron donors for photosystem I and nicely corroborates our chemios-motic concept of artificial energy conservation (see Section III).

B. THERMODYNAMIC AND KINETIC COMPETENCE

Kraayenhof (1969) demonstrated, that highly coupled chloroplasts could catalyze photophosphoylation against a phosphate potential of up to 15.5 kcal under steady-state conditions ("static head" for phosphoryl-ation; see Rottenberg, 1976). A detailed discussion of the phosphate potential and an assessment of what its value might be *in vivo* are presented by Hall (1976). A value, similar to that of Kraayenhof, has been reported for mitochondrial respiration (see Slater *et al.*, 1973). The electrochemical proton potential, if solely responsible for phosphoryla-tion, should exceed this value. As discussed in Section IV,C, the highest pH difference reported is around 3.5 units, to which the membrane potential, ranging from 0 to 100 mV (see Section V,B), must be added. Together this makes a total free energy of about 200–300 mV, or 4.6–6.9 kcal/mole H^+. The values for H^+/ATP under consideration are either 2 or 3 (see Table IV). It is clear that 2 H^+ might just suffice to match the phosphate potential, if 15.5 kcal is an overestimate, which might be the case (see Hall, 1976), and a membrane potential of 100 mV in the steady state indeed could simply be added (Gräber and Witt, 1976; Witt, 1975). The latter is not justified in view of the profiles for electric potential and pH difference between the two aqueous bulk phases, across the membrane (Rumberg and Muhle, 1976) (see Fig. 6). With a lower contribution by a membrane potential, a value between 5 and 6 kcal/mole H^+ seems more realistic, and therefore a stoichiometry of 3 H^+/ATP, leaving some room for proton leakage, is most frequently considered at present (Portis *et al.*, 1975; Jagendorf, 1975; Pick *et al.*, 1975; Rottenberg, 1975, 1976).

Also in mitochondrial systems an H^+/ATP-ratio of 2 (see Thayer and Hinkle, 1973) seems inadequate to balance the phosphate potential measured (Slater *et al.*, 1973), whereas in bacterial chromatophores contradictory reports on the extent of the maximal electrochemical proton potential have appeared [compare 340 mV in Casadio *et al.* (1974) with 210 mV in Schuldiner *et al.* (1974)]. Only the value reported by Casadio *et al.* would energetically suffice with a stoichiometry of 2 H^+/ATP, which has recently been reported independently by Jackson *et al.* (1975). Rottenberg (1975) summarized and discussed all available data on the extent of the electrochemical proton potential in electron transporting membranes.

Lower limits of the pH difference (Rumberg and Schröder, 1974; Portis and McCarty, 1974; Pick *et al.*, 1974, 1975), or the membrane potential (Junge *et al.*, 1970), or both (Gräber and Witt, 1976), required to drive photophosphorylation have been reported; they are frequently referred to as threshold values, a term that implies something beyond the mere mass action between the driving force of H^+ and ATP formation. This implication is not necessary. Naturally, at low driving force only minute amounts of ATP, which could escape measurement, have to be formed to exert the compensating back pressure. However, it is possible, but not yet proved, that the conformational change of CF_1 necessary for the ATPase to be activated (see Section IX,C) and probably representing the transition to the active form in phosphorylation as well, requires triggering by a minimal electric potential, as suggested by Junge (1970), or by a minimal pH difference. If this were the case, the threshold value for instance, should be independent of phosphate potential, which has been found (Pick *et al.*, 1975), or has not been found (Rumberg and Schröder, 1974). A lower limit of about 3 pH units also exists for acid-base phosphorylation (Jagendorf and Uribe, 1966; Schuldiner *et al.*, 1973). The threshold of light intensity for photophosphorylation, the so-called intensity lag debated in the literature, can be related to this minimum requirement of proton potential (see Jagendorf, 1975, p. 447, for complete reference). Gräber and Witt (1976) in their recent extensive work demonstrated the interchangeability of membrane potential and pH difference for this minimal driving force. An earlier claim—that photophosphorylation requires an electric field and cannot proceed by the action of a pH difference alone (Boeck and Witt, 1972)—which has been taken as evidence against a straightforward chemiosmotic mechanism of coupling (Williams, 1974)—thus seems to be superseded. Williams (1969, q.v.) suggested that a local proton potential that is not in equilibrium with the pH of the inner thylakoid space and the delocalized membrane potential, drives ATP formation. This variant of chemiosmotic coupling has been considered particularly for photo-phosphorylation by Dilley and Giaquinta (1975). It is supported by the recent studies of Ort *et al.* (1976a,b) on ATP formation and proton uptake during msec-range light flashes, demonstrating that the time lag in the onset of photophosphorylation is shorter than expected from the risetime of the electrochemical proton potential difference between the aqueous phases on either side of the membrane. Furthermore, the lag does not respond appreciably if the rise of the proton potential is delayed by addition of permeant ions or buffers. However, the values for the membrane potential and the pH difference during this presteady state condition in the presence of, for instance, valinomycin plus K^+ and permeant buffers are not known, and might be higher than the authors reasoned.

As discussed in Section V,A and Fig. 5, the rise of the electric field is certainly fast enough to account for the initial rates of photophosphory-lation. The decay of the pH difference and of the capacity for postillumi-nation phosphorylation (X_e) in the dark are also correlated (Izawa, 1970; see Jagendorf, 1975); in this case the membrane potential plays a minor role. Application of the thermodynamics of irreversible processes to the energy flow in electron transport phosphorylation also leads to the conclusion that the electrochemical proton potential fulfills the neces-sary criteria for an intermediate in photophosphorylation of chloroplasts (Rottenberg, 1976). A similar conclusion was reached for bacterial chromatophores (Casadio *et al.*, 1975). This is not so for oxidative phosphorylation in mitochondria, where more direct coupling between electron transport and ATP formation is suggested by the observation of a higher degree of coupling between input force and output force, i.e., between electron transport and ATP formation, than between electron flow and proton potential, and between proton potential and ATP formation (see Rottenberg, 1976). This fact argues against the delocal-ized potential being an intermediate, and could again be accounted for by a local proton potential in the membrane which is not in free equilibrium with the one of the inner bulk aqueous phase (Williams, 1969). However, Thayer and Hinkle (1975b), in contradiction, reported from stop-flow measurements that in submitochondrial vesicles ATP formation is more efficiently coupled to an artificially imposed proton potential than to electron transport.

IX. Regulatory Functions of the Electrochemical Proton Potential and Conformational Changes

Photosynthetic control, in analogy to respiratory control, is understood as the back pressure of the high-energy intermediate on electron transport. It is released by ADP and P_i, or by uncouplers, which results in a characteristic stimulation of electron flow. According to the chemiosmotic hypothesis it is the electrochemical proton potential, which should control electron transport. This is expected only if the rate of the limiting step in steady-state electron transport is directly related to the dissipative rate for the electrochemical proton potential. However, photosynthetic control is not the only way by which electron transport could be influenced by an electrochemical proton potential. Optima of internal and external pH for electron transport have been reported (Section IX,A). In addition, an inhibitory effect of high internal pH on the water-splitting reaction has been found (Harth et al., 1974) (see Sections I and IX,B). The electrochemical proton potential should also influence transmembrane shuttles of artificial redox compounds if charged species and protonization reactions participate (see Section IX,A). Finally, conformational changes, either of electron transfer components (see Section IX,B) or of the ATP-forming complex (see Section IX,C) have been observed and might be related to the electrochemical proton potential. Even if the H^+ potential were not the obligatory intermediate in energy transduction, but in equilibrium with conformational energy or some other form of local energy, it would function as an energy buffer delocalized over the whole membrane compartment and still would exert photosynthetic control and the other effects.

Besides this fundamental regulatory function in energy flow, the role of proton uptake in regulation of the Calvin cycle has been mentioned (Section II, Figs. 1 and 3). This is attributed to the change of FDPase activity from almost zero to full in the range from pH 7.5 to 8.5, which is exactly the observed change in pH with stroma after the transition from dark to light (Werdan et al., 1975). In addition, the affinity of RuDP carboxylase is substantially increased at pH 8.5 compared to 7.5 (Bowes et al., 1975).

A. Control of Native and Artificial Electron Transport

1. Native Electron Flow

Photosynthetic control in chloroplasts is predominantly exerted by the pH difference, not by the membrane potential, because the latter is small in the steady state. In chemiosmotic terms, the control is released and electron transport is stimulated by increasing the proton permeability, e.g., by the action of uncouplers as depicted in Fig. 7a,b. The rate-limiting step in electron flow from water to photosystem I is the turnover of plastoquinone, a protolytic reaction, and it seems to follow that it is the primary site of control by the pH difference (see Fig. 8a). At external pH of 8.0, it is the internal proton activity that governs the rate of plastohydroquinone oxidation (Rumberg and Siggel, 1969; Siggel, 1975, 1976). More specifically, it probably is kinetic control of the commutation reaction to the semiquinone anion (Stiehl and Witt, 1969) which is limited by the low dissociation of the hydroquinone at neutral pH (Bishop and Tong, 1964) and is preceding the actual oxidation. Water oxidation is less affected by the pH difference (Siggel, 1975).

Photosynthetic control seems to be complicated by the existence of an apparent optimum for electron transport at external pH somewhat above 8.0 (see Good *et al.*, 1966) and by the fact that uncouplers stimulate electron flow in the lower, but inhibit it in the higher, pH range (Avron, 1972). Thus the optimum is shifted to lower pH upon addition of uncouplers. It remains at almost the same pH after addition of ADP and

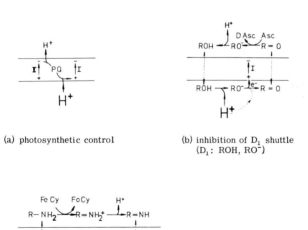

(a) photosynthetic control

(b) inhibition of D_1 shuttle
(D_1: ROH, RO$^-$)

(c) stimulation of A_2 shuttle
(A_2: R = NH, R = NH$_2^+$)

FIG. 8. Inhibition and stimulation of photosynthetic electron transport by the pH difference across the chloroplast membrane. FoCy, ferrocyanide; DAsc, dehydroascorbate; ROH/RO$^-$ and R=O, hydroquinoid and quinoid form of a phenolic donor for photosystem I (D_1); RNH$_3^+$/RNH$_2$ and R=NH$_2^+$/R=NH, the reduced and oxidized forms of *p*-phenylenediamines. For other abbreviations, see legends to Figs. 1 and 2.

P_i. One is tempted to attribute this to an optimum for photophosphory-lation around pH 8.0. Indications for a corresponding optimum in the reverse ATPase reaction have been reported (McCarty and Racker, 1968), but since this activity is maintained by the proton potential across the membrane (Section IX,C), its dependence on pH must be complex. Furthermore, it is unlikely that phosphorylation is rate limiting during electron flow from water to photosystem I in view of the very high rates found for cyclic photophosphorylation. It is interesting to note that the minimal pH difference required to drive photophosphorylation (see Section 8,B), decreases with external pH from 9.0 to 7.0, suggesting an optimum for photophosphorylation lower than pH 8.0 (Pick *et al.*, 1975). We suggest, however, that this reflects the lower leak of protons at lower pH (see Section IV). The finding that basal and coupled electron transport both exhibit an optimum at external pH 8.0 is another indication for the possibility that the leak of protons and their use in photophosphorylation occur via the same channel in the ATP-forming complex (Section VII,A).

In an extensive study, Bamberger *et al.* (1973) investigated the rate of electron transport from water to ferricyanide, simultaneously measuring the pH difference across the membrane. They found that electron transport exhibits a presteady-state transient, which could be correlated with an apparent optimum for electron transport at an internal pH of 5.0. Compared to the steady-state rate, the transient was slower at external pH above 8.0, and faster below 8.0, depending on whether the internal pH moved into, or out of, the optimum upon internal acidification. The optimum of internal pH around 5.0 shifted towards higher values when the pH difference across the membrane was attenuated by addition of uncouplers or by lowering the light intensity. The authors concluded that a mean value of internal and external pH governs a reaction step in the membrane. This also follows from a recently developed theoretical model for a vectorial plastoquinone redox reaction (Chernavsky *et al.*, 1975). Specifically, we would suggest, according to Fig. 8a, that at low mean pH, proton liberation in plastoquinone oxidation is rate limiting, while at high mean pH, it is possibly the protonization of plastoquinone anions on the outside (see Section IV,B). At a given pH difference an optimal mean pH is indeed expected for optimal turnover of plastoqui-none. In this view we still have electron transport controlled by the dependence of the rate-limiting steps on H^+ concentration, but no pH optimum for an enzymatic step in the usual sense.

Photosynthetic control in the region between photosystem II and cytochrome f has also been demonstrated by the phenomenon of reversed electron flow (Rienits *et al.*, 1973, 1974; Shahak *et al.*, 1975).

2. Artificial Electron Flow

In partial reactions of photosynthetic electron transport, an effect of the pH difference on transmembrane shuttles of artificial redox compounds, discussed in Section III, can be discerned from electron transport control. The two effects might actually occur in opposite direction (Trebst et al., 1975). They are linked to the distribution of the redox compounds following the pH difference, according to their acidic and basic nature and their permeability.

In a systematic investigation of compounds acting as donors for photosystem I (D_1 in Figs. 1a and 2b), it was found that photoreductions by photosystem I with phenols, e.g., $DPIPH_2$, carrying acidic OH groups, was highly stimulated by uncouplers, but with other compounds, such as p-phenylenediamines, there was no stimulation. The stimulation of electron flow was independent of coupled ATP formation, because the reaction with p-phenylenediamines was even better coupled (Hauska et al., 1975b). The explanation is given in Fig. 9b. If the phenolate anion (RO^-) is more reactive as electron donor for plastocyanine inside than the neutral form (ROH) of the reduced donor (Diebler, 1963), but is relatively impermeable, a high internal proton concentration would force the donor out of the internal space, in addition to controlling the oxidation reaction proper (dashed in Fig. 8b). Lowering the internal proton concentration by addition of uncouplers stimulates the reaction by increasing the steady-state concentration of the reactive phenolate. Phenylenediamines, on the other hand, are accumulated inside at low internal pH, forming ammonium ions like other amines (see Fig. 7e). Since the reactive species is the free amino form, which is supposed to equilibrate rapidly through the membrane, its steady-state concentration inside at constant external pH should not depend on the pH difference, and no stimulation of the reaction by uncouplers beyond release of electron transport control is expected. The latter is found at a very high concentration of p-phenylenediamine only (Gould, 1975b), showing that not the oxidation reaction, but rather another part of the shuttle through the membrane might be rate limiting.

A similar explanation, with opposite signs, has been proposed for the observation that electron transport from water is paradoxically inhibited by uncouplers if p-phenylenediamines acted as A_2 in the presence of DBMIB (Trebst and Reimer, 1973b; Trebst et al., 1975; Cohen et al., 1975). At lower external pH normal stimulation of electron transport was found. The explanation is formulated in Fig. 8c. If one assumes that an iminium ion ($R{=}NH_2^+$) is the active species being reduced inside by plastoquinol, a high internal proton concentration should increase its steady-state concentration. Furthermore, the product (RNH_2) would be constantly removed by protonation. Uncouplers should inhibit the reaction by increasing the pH inside way above the pKs of the imine and amine. At lower pH, the loss of protons from plastoquinol would be rate limiting again (see Fig. 8a), and uncouplers should stimulate, i.e., the usual case of photosynthetic control. According to this mechanism, protons liberated from plastoquinol inside are taken up again by the phenylenediamine and shuttled back to the outside. This possibility has been termed "stoichiometric uncoupling" (Trebst and Reimer, 1973b). The analog reaction with substituted quinones as A_2 shows neither inhibition nor stimulation by uncouplers at external pH 8.0 (Trebst *et al.*, 1976). No inhibition is expected because the pK for the formation of oxonium products is much too low, compared to the analogous iminium formation.

Lack of electron transport control in photoreductions by photosystem II was put forward as an argument for a different coupling mechanism in photosystems II and I (see Section III). However, if the protolytic oxidation steps in this partial reaction, either oxygen evolution or the oxidation of the artificial hydroquinone (or plastohydroquinone if involved), are not rate limiting, control by the pH difference is not expected.

B. CONFORMATIONAL CHANGES OF THE ELECTRON TRANSPORT
     SYSTEM

Structural changes of the chloroplast compartment are related to the high energy state—more specifically, to ion and water flow secondary to proton accumulation (see Section IV) (Murakami *et al.*, 1975). Light-dependent conformational changes closer to a molecular level within the membrane are linked to the osmotic changes, as visualized by fluorescence transients, for example (see Section VI,A). A number of other probes for conformational changes in the chloroplast membrane have recently emerged (see Dilley and Giaquinta, 1975, for a recent review).

Labeling with the membrane impermeable probe diazobenzene sulfonic acid (DABS) leads to an inhibition of photosystem II activity. The inhibition of electron flow as well as the incorporation of radioactive label into the membrane by ^{35}S-labeled DABS is markedly increased (4-fold) in the light compared with labeling of the membrane in the dark (Giaquinta *et al.*, 1974). The O_2 evolution system is specifically inhibited by illumination during DABS-labeling, while the electron donor system (D_2) for photosystem II is not affected. The light increased inhibition, and labeling has been interpreted to indicate a conformational change of the membrane in the light, which exposes the water-splitting reaction to the outside and renders it accessible to the impermeable modifier. Detailed study of the conditions for the inactivation of oxygen evolution by light indicated that not just excitation of photosystem II, but actual electron flow through photosystem II and Q to PQ, is required to bring about the conformational change (Giaquinta et al., 1975). DCMU, which inhibits electron flow between Q and PQ, would block the light-induced change. Recent results indicate that energization of the membrane by photosystem II requires proton release from water in addition to electron flow. This is concluded from the result that DCMU-insensitive silicomolybdate photoreduction by photosystem II, which is not coupled to ATP formation, does not yield high DABS-labeling in the light (Giaquinta et al., 1975). The high energy state and the proton release by photosystem I do not substitute for photosystem II activity, suggesting the rather interesting fact that the proton translocation in the energy conservation loop of photosystem II releases protons into a different space than the loop involving photosystem I and plastoquinone. It also suggests that the conformational change is not essential for oxygen evolution.

Iodination of the membrane catalyzed by an impermeable peroxidase shows similarities to DABS labeling (Arntzen et al., 1974). At high levels of iodination, oxygen evolution, but not electron donor systems for photosystem II, is inhibited. Glutaraldehyde fixation of the membrane eliminates these properties. From this a structural disorganization of the membrane by iodination is indicated. Again, these results suggest that the conformational change is not essential for oxygen evolution.

Recently similar experiments have been carried out with p-nitrothiophenol. Like DABS, this probe also inactivates photosystem II only in the light, but not in the dark (Kobayashi et al., 1976).

Inhibition (rather than the usual stimulation) of electron flow by uncouplers at high external pH has been explained by a shifting of the internal pH into an unfavorable range (see Section IX,A). Recently, it has been shown that the inhibition of electron flow at high external pH in the presence of pH-equilibrating uncouplers is due to a specific inactivation of the water-splitting reaction, specific because artificial donor systems for photosystem II remain unaffected (Harth et al., 1974; Trebst et al., 1975; Reimer and Trebst, 1975; Cohn et al., 1975). This inactivation of oxygen evolution by high internal pH is possible only in the light, but not in the dark, and therefore again might indicate a conformational change of the water-splitting reaction in the light. Alternatively, the higher oxidation states of Y ($S_0 \rightarrow S_4$), formed in the light only, might be sensitive to high internal pH. This effect of internal pH suggests that light exposes the water-splitting system to the internal space. The contradiction to the light-induced reaction of DABS from outside is reconciled by the assumption that the water-splitting complex is plugged through the membrane (see Section II).

Photosystem I activity seems also to be connected with conformational changes in the light. This has been suggested by DABS-labeling and inhibition experiments of photosystem I in the light vs dark (Selman *et al.*, 1974). This interpretation is, however, somewhat weakened by the observation that DABS itself is altered by light and converted to a more reactive species, which may account for higher labeling in the light (Lockau and Selman, 1976). EDAC, a water-soluble carbodiimide, inhibits electron transport, but only after preillumination of chloroplasts (McCarty, 1974). The point of inhibition is close to, but not at, plastocyanine, the endogenous electron donor for photosystem I. Electron transport through photosystem II alone is not affected by EDAC. A conformational change in the vicinity of photosystem I is indicated also by the observation that the accessibility of cytochrome *f* in the membrane to ferricyanide is markedly enhanced after a number of turnovers in the light (Horton and Cramer, 1974).

It might be of interest to refer to a conformational change found for the mitochondrial cytochrome oxidase, and its possible role in energy conservation (Wikström, 1975).

C.   Conformational Changes of the ATP-Forming Complex

Coupling factor 1 (CF_1) exists in several conformations on the chloroplast membrane in an energy-dependent manner. The transition longest known is from a "closed" to an "open" conformation upon illumination (see Jagendorf, 1975). The open form is susceptible to inhibition by the SH-reagent *N*-ethylmaleimide (McCarty and Fagan, 1973) and to activation of ATPase activity by SH-compounds or proteolysis (Petrack and Lipmann, 1961; Bakker-Grunwald, 1974). This activation results in removal or alteration of one of the five different subunits of CF_1 (see Nelson *et al.*, 1975), which is analogous to the more loosely bound ATPase inhibitor of mitochondria (Pullman and Monroy, 1963).

The transition from a closed to an open form is also induced by an artificially imposed pH difference across the membrane in the dark (Kaplan *et al.*, 1967; Ryrie and Jagendorf, 1972), which documents the interaction of the proton potential with conformational changes. It is feasible indeed that the free energy of the proton potential is transmitted to the chemical free energy of ATP via a strained conformation of CF_1 (see Boyer *et al.*, 1975; Harris and Slater, 1975), a notion supported by the further evidence that ATP and other adenine nucleotides are trapped (or tightly bound) in the closed form of CF_1 in all systems studied and are released from the open form after energization of the membrane (see Boyer *et al.*, 1975; Harris and Slater, 1975; Pflugshaupt and Bachofen, 1975). Significantly again, this release can be brought about by an artificial pH gradient in the dark (Strotmann *et al.*, 1976; see also Boyer *et al.*, 1975). Furthermore, studies of exchange reactions suggest that energy input is needed to liberate ATP from, as well as to bind P_i to, the closed form, but not for formation of the anhydride of the tightly bound ATP. The change from a closed to an open form can be stimulated by a partial reaction of electron transport, involving energy conservation by just one photosystem, and expresses itself in the partial reaction with the other photosystem, for instance by its susceptibility to inhibition by *N*-ethylmaleimide—a clear demonstration that there are no different domains of energy conservation in either photosystem I or II (Grebanier and Jagendorf, 1976).

Another, possibly different, change, relevant to the proton potential, has been reported for CF_1 in chloroplasts. It was derived from the finding that ATP or ADP, at micromolar concentrations stimulated the extent of the proton uptake (McCarty *et al.*, 1971), an effect that is expressed more at higher pH values and above a certain level of energization (Portis *et al.*, 1975). It has been concluded that, above a certain pH difference across the membrane, the dissipative proton leak through the ATP-forming complex is suddenly increased by a conformational change of CF_1, which is prevented by ATP. The ATP-forming complex in this view can be imagined as a gated proton translocator (Portis *et al.*, 1975), representing the valve through which energy transmission is controlled. The attenuation of basal electron transport by low concentration of ATP or ADP is an early, corroborative result (Avron *et al.*, 1958; see Schröder *et al.*, 1972). Perhaps the puzzling stimulation of proton uptake by phosphorylating conditions in chromatophores from *Rhodopseudomonas capsulata* likewise reflects interference of conformational changes (Melandri *et al.*, 1970). Conformational changes of coupling factor 1 in mitochondria have been observed as well (see Wikström and Saari, 1976).

X. Models for the Mechanism of Proton Translocation

Proton translocation is linked to protolytic steps in vectorial electron transport, but this notion does not specify a molecular reaction mechanism. Several models have come into discussion, and their number is increasing.

Of the two protolytic reactions in photosynthetic electron transport, the translocation of protons by water oxidation poses no special problem, since water is present in abundance and penetrates the membrane.

Proton translocation by plastoquinol in the second loop of electron transport is more difficult. Simple diffusion of the reduced and oxidized form, which has been implied in Figs. 2a, 4, and 8a, seems reasonable only at first sight. It is mechanistically important that plastoquinone is in 5- to 6-fold excess over the photocenters and other electron carriers, fulfilling an interconnecting function between several electron-transport chains (see Witt, 1971; Siggel *et al.*, 1972). Stiehl and Witt (1969) were the first to publish a quantitative model, based on investigations in flashing light. A simplified version is given in Fig. 9a, and involves the semiquinone anion of plastoquinone not only as reductant formed in photosystem II, but also as the species reacting toward photosystem I. The latter is based on the finding that the rate of PQH_2 oxidation is proportional to the product of the concentrations for PQH_2 and PQ. The commutation of PQH_2 and PQ, not the oxidation of PQH_2, is considered to be the rate-limiting step. This proposal seems reasonable in view of the low dismutation constant for benzoquinones at physiological pH (Diebler *et al.*, 1961; Bishop and Tong, 1964), which is caused by the very low dissociation of the hydroquinones into anionic forms. The model in Fig. 9a still rests on a formal movement of PQH_2 though the membrane core, which could occur via diffusion or via multiple hopping of the reducing equivalents within the plastoquinone pool. In view of a lipid bilayer, tumbling of plastoquinone with its long hydrophobic side chain might, however, be unfavorable.

Siggel (1975, 1976) extended these studies and added an alternative model. It is formulated in Fig. 9b, and essentially constitutes a proton pump A, which is driven by PQH_2 oxidation, oxidized plastoquinone being somehow also involved. This model comes close to the conformational concept for energy conservation (see Boyer *et al.*, 1975; Boyer, 1975b). It avoids the need for tumbling of PQH_2, but suffers from the unspecified nature of the proton pump A. In that context the proton-pumping purple membrane of Halobacteria, with bacteriorhodopsin as the only component, ought to be mentioned—a system beautiful for its simplicity (see Oesterhelt *et al.*, 1976). Although the detailed mechanism is not elucidated yet, it is established that an electron transport loop is not required for proton translocation. Instead it is driven by the cycle of the light-induced changes of retinal, volving protonation and deprotonation on opposite sides of the membrane.

Cytochrome *b* might fulfill a role in this direction in respiratory as well as photosynthetic electron transport, as has been suggested for mitochondria first (see Papa *et al.*, 1975; Papa, 1976). In chloroplasts, *b*-type cytochromes exhibit properties that make them good candidates for a proton pump together with plastoquinone. Cytochrome b_6, for instance, can be isolated in a complex together with cytochrome *f* (Nelson and

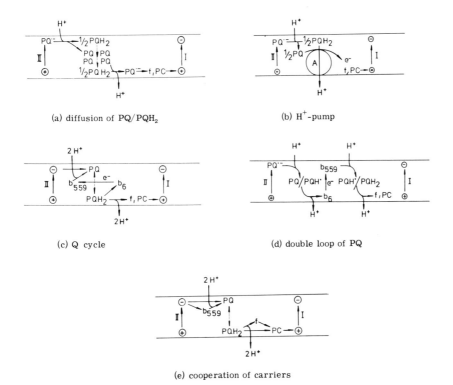

(a) diffusion of PQ/PQH₂

(b) H⁺-pump

(c) Q cycle

(d) double loop of PQ

(e) cooperation of carriers

FIG. 9. Models for the mechanism of proton translocation in the plastoquinone region of electron transport in chloroplasts. Abbreviations as in the legends for Figs. 1 and 2. (a) Stiehl and Witt, 1969; (b) Siggel, 1975, 1976; (c) Mitchell, 1975a; (d) analog to Crofts *et al.*, 1975b.

Neumann, 1972), which possesses the activity of a plastoquinol–plasto-cyanine reductase (Wood and Bendall, 1975). More intriguing is the fact that cytochrome b_{559} changes from a high to a low potential form when acidified (Cramer *et al.*, 1975; Horton and Cramer, 1976). This transition has an approximate pK of 5.5, which is significantly close to the expected pK for the plastosemiquinone (Bridge and Porter, 1958). Furthermore, the low-potential form is obtained by perturbation of the chloroplast membrane, for instance by extraction with organic solvents, which removes plastoquinone. The high-potential form is restored upon readdition of plastoquinone (Cox and Bendall, 1974).

A more sophisticated interplay of b cytochromes and plastoquinone has recently been suggested (Fig. 9c; Mitchell, 1975a,c,d). The model is called Q cycle and was constructed to explain energy conservation at site II and site III, and hitherto unresolved anomalies in the redox behavior of the cytochrome b–c_1–ubiquinone region of the mitochondrial membrane. In essence it results in a double loop during the cooperation of quinone and *b* cytochromes, yielding an H^+/e of 2. This is a radical departure from the concept of independent energy-conserving sites II and III, because they appear to be tied together in the Q cycle. The model was transferred to photosynthetic electron transport for reasons of generalization. Mitchell's Q cycle in Fig. 9c might become more intelligible via the linear reaction sequence of Fig. 9d, which has been adopted to explain proton translocation in cyclic electron transport of bacterial chromatophores (Crofts *et al.*, 1975b). The essential feature is that the redox reaction of plastoquinone/ plastoquinol is split into the two single-electron steps, separated by the action of the *b* cytochromes. It rests upon the fact that with a E_{m7} for PQ/PQH_2 around 50 mV, the couple $PQ/PQH^{\cdot}$ should be much more reducing (E_{m7} ca. -200 mV), and the couple $PQH^{\cdot}/PQH_2$ much more oxidizing (E_{m7} ca. 300 mV), reflecting the instability of the semiquinone at neutral pH (see Wood, 1974a). However, the scheme in Fig. 9d is unsatisfactory, for it requires diffusion of all forms of plastoquinone through the membrane on one hand, and separation of the two redox couples on the other. Furthermore, it is unrealistic, in view of the low pK for the semiquinone, to attribute a proton-translocating role to the $PQ/PQH^{\cdot}$ couple. These weaknesses are eliminated in Mitchell's "Q cycle" (Fig. 9c), in which the semiquinone action is localized twice on either side of the membrane, taking into account its short lifetime. It is not a linear scheme. The essential feature is the assumption, that two electron donors (PS II and b_{559}) cooperate in plastoquinone reduction, and two acceptors (*f*, PC, and b_6) cooperate in plastoquinol oxidation. Electron pressure from photosystem II would form the reactive semiquinone anion from plastoquinone, which immediately oxidizes cytochrome b_{559} consuming 2 protons to form PQH_2. Plastoquinol traverses the membrane and reacts with the strong oxidant cytochrome *f* (or plastocyanine), giving semiquinone anion and 2 protons. The semiquinone anion rapidly reduces cytochrome b_6. The resulting plastoquinone diffuses back, and the cycle is closed when cytochrome b_6 reduces cytochrome b_{559}. The important consequence for energy conservation is that the quinone reaction in this model, as in the one of Fig. 9d, is split into two electron-transport loops, yielding a H^+/e ratio of 2. This corresponds to two energy-coupling sites, being essential for the situation in mitochondria. It is not essential to explain energy conservation in chloroplasts in terms of chemiosmotic loops, but it seems worthwhile to discuss its implications. A Q cycle in chloroplasts would result in a H^+/e ratio of 3 for electron flow from water to photosystem I, which has indeed been measured occasionally, but a value of 2 predominates (see Section IV,C, Table III). On the other hand, a value of 2 is not necessarily in contradiction to a Q cycle. It might actually ease the pressure to put water oxidation always on the inside of chloroplasts in order to formulate a loop responsible for energy conservation in photosystem II. Even without the water protons participating, the Q cycle still provides two coupling sites, almost inseparable now. In photoreductions by photosystem II electron acceptors for photosystem II would have to be assumed to interact with PQH_2 inside, carrying one proton back outside. After this "stoichiometric uncoupling" only half the internal protons would be left available for ATP synthesis (see Sections III and IX,A and Fig. 8c). The Q cycle includes an additional electrogenic step from cytochromes b_6 to b_{559} in Fig. 9d, and also in Fig. 9c, which, without further assumptions, should show up in the field indicating absorption change at 515 nm. A corresponding second phase has been observed in chromatophores of photosynthetic bacteria, but not in chloroplasts (see Section V,A). The Q cycle might explain why light-induced redox changes of the b cytochromes do not fit an involvement of a linear chain between the photosystems. Because the formation of the reducing semiquinone is dependent on oxidation of PQH_2, a transient reduction of the b cytochromes in photosystem I light is expected, followed by oxidation, especially in strong light. The changes might be masked by equilibration with the plastoquinone pool, since the oxidation of PQH_2 is the limiting rate also in these models.

Possibly, a simplified version of Mitchell's scheme might best account for the present evidence in chloroplasts (Fig. 9e). It would exclude the double loop of the Q cycle, i.e., the reaction between the two b cytochromes carrying one electron back outside. In this "cooperational scheme" the H^+/e ratio would be only 1, i.e., half of Mitchell's Q cycle, but the other essential feature is preserved, i.e., that plastoquinone is reduced by two carriers in sequence (Q and b_{559}) to form the plastohydroquinone, and that the hydroquinone also is oxidized by two carriers in sequence (f and PC). This version calls for a cooperation of electron carriers in the reduction and oxidation of plastoquinone in order to ensure proton translocation across the membrane. Enzymatic catalysis of plastoquinone reduction and oxidation has been suggested in a theoretical model for proton translocation by Chernavsky et al. (1975), without specification of carriers involved. It is feasible that cytochrome b_{559} and cytochrome f, in addition to redox interaction, bind plastoquinone and plastoquinol, respectively. The semiquinone formation is thereby facilitated, possibly via interaction with the heme. The kinetic evidence for an intermediate between Q and plastoquinone, called B by Bouges-Bocquet (1973) and R by Velthuys and Amesz (1974; see also Diner, 1975), might be pertinent here, as well as the genetic evidence for an intermediate between plastoquinone and cytochrome f (Levine and

Smillie, 1962; see Levine, 1969). The suggestions that the ratio of high-potential to low-potential cytochrome b_{559} might regulate energy coupling (Cramer *et al.*, 1971), and that under special conditions the plastoquinone anion might act across the membrane, without participation of protons, resulting in inefficient energy coupling (Dilley and Giaquinta, 1975), are also of importance in this context. Cytochrome b_6 and ferredoxin might fulfill a role in plastoquinone reduction during cyclic electron transport analogous to the cooperation of cytochrome b_{559} and Q in electron flow from photosystem II.

All these speculations are severely limited by the observation, that electrons from photosystem II take only a few milliseconds to arrive at the rate-limiting step of PQH_2 oxidation. This can be concluded from a corresponding lag in the kinetics of P_{700} reduction after a flash (Haehnel, 1976).

The action of the inhibitor DBMIB in these models can be attributed to interference with the subtle geometry in the Q cycle, as well as in the cooperational scheme, possibly blocking the action or formation of $PQ^{\cdot-}$ forms, and similar to the action of antimycin in mitochondria and bacterial chromatophores (Mitchell, 1975a). A corresponding effect has recently been postulated for valinomycin, at higher concentrations, in electron flow of chloroplasts and chromatophores (Trebst, 1976).

These inhibitory actions can be overcome by supplying the stable "semiquinone" $TMPD^+$ (see Trebst, 1976). The bypass of DBMIB inhibition by TMPD has been discussed in Section III (see Fig. 2a). It is proposed that $TMPD^+$ may take the role of one endogenous carrier in the cooperational scheme, when an inhibition disturbs the cooperative oxidation of plastoquinone.

Proton translocation with artificial donor compounds can be satisfactorily explained by a cycle of simple diffusion of the reduced and oxidized form, as discussed in Section III and depicted in Fig. 2b. Investigations of proton translocation during vectorial redox reactions in liposomal systems support this notion (Hinkle, 1973; Deamer *et al.*, 1972; Hauska and Prince, 1974). However, also in artificial proton translocation a cooperation of two different artificial electron donors for photosystem I was detected. Hydroquinones with normally high pK values are generally poor electron donors for photosystem I, in contrast to acidic hydroquinones or substituted phenylenediamines (Hauska *et al.*, 1974). Their donor activity is highly stimulated by the presence of TMPD. In corroboration, it could be shown that hydroquinones are poor reductants for oxidized plastocyanine *in vitro*, compared to *p*-phenylenediamines (Wood, 1974b). The differential behavior can be explained, since the later have a much higher tendency to form semiquinone intermediates at physiological pH (Tong and Glesmann, 1964;

Bishop and Tong, 1964). The oxidation of a hydroquinone by plastocy-anine in the membrane seems to be mediated by TMPD, in some way lowering the activation energy of the first step to the semiquinone. A similar function should be considered for the cytochrome $f-b_6$ complex, which has plastoquinone–plastocyanine reductase activity *in vitro* (Wood and Bendall, 1975), as mentioned above.

The mechanism of proton translocation through the "channel" in the ATP-forming complex is not known. It might involve the sequential participation of protic amino acid residues or lipids, together with conformational changes of the complex. A chemiosmotic model has been put forward by Mitchell (1974, 1975b), which has received vigorous resonance (Boyer, 1975a,b; Williams, 1975). The final acceptance of the chemiosmotic theory will depend on the elucidation of this mechanism.

XI. Conclusion

In reviewing the present state of knowledge in photosynthetic electron transport and photophosphorylation, vectorial electron flow leading to an electric potential and a pH gradient across the thylakoid membrane seems to be established. Two loops comprising an electrogenic photo-system and a proton translocating electroneutral redox reaction across the membrane are recognized and constitute two native energy-conserv-ing sites in noncyclic photophosphorylation. In addition, either one of the electrogenic photosystems might be combined with an artificial proton translocating electron donor to constitute an artificial energy-conserving site in partial reactions of noncyclic or cyclic electron flow. Such light-driven ATP formation with very high rates might be forced onto an electron flow sequence that is not coupled in the native state.

The stoichiometric relationships H^+/e, H^+/ATP, and even ATP/e_2 are still not established beyond doubt. The H^+/e ratio in noncyclic electron flow via both photosystems in all probability is 2, but higher values have been found occasionally. There is less agreement as to the H^+/ATP ratio, ranging from to 2 to even 4. For energetic reasons a value of 3 is favored. Taking a H^+/e ratio of 2 and a H^+/ATP ratio of 3, an ATP/e_2 ratio of 1.33 for two coupling sites in noncyclic electron flow, and of 0.66 for each individual site, would result. Indeed this comes close to the measured values in washed thylakoid preparations (type C chloro-plasts). Higher ATP/e_2 stoichiometries have been reported for type B chloroplasts.

The electrochemical proton potential can drive ATP synthesis, the electrical and osmotic portions being fully interchangeable. Usually in chloroplasts the pH gradient prevails in the steady state. Although the requirements for the electrochemical proton potential to act as an obligatory intermediate according to the chemiosmotic coupling theory are fulfilled, this role is not universally accepted. In particular, the action of a local proton potential in the membrane, not in equilibrium with the inner thylakoid space, is seriously considered. The mechanistic aspects of proton translocation by electron transport components and by the ATP-forming complex are not satisfactorily resolved. Although biochemical knowledge of the functional and regulatory dynamics in the ATP-forming complex has accumulated, this information has not been incorporated into the formation of a generally accepted mechanism.

Concepts for the molecular mechanism of proton translocation linked to electron transport, in particular to the function of plastoquinone, have recently received new stimulus. The Q cycle of Mitchell, with its functional cooperation of quinones and cytochromes required for efficient proton translocation, might clarify the role of b cytochromes also for photosynthetic electron flow. On the other hand, the double loop in the Q cycle might reopen the discussion as to the location of the energy-conserving sites in photosynthetic electron flow from water of photosystem I. It would allow that protons from water oxidation are not needed to formulate the electron transport loop required to explain chemiosmotic coupling in photosystem II.

The generalization of membrane topography, of proton translocation linked to vectorial electron transport, and of membrane-bound ATPase in mitochondria, chloroplasts, and bacteria seems justified. This universality is a consequence of the chemiosmotic concept, and surely will further stimulate bioenergetic research from eukaryotes to anaerobic bacteria.

ACKNOWLEDGMENTS

Many investigators of the field have supported our efforts for this review by communication of their views or by contribution of manuscripts prior to publication. This support is gratefully acknowledged. Furthermore, we would like to thank Drs. W. A. Cramer, A. R. Crofts, U. Heber, R. E. McCarty, B. A. Melandri, B. Rumberg, U. Siggel, H. T. Witt, and P. M. Wood for clarifying discussions, and our daily environment for encouraging patience.

REFERENCES

Amesz, J. (1973). *Biochim. Biophys. Acta* **301,** 35.
Anderson, J. M. (1975). *Biochim. Biophys. Acta* **416,** 191.
Arnon, D. I., Whatley, F. R., and Allen, M. B. (1957). *Nature (London)* **180,** 182.
Arntzen, C. J., and Briantais, J.-M. (1975). *In* "Bioenergetics of Photosynthesis" (Govindjee, ed.), p. 52. Academic Press, New York.
Arntzen, C. J., Dilley, R. A., and Neumann, J. (1971). *Biochim. Biophys. Acta* **245,** 409.

Arntzen, C. J., Vernotte, C., Briantais, J.-M., and Armond, P. (1974). *Biochim. Biophys. Acta* **368**, 39.

Ausländer, W., and Junge, W. (1974). *Biochim. Biophys. Acta* **357**, 285.

Ausländer, W., Heathcote, P., and Junge, W. (1974). *FEBS Lett.* **47**, 229.

Avron, M. (1972). *Photosynth., Two Centuries Its Discovery Joseph Priestley, Proc. Int. Congr. Photosynth. Res., 2nd, 1971.* Vol. 2, p. 861.

Avron, M. (1975a). *In* "The Structural Basis of Membrane Function" (Y. Hatefi, ed.). Academic Press, New York.

Avron, M., ed. (1975b). *Proc. Int. Congr. Photosynth., 3rd, 1974.*

Avron, M. (1975c). *In* "Bioenergetics of Photosynthesis" (Govindjee, ed.), p. 374. Academic Press, New York.

Avron, M., Krogmann, W. D., and Jagendorf, A. T. (1958). *Biochim. Biophys. Acta* **30**, 144.

Bakker-Grunwald, T. (1974). *Biochim. Biophys. Acta* **368**, 386.

Bakker-Grunwald, T., and van Dam, K. (1973). *Biochim. Biophys. Acta* **292**, 808.

Baltscheffsky, M., and Hall, D. O. (1974). *FEBS Lett.* **39**, 345.

Bamberger, E. J., Rottenberg, H., and Avron, M. (1973). *Eur. J. Biochem.* **34**, 557.

Barber, J. (1972). *Biochim. Biophys. Acta* **275**, 105.

Barber, J., and Kraan, G. P. B. (1970). *Biochim. Biophys. Acta* **197**, 49.

Barber, J., and Telfer, A. (1974). *In* "Membrane Transport in Plants" (U. Zimmermann and J. Dainty, eds.), p. 281. Springer-Verlag, Berlin and New York.

Bassham, J. A. (1971). *Science* **172**, 526.

Bauer, R., and Wijnands, M. J. G. (1974). *Z. Naturforsch., Teil C* **29**, 725.

Berzborn, R. J., Kopp, F., and Mühlethaler, K. (1974). *Z. Naturforsch., Teil C* **29**, 694.

Bishop, C. A., and Tong, L. K. J. (1964). *J. Am. Chem. Soc.* **87**, 501.

Boeck, M., and Witt, H. T. (1972). *Photosynth., Two Centuries Its Discovery Joseph Priestley, Proc. Int. Congr. Photosynth. Res., 2nd, 1971* Vol. 2, p. 903.

Boguslavsky, L. I., Kondrashin, A. A., Kozlow, I. A., Metelsky, S. T., Skulachev, V. P., and Volkov, A. G. (1975). *FEBS Lett.* **50**, 223.

Böhme, H., Reimer, S., and Trebst, A. (1971). *Z. Naturforsch., Teil B* **26**, 341.

Bouges-Bocquet, B. (1973). *Biochim. Biophys. Acta* **314**, 250.

Bowes, G., Ogren, W. L., and Hagemann, R. H. (1975). *Plant Physiol.* **56**, 630.

Boyer, P. D. (1975a). *FEBS Lett.* **50**, 91.

Boyer, P. D. (1975b). *FEBS Lett.* **58**, 1.

Boyer, P. D., Smith, D. J., Rosing, J., and Kayalar, C. (1975). *In* "Electron Transfer Chains and Oxidative Phosphorylation" (E. Quagliarello *et al.*, eds.), p. 361. Am. Elsevier, New York.

Bradeen, D. A., and Winget, G. D. (1974). *Biochim. Biophys. Acta* **333**, 331.

Bridge, N. K., and Porter, G. (1958). *Proc. R. Soc. London, Ser. A* **244**, 259.

Buchholz, J., Heinze, F., and Rumberg, B. (1975). *Abstr. Int. Biophys. Congr., 5th,* Abstract 334.

Bulychev, A. A., Andrianov, V. K., Kurella, G. A., and Litvin, F. F. (1971). *Sov. Plant Physiol. (Engl. Transl.)* **18**, 204.

Carmeli, C. (1970). *FEBS Lett.* **7**, 297.

Carmeli, C., and Racker, E. (1973). *J. Biol. Chem.* **243**, 8281.

Carmeli, C., Lifschitz, Y., and Gephstein, A. (1975). *Biochim. Biophys. Acta* **376**, 249.

Casadio, R., Baccarini-Melandri, A., and Melandri, B. A. (1974). *Eur. J. Biochem.* **47**, 121.

Casadio, R., Baccarini-Melandri, A., and Melandri, B. A. (1975). *In* "Electron Transfer Chains and Oxidative Phosphorylation" (E. Quagliarello *et al.*, eds.), p. 407. Am. Elsevier, New York.

Chance, B., and Mela, L. (1966). *J. Biol. Chem.* **241,** 4588.

Chance, B., and Montal, M. (1971). *Curr. Top. Membr. Transp.* **2,** 99.

Chance, B., Nishimura, M., Avron, M., and Baltscheffsky, M. (1966). *Arch. Biochem. Biophys.* **117,** 158.

Chance, B., Crofts, A. R., Nishimura, M., and Price, B. (1970). *Eur. J. Biochem.* **13,** 364.

Chance, B., Baltscheffsky, M., Vanderkoi, J., and Cheng, W. (1974). *In* "Perspectives in Membrane Biology" (S. Estrada-O. and C. Gitler, eds.), p. 329. Academic Press, New York.

Chernavsky, D. S., Chernavskaya, N. M., Günther, K., and Hache, A. (1975). *Stud. Biophys.* **49,** 91.

Cockrell, R. S., and Racker, E. (1969). *Biochem. Biophys. Res. Commun.* **35,** 414.

Cockrell, R. S., Harris, E. J., and Pressmann, B. C. (1967). *Nature (London)* **215,** 1487.

Cogdell, R. J., and Crofts, A. R. (1974). *Biochim. Biophys. Acta* **347,** 264.

Cohen, W. S., and Jagendorf, A. T. (1972). *Arch. Biochem. Biophys.* **150,** 235.

Cohen, W. S., and Sherman, L. A. (1971). *FEBS Lett.* **16,** 319.

Cohen, W. S., Cohn, D. E., and Bertsch, W. (1975). *FEBS Lett.* **49,** 350.

Cohn, D. E., Cohen, W. S., and Bertsch, W. (1975). *Biochim. Biophys. Acta* **376,** 97.

Cost, K., and Frenkel, A. W. (1967). *Biochemistry* **6,** 663.

Cox, R. D., and Bendall, D. S. (1974). *Biochim. Biophys. Acta* **347,** 49.

Cramer, W. A., Fan, H. N., and Böhme, H. (1971). *J. Bioenerget.* **2,** 289.

Cramer, W. A., Horton, P., and Wever, R. (1975). *In* "Electron Transfer Chains and Oxidative Phosphorylation" (E. Quagliarello *et al.*, eds.), p. 31. Am. Elsevier, New York.

Crofts, A. R. (1966). *Biochem. Biophys. Res. Commun.* **24,** 725.

Crofts, A. R. (1967). *J. Biol. Chem.* **242,** 3352.

Crofts, A. R. (1968). *Regul. Funct. Biol. Membr., Proc. Sigrid Juselius Symp., 2nd, 1967* BBA Libr., Vol. 11, p. 247.

Crofts, A. R., Wraight, C. A., and Fleischmann, D. E. (1971). *FEBS Lett.* **15,** 89.

Crofts, A. R., Jackson, J. B., Evans, E. H., and Cogdell, R. J. (1972). *Photosynth., Two Centuries Its Discovery Joseph Priestley, Proc. Int. Congr. Photosynth. Res., 2nd, 1971* Vol. 2, p. 873.

Crofts, A. R., Holmes, N. G., and Crowther, D. (1975a). *Fed. Eur. Biochem. Soc., Meet., 10th,* Vol. 40, p. 239

Crofts, A. R., Crowther, D., and Tierney, G. V. (1975b). *In* "Electron Transfer Chains and Oxidative Phosphorylation" (E. Quagliarello *et al.*, eds.), p. 233. Am. Elsevier, New York.

Deamer, D. W., Prince, R. C., and Crofts, A. R. (1972). *Biochim. Biophys. Acta* **274,** 323.

de Kouchkovsky, Y. (1974). *C. R. Hebd. Seances Acad. Sci., Ser. D* **278,** 667.

de Kouchkovsky, Y., and de Kouchkovsky, F. (1974). *Biochim. Biophys. Acta* **368,** 113.

Diebler, H. (1963). *Ber. Bunsenges. Phys. Chem.* **67,** 396.

Diebler, H., Eigen, M., and Mathies, P. (1961). *Z. Naturforsch., Teil B* **16,** 629.

Dilley, R. A. (1966). *Brookhaven Symp. Biol.* **19,** 258.

Dilley, R. A. (1970). *Arch. Biochem. Biophys.* **137,** 270.

Dilley, R. A. (1971). *Curr. Top. Bioenerg.* **4,** 237.

Dilley, R. A., and Giaquinta, R. T. (1975). *Curr. Top. Membr. Transp.* **6,** 49.

Dilley, R. A., and Vernon, L. P. (1967). *Proc. Natl. Acad. Sci. U.S.A.* **57,** 395.

Diner, B. (1975). *Proc. Int. Congr. Photosynth. 3rd, 1974* p. 589.

Duysens, L. N. M. (1954). *Nature (London)* **173,** 642.

Ellenson, J. L., and Sauer, K. (1976). *Photochem. Photobiol.* **23,** 113.

Emrich, H. M., Junge, W., and Witt, H. T. (1969a). *Z. Naturforsch., Teil B* **24,** 1144.

Emrich, H. M., Junge, W., and Witt, H. T. (1969b). *Naturwissenschaften* **56**, 514.

Ernster, L., Estabrook, R. W., and Slater, E. C., eds. (1974). ''Dynamics of Energy Transducing Membranes,'' BBA Libr., Vol. 13. Elsevier, Amsterdam.

Estrada-O. S., and Gitler, C., eds. (1974). ''Perspectives in Membrane Biology.'' Academic Press, New York.

Evans, H. E., and Crofts, A. R. (1973). *Biochim. Biophys. Acta* **292**, 130.

Evans, E. H., and Crofts, A. R. (1974). *Biochim. Biophys. Acta* **333**, 44.

Fiolet, J. T. W., and van de Vlugt (1975). *FEBS Lett.* **53**, 287.

Fiolet, J. T. W., Bakker, E. P., and van Dam, K. (1974). *Biochim. Biophys. Acta* **368**, 432.

Forti, G., Avron, M., and Melandri, B. A., eds. (1972). *Photosynth., Two Centuries Its Discovery Joseph Priestley, Proc. Int. Congr. Photosynth. Res., 2nd 1971.*

Fowler, C. F., and Kok, B. (1974a). *Biochim. Biophys. Acta* **357**, 299.

Fowler, C. F., and Kok, B. (1974b). *Prog. Photobiol., Proc. Int. Congr. Photobiol., 6th, 1972* Abstract 417.

Fowler, C. F., and Kok, B. (1976). *Biochim. Biophys. Acta* **423**, 510.

Gaensslen, R. E., and McCarty, R. E. (1971). *Arch. Biochem Biophys.* **147**, 55.

Giaquinta, R. T., Dilley, R. A., Selman, B. R., and Anderson, B. J. (1974). *Arch. Biochem. Biophys.* **162**, 200.

Giaquinta, R. T., Ort, D. R., and Dilley, R. A. (1975). *Biochemistry* **14**, 4392.

Gimmler, H., Schäfer, G., and Heber, U. (1975). *Proc. Int. Congr. Photosynth., 3rd, 1974* Vol. 2, p. 1381.

Girault, G., Galmiche, J. M., and Vermeglio, A. (1975). *Proc. Int. Congr. Photosynth., 3rd, 1974* Vol. 2, p. 839.

Good, N., Izawa, S., and Hind, G. (1966). *Curr. Top. Bioenerg.* **1**, 76.

Gould, J. M. (1975a). *Biochem. Biophys. Res. Commun.* **64**, 673.

Gould, J. M. (1975b). *Biochim. Biophys. Acta* **387**, 135.

Gould, J. M., and Izawa, S. (1973). *Biochim. Biophys. Acta* **314**, 211.

Gould, J. M., and Izawa, S. (1974). *Biochim. Biophys. Acta* **333**, 509.

Gould, J. M., and Ort, D. R. (1973). *Biochim. Biophys. Acta* **325**, 157.

Gräber, P., and Witt, H. T. (1974). *Biochim. Biophys. Acta* **333**, 389.

Gräber, P., and Witt, H. T. (1975a). *FEBS Lett.* **59**, 184.

Gräber, P., and Witt, H. T. (1975b). *Proc. Int. Congr. Photosynth., 3rd, 1974* Vol. 2, p. 951.

Gräber, P., and Witt, H. T. (1976). *Biochim. Biophys. Acta* **423**, 141.

Grebanier, A., and Jagendorf, A. T. (1976). In preparation.

Green, D. E., ed. (1974). ''The Mechanism of Energy Transduction in Biological Systems,'' Annals, Vol. 227. N.Y. Acad. Sci., New York.

Grinius, L., Slusnyte, R., and Griniuviene, B. (1975). *FEBS Lett.* **57**, 290.

Gromet-Elhanan, Z. (1974). *J. Biol. Chem.* **249**, 2522.

Gross, E., Dilley, R. A., and San Pietro, A. (1969). *Arch. Biochem. Biophys.* **134**, 450.

Grünhagen, H. H., and Witt, H. T. (1970). *Z. Naturforsch., Teil B* **25**, 373.

Haehnel, W. (1973). *Biochim. Biophys. Acta* **305**, 618.

Haehnel, W. (1976). *Biochim. Biophys. Acta* **423**, 499.

Hall, D. O. (1972). *Nature (London), New Biol.* **235**, 125.

Hall, D. O. (1976). *In* ''The Intact Chloroplast; Structure and Function'' (J. Barber, ed.). ASP Biol. and Med. Press, Amsterdam (in press).

Hall, D. O., Reeves, S. G., and Baltscheffsky, H. (1971). *Biochem. Biophys. Res. Commun.* **43**, 359.

Hare, J. H. (1975). *Biochem. Biophys. Res. Commun.* **66**, 1329.

Harold, F. M., and Altendorf, K. (1974). *Curr. Top. Membr. Transp.* **5**, 1.
Harris, D. A., and Slater, E. C. (1975). *In* "Electron Transfer Chains and Oxidative Phosphorylation" (E. Quagliarello *et al.*, eds.), p. 361. Am. Elsevier, New York.
Harth, E., Oettmeier, W., and Trebst, A. (1974). *FEBS Lett.* **43**, 231.
Hatefi, Y., ed. (1975). "The Structural Basis of Membrane Function." Academic Press, New York (in press).
Hatefi, Y., Hanstein, W. G., Galante, Y., and Stiggall, D. L. (1975). *Fed. Proc., Fed. Am. Soc. Exp. Biol.* **34**, 1699.
Hauska, G. (1972). *FEBS Lett.* **28**, 217.
Hauska, G. (1975). *Ber. Dtsch. Bot. Ges.* **88**, 303.
Hauska, G., and Prince, R. C. (1974). *FEBS Lett.* **41**, 35.
Hauska, G., and Sane, P. V. (1972). *Z. Naturforsch., Teil B* **27**, 938.
Hauska, G., McCarty, R. E., and Olson, J. S. (1970). *FEBS Lett.* **7**, 151.
Hauska, G., Trebst, A., and Draber, W. (1973). *Biochim. Biophys. Acta* **305**, 632.
Hauska, G., Reimer, S., and Trebst, A. (1974). *Biochim. Biophys. Acta* **357**, 1.
Hauska, G., Trebst, A., Kötter, C., and Schulz, H. (1975a). *Z. Naturforsch., Teil C* **30**, 505.
Hauska, G., Oettmeier, W., Reimer, S., and Trebst, A. (1975b). *Z. Naturforsch., Teil C* **30**, 37.
Heath, R. L. (1972). *Biochim. Biophys. Acta* **256**, 645.
Heath, R. L., and Hind, G. (1972). *J. Biol. Chem.* **247**, 2917.
Heathcote, P., and Hall, D. O. (1974). *Biochem. Biophys. Res. Commun.* **56**, 767.
Heathcote, P., and Hall, D. O. (1975). *Proc. Int. Congr. Photosynth., 3rd, 1974* Vol. 1, p. 463.
Heber, U. (1969). *Biochim. Biophys. Acta* **180**, 302.
Heber, U. (1974). *Annu. Rev. Plant Physiol.* **25**, 393.
Heber, U. (1976). *J. Bioenerg.* **8**, 157.
Heber, U., and Kirk, M. R. (1975). *Biochim. Biophys. Acta* **376**, 136.
Heber, U., and Krause, G. (1972). *Photosynth., Two Centuries Its Discovery Joseph Priestley, Proc. Int. Congr. Photosynth. Res., 2nd, 1971* Vol. 2, p. 1023.
Heldt, H. W., Werdan, K., Milovancev, M., and Geller, G. (1973). *Biochim. Biophys. Acta* **314**, 224.
Hind, G., and Jagendorf, A. T. (1963). *Proc. Natl. Acad. Sci. U.S.A.* **49**, 715.
Hind, G., and McCarty, R. E. (1973). *Photophysiology* **8**, 113.
Hind, G., Nakatani, H. Y., and Izawa, S. (1974). *Proc. Natl. Acad. Sci. U.S.A.* **74**, 1484.
Hinkle, P. (1970). *Biochem. Biophys. Res. Commun.* **41**, 1375.
Hinkle, P. C. (1973). *Fed. Proc., Fed. Am. Soc. Exp. Biol.* **32**, 1988.
Hinkle, P. C., and Horstman, L. L. (1971). *J. Biol. Chem.* **246**, 6024.
Hiyama, T., and Ke, B. (1972). *Biochim. Biophys. Acta* **267**, 160.
Horton, P., and Cramer, W. A. (1974). *Biochim. Biophys. Acta* **368**, 348.
Horton, P., and Cramer, W. A. (1976). *Biochim. Biophys. Acta* **430**, 122.
Itoh, S., Murata, N., and Takamiya, A. (1971). *Biochim. Biophys. Acta* **245**, 109.
Izawa, S. (1970). *Biochim. Biophys. Acta* **223**, 165.
Izawa, S., and Good, N. E. (1968). *Biochim. Biophys. Acta* **162**, 380.
Izawa, S., and Hind, G. (1967). *Biochim. Biophys. Acta* **143**, 377.
Izawa, S., and Ort, D. O. (1974). *Biochim. Biophys. Acta* **357**, 127.
Izawa, S., Connolly, T. N., Winget, G. D., and Good, N. E. (1966). *Brookhaven Symp. Biol.* **19**, 169.
Izawa, S., Gould, J. M., Ort, D. R., Felker, P., and Good, N. E. (1973). *Biochim. Biophys. Acta* **305**, 119.

Izawa, S., Ort, D. R., Gould, J. M., and Good, N. E. (1975). *Proc. Int. Congr. Photosynth., 3rd, 1974* Vol. 1, p. 449.

Jackson, J. B., and Crofts, A. R. (1969a). *FEBS Lett.* **4**, 185.

Jackson, J. B., and Crofts, A. R. (1969b). *Eur. J. Biochem.* **10**, 226.

Jackson, J. B., and Crofts, A. R. (1971). *Eur. J. Biochem.* **18**, 120.

Jackson, J. B., Crofts, A. R., and von Stedingk, L. V. (1968). *Eur. J. Biochem.* **6**, 41.

Jackson, J. B., Saphon, S., and Witt, H. T. (1975). *Biochim. Biophys. Acta* **408**, 83.

Jagendorf, A. T. (1975). *In* "Bioenergetics of Photosynthesis" (Govindjee ed.), p. 413. Academic Press, New York.

Jagendorf, A. T., and Hind, G. (1963). *N.A.S.—N.R.C., Publ.* **1145**, 509.

Jagendorf, A. T., and Uribe, E. (1966). *Proc. Natl. Acad. Sci. U.S.A.* **55**, 170.

Jennings, R. C., Garlaschi, F. M., and Forti, G. (1975). *In* "Electron Transfer Chains and Oxidative Phosphorylation" (E. Quagliarello *et al.*, eds.), p. 277. Am. Elsevier, New York.

Joliot, P., and Delosme, R. (1974). *Biochim. Biophys. Acta* **357**, 267.

Joliot, P., and Kok, B. (1975). *in* "Bioenergetics of Photosynthesis" (Govindjee, ed.), p. 388. Academic Press, New York.

Junge, W. (1970). *Eur. J. Biochem.* **14**, 582.

Junge, W. (1975). *Ber. Dtsch. Bot. Ges.* **88**, 296.

Junge, W., and Ausländer, W. (1974). *Biochim. Biophys. Acta* **333**, 59.

Junge, W., and Ausländer, W. (1975). *FEBS Lett.* **59**, 310.

Junge, W., and Witt, H. T. (1968). *Z. Naturforsch., Teil B* **23**, 244.

Junge, W., Rumberg, B., and Schröder, H. (1970). *Eur. J. Biochem.* **14**, 575.

Kagawa, Y. (1972). *Biochim. Biophys. Acta* **265**, 297.

Kagawa, Y., and Racker, E. (1966). *J. Biol. Chem.* **241**, 2467.

Kahn, J. S. (1971). *Biochim. Biophys. Acta* **245**, 144.

Kaplan, J. H., Uribe, E., and Jagendorf, A. T. (1967). *Arch. Biochem. Biophys.* **120**, 365.

Karlish, S. J. D., and Avron, M. (1971). *Eur. J. Biochem.* **20**, 51.

Karlish, S. J. D., Shavit, N., and Avron, M. (1969). *Eur. J. Biochem.* **9**, 291.

Ke, B. (1973). *Biochim. Biophys. Acta* **301**, 1.

Kimimura, M., and Katch, S. (1972). *Biochim. Biophys. Acta* **283**, 279.

Kobayashi, Y., Inoue, Y., and Shibata, K. (1976). *Biochim. Biophys. Acta* **423**, 80.

Kraan, G. P. B., Amesz, J., Velthuys, B. R., and Steeneers, R. G. (1970). *Biochim. Biophys. Acta* **223**, 129.

Kraayenhof, R. (1969). *Biochim. Biophys. Acta* **180**, 213.

Kraayenhof, R. (1970). *FEBS Lett.* **6**, 161.

Kraayenhof, R., and Slater, E. C. (1975). *Proc. Int. Congr. Photosynth., 3rd, 1974* Vol. 2, p. 985.

Kraayenhof, R., Kartan, M. B., and Grunwald, T. (1971). *FEBS Lett.* **19**, 5.

Krause, G. H. (1974). *Biochim. Biophys. Acta* **333**, 301.

Kulandaivelu, G., and Senger, H. (1976). *Biochim. Biophys. Acta* **430**, 94.

Larkum, A. W. D., and Bonner, W. D. (1972). *Biochim. Biophys. Acta* **256**, 396.

Lavorel, J. (1975). *In* "Bioenergetics of Photosynthesis" (Govindjee, ed.), p. 225. Academic Press, New York.

Leigh, J. S., Netzel, T. L., Dutton, P. L., and Rentzepis, P. M. (1974). *FEBS Lett.* **48**, 136.

Leiser, M., and Gromet-Elhanan, Z. (1974). *FEBS Lett.* **43**, 267.

Leiser, M., and Gromet-Elhanan, Z. (1975a). *J. Biol. Chem.* **250**, 84.

Leiser, M., and Gromet-Elhanan, Z. (1975b). *J. Biol. Chem.* **250**, 90.

Levine, R. P. (1969). *Ann. Rev. Plant Physiol.* **20**, 523.

Levine, R. P., and Smillie, R. M. (1962). *J. Biol. Chem.* **238**, 4052.
Lew, V. L., Glynn, I. M., and Ellory, J. C. (1970). *Nature (London)* **225**, 865.
Lockau, W., and Selman, B. R. (1976). *Z. Naturforsch.* **31c**, 48.
Losada, M., Whatley, F. R., and Arnon, D. I. (1961). *Nature (London)* **190**, 606.
Lynn, W. S. (1968). *Biochemistry* **7**, 3811.
McCarty, R. E. (1969). *J. Biol. Chem.* **244**, 4292.
McCarty, R. E. (1970). *FEBS Lett.* **9**, 313.
McCarty, R. E. (1974). *Arch. Biochem. Biophys.* **161**, 93.
McCarty, R. E. (1976). *In* "Encyclopedia of Plant Physiology, New Series" (A. Pirson and M. Zimmermann, eds.), Vol. 3. Springer-Verlag, Berlin and New York.
McCarty, R. E., and Fagan, J. (1973). *Biochemistry* **12**, 1503.
McCarty, R. E., and Racker, E. (1966). *Brookhaven Symp. Biol.* **19**, 202.
McCarty, R. E., and Racker, E. (1967). *J. Biol. Chem.* **242**, 3435.
McCarty, R. E., and Racker, E. (1968). *J. Biol. Chem.* **243**, 129.
McCarty, R. E., Fuhrman, J. S., and Tsuchija, Y. (1971). *J. Biol. Chem.* **240**, 2522.
Makinose, M., and Hasselbach, W. (1971). *FEBS Lett.* **12**, 271.
Malkin, S., and Hardt, H. (1972). *Photosynth., Two Centuries Its Discovery Joseph Priestley, Proc. Int. Congr. Photosynth. Res., 2nd, 1971* Vol. 1, p. 253.
Maloney, R. C., Kashket, E. R., and Wilson, T. H. (1974). *Proc. Natl. Acad. Sci., U.S.A.* **71**, 3896.
Mayne, B. C., and Clayton, R. K. (1966). *Proc. Natl. Acad. Sci. U.S.A.* **55**, 494.
Melandri, B. A., Baccarini-Melandri, A., San Pietro, A., and Gest, H. (1970). *Proc. Natl. Acad. Sci. U.S.A.* **67**, 477.
Melandri, B. A., Baccarini-Melandri, A., Crofts, A. R., and Cogdell, R. J. (1972). *FEBS Lett.* **24**, 141.
Metzner, H., ed. (1969). *Prog. Photosynth. Res., Proc. Int. Congr. [1st], 1968.*
Miles, C. D., and Jagendorf, A. T. (1969). *Arch. Biochem. Biophys.* **129**, 711.
Mitchell, P. (1961). *Nature (London)* **191**, 144.
Mitchell, P. (1966). "Chemiosmotic Coupling in Oxidative and Photosynthetic Phosphorylation." Glynn Res., Bodmin, Cornwall, England.
Mitchell, P. (1967). *Fed. Proc., Fed. Am. Soc. Exp. Biol.* **26**, 1370.
Mitchell, P. (1968). "Chemiosmotic Coupling and Energy Transduction." Glynn Res., Bodmin, Cornwall, England.
Mitchell, P. (1970). *In* "Membranes and Ion Transport" (E. E. Bittar, ed.), Vol. 1, p. 192. Wiley, New York.
Mitchell, P. (1974). *FEBS Lett.* **43**, 189.
Mitchell, P. (1975a). *In* "Electron Transfer Chains and Oxidative Phosphorylation" (E. Quagliarello *et al.*, eds.), p. 305. Am. Elsevier, New York.
Mitchell, P. (1975b). *FEBS Lett.* **50**, 95.
Mitchell, P. (1975c). *FEBS Lett.* **56**, 1.
Mitchell, P. (1975d). *FEBS Lett.* **59**, 137.
Mitchell, P., and Moyle, J. (1965a). *Nature (London)* **208**, 147.
Mitchell, P., and Moyle, J. (1965b). *Nature (London)* **208**, 1205.
Mitchell, P., Moyle, J., and Smith, L. (1968). *Eur. J. Biochem.* **4**, 9.
Montal, M., Chance, B., and Lee, C. P. (1969). *Biochem. Biophys. Res. Commun.* **36**, 428.
Montal, M., Nishimura, N., and Chance, B. (1970). *Biochim. Biophys. Acta* **223**, 183.
Murakami, S., Torres-Pereira, J., and Packer, L. (1975). *In* "Bioenergetics of Photosynthesis" (Govindjee, ed.), p. 555. Academic Press, New York.
Murata, N., and Sugahara, K. (1969). *Biochim. Biophys. Acta* **189**, 182.
Nelson, N., and Neumann, J. (1972). *J. Biol. Chem.* **247**, 1817.

Nelson, N., Nelson, H., Naim, Y., and Neumann, J. (1971). *Arch. Biochem. Biophys.* **145**, 263.

Nelson, N., Kamienietzky, K., Deters, D. W., and Nelson, H. (1975). *In* "Electron Transfer Chains and Oxidative Phosphorylation" (E. Quagliarello *et al.*, eds.), p. 305. Am. Elsevier, New York.

Neumann, J., and Jagendorf, A. T. (1964). *Arch. Biochem. Biophys.* **107**, 109.

Neumann, J., Ke, B., and Dilley, R. A. (1970). *Plant Physiol.* **46**, 86.

Neumann, J., Arntzen, C. J., and Dilley, R. A. (1971). *Biochemistry* **10**, 866.

Nieuwenhuis, F. J. R., Thomas, A. A. M., and van Dam, K. (1974). *Biochem. Soc. Trans.* **2**, 512.

Nishizaki, Y., and Jagendorf, A. T. (1971). *Biochim. Biophys. Acta* **226**, 172.

Oesterhelt, D., Hartmann, R., Fischer, U., Michel, H., and Schreckenbach, T. (1975). *Fed. Eur. Biochem. Soc., Meet. 10th,* Vol. 40, p. 234.

Oettmeier, W., Reimer, S., and Trebst, A. (1974). *Plant Sci. Lett.* **2**, 267.

Orlich, G. (1974). Ph.D. Thesis, Ruhr-Universitat, Bochum Germany.

Ort, D. R. (1975). *Arch. Biochem. Biophys.* **166**, 629.

Ort, D. R., and Izawa, S. (1974). *Plant Physiol.* **53**, 370.

Ort, D. R., Izawa, S., Good, N. E., and Krogmann, D. W. (1973). *FEBS Lett.* **31**, 119.

Ort, D. R., Dilley, R. A., and Good, N. E. (1976a). *Biochim. Biophys. Acta* (in press).

Ort, D. R., Dilley, R. A., and Good, N. E. (1976b). *Biochim. Biophys. Acta* (in press).

Ouitrakul, R., and Izawa, S. (1973). *Biochim. Biophys. Acta* **305**, 105.

Papa, S. (1976). *Biochim. Biophys. Acta, Rev. Bioenerg.* **456**, 39.

Papa, S., Lorusso, M., Guerreri, F., and Izzo, G. (1975). *In* "Electron Transfer Chains and Oxidative Phosphorylation" (E. Quagliarello *et al.*, eds.), p. 317. Am. Elsevier, New York.

Papageorgiou, G. (1975a). *in* "Bioenergetics of Photosynthesis" (Govindjee, ed.), p. 319. Academic Press, New York.

Papageorgiou, G. (1975b). *Arch. Biochem. Biophys.* **166**, 390.

Park, R. B., and Sane, P. V. (1971). *Annu. Rev. Plant Physiol.* **22**, 395.

Petrack, B., and Lipmann, F. (1961). *In* "Light and Life" (W. D. McElroy and B. Glass, eds.), p. 621. John Hopkins Press, Baltimore, Maryland.

Pflugshaupt, C., and Bachofen, R. (1975). *J. Bioenerg.* **7**, 51.

Pick, U., and Avron, M. (1976). *Biochim. Biophys. Acta* **440**, 189.

Pick, U., Rottenberg, H., and Avron, M. (1973). *FEBS Lett.* **32**, 91.

Pick, U., Rottenberg, H., and Avron, M. (1974). *FEBS Lett.* **48**, 32.

Pick, U., Rottenberg, H., and Avron, M. (1975). *Proc. Int. Congr. Photosynth., 3rd, 1974* Vol. 2, p. 967.

Pirson, A., and Zimmermann, M., eds. (1976). "Encyclopedia of Plant Physiology, New Series," Vols. 3 and 4. Springer-Verlag, Berlin and New York (in press).

Portis, A. R., and McCarty, R. E. (1973). *Arch. Biochem. Biophys.* **156**, 621.

Portis, A. R., and McCarty, R. E. (1974). *J. Biol. Chem.* **249**, 6250.

Portis, A. R., Magnusson, R. P., and McCarty, R. E. (1975). *Biochem. Biophys. Res. Commun.* **64**, 877.

Postma, P. W., and van Dam, K. (1976). *Trends Biochem. Sci.,* Vol. 1, p. 16.

Pullman, M. E., and Monroy, G. C. (1963). *J. Biol. Chem.* **238**, 3762.

Quagliarello, E., Papa, S., Palmieri, I., Slater, E. C., and Siliprandi, N., eds. (1975). "Electron Transfer Chains and Oxidative Phosphorylation." Am. Elsevier, New York.

Racker, E. (1975). *In* "Electron Transfer Chains and Oxidative Phosphorylation" (E. Quagliarello *et al.*, eds.), p. 401. Am. Elsevier, New York.

Racker, E., Hauska, G., Lien, S., Berzborn, R. J., and Nelson, N. (1972). *Photosynth.,*

*Two Centuries Its Discovery Joseph Priestley, Proc. Int. Congr. Photosynth. Res.,
2nd, 1971* Vol. 2, p. 1097.
Radmer, R., and Kok, B. (1975). *Annu. Rev. Biochem.* **44,** 409.
Reeves, S. G., and Hall, D. O. (1973). *Biochim. Biophys. Acta* **314,** 66.
Reid, R. A., Moyle, J., and Mitchell, P. (1966). *Nature (London)* **212,** 257.
Reimer, S., and Trebst, A. (1975). *Biochem. Physiol. Pflanz.* **168,** 225.
Reinwald, E., Stiehl, H. H., and Rumberg, B. (1968). *Z. Naturforsch., Teil B* **23,** 1616.
Renger, G. (1973). *Biochim. Biophys. Acta* **314,** 390.
Rienits, K. G., Hardt, H., and Avron, M. (1973). *FEBS Lett.* **33,** 28.
Rienits, K. G., Hardt, H., and Avron, M. (1974). *Eur. J. Biochem.* **43,** 291.
Rottenberg, H. (1975). *J. Bioenerg.* **7,** 61.
Rottenberg, H. (1976). *Prog. Surf. Membr. Sci.* (in press).
Rottenberg, H., and Grunwald, T. (1972). *Eur. J. Biochem.* **25,** 71.
Rottenberg, H., and Lee, C. P. (1975). *Biochemistry* **14,** 2675.
Rottenberg, H., Grunwald, T., and Avron, M. (1971). *FEBS Lett.* **13,** 41.
Rottenberg, H., Grunwald, T., and Avron, M. (1972). *Eur. J. Biochem.* **25,** 54.
Rumberg, B., and Muhle, H. (1976). *J. Bioelectrochem. Bioenerget. Proc. Symp.
Bioelectrochem. 3rd, 1975* (in press).
Rumberg, B., and Schröder, H. (1974). *Prog. Photobiol., Proc. Int. Congr., 6th, 1972*
abstract 36.
Rumberg, B., and Siggel, U. (1969). *Naturwissenschaften* **56,** 130.
Ryrie, I. J., and Jagendorf, A. T. (1972). *J. Biol. Chem.* **247,** 4453.
Saha, S., Ouitrakul, R., Izawa, S., and Good, N. (1971). *J. Biol. Chem.* **246,** 3204.
Samoray, D., and Hauska, G. (1975). *Proc. Int. Congr. Photosynth., 3rd, 1974* Vol. 2, p.
1055.
Saphon, S., Jackson, J. B., Lerbs, U., and Witt, H. T. (1975a). *Biochim. Biophys. Acta*
408, 58.
Saphon, S., Jackson, J. B., and Witt, H. T. (1975b). *Biochim. Biophys. Acta* **408,** 67.
Schliephake, W., Junge, W., and Witt, H. T. (1968). *Z. Naturforsch., Teil B* **23,** 1571.
Schmid, G. H., Radunz, A., and Menke, W. (1975). *Z. Naturforsch., Teil C* **30,** 201.
Schmid, R., and Junge, W. (1975). *Proc. Int. Congr. Photosynth., 3rd, 1974* Vol. 2, p. 821.
Scholes, P., Mitchell, P., and Moyle, J. (1969). *Eur. J. Biochem.* **8,** 450.
Schröder, H., Muhle, H., and Rumberg, B. (1972). *Photosynth., Two Centuries Its
Discovery Joseph Priestley, Proc. Int. Congr. Photosynth. Res., 2nd, 1971* p. 919.
Schröder, H., Siggel, U., and Rumberg, B. (1975). *Proc. Int. Congr. Photosynth., 3rd,
1974* Vol. 2, p. 1031.
Schuldiner, S., Rottenberg, H., and Avron, M. (1972a). *Eur. J. Biochem.* **25,** 64.
Schuldiner, S., Rottenberg, H., and Avron, M. (1972b). *FEBS Lett.* **28,** 173.
Schuldiner, S., Rottenberg, H., and Avron, M. (1973). *Eur. J. Biochem.* **39,** 455.
Schuldiner, S., Padan, E., Rottenberg, H., Gromet-Elhanan, Z., and Avron, M. (1974).
FEBS Lett. **49,** 174.
Schwartz, M. (1968). *Nature (London)* **219,** 915.
Selman, B. R. (1976). *Bioenergetics* **8,** 143.
Selman, B. R., and Psczolla, G. (1976). *FEBS Lett.* **61,** 135.
Selman, B. R., Giaquinta, R. T., and Dilley, R. A. (1974). *Arch. Biochem. Biophys.* **162,**
210.
Selman, B. R., Johnson, G. L., Dilley, R. A., and Voegeli, K. K. (1975). *Proc. Int.
Congr. Photosynth., 3rd, 1974* Vol. 2, p. 897.
Senior, A. E. (1973). *Biochim. Biophys. Acta* **301,** 249.
Shahak, Y., Hardt, H., and Avron, M. (1975). *FEBS Lett.* **54,** 151.
Shavit, N., Degani, H., and San Pietro, A. T. (1970). *Biochim. Biophys. Acta* **216,** 208.

Shen, Y. K., and Shen, C. M. (1962). *Sci. Sinica* **11**, 1097.

Siggel, U. (1975). *Proc. Int. Congr. Photosynth., 3rd, 1974* Vol. 1, p. 645.

Siggel, U. (1976). *J. Bioelectrochem. Bioenerg., Proc. Symp. Bioelectrochem., 3rd, 1975* (in press).

Siggel, U., Renger, G., Stiehl, H. H., and Rumberg, B. (1972). *Biochim. Biophys. Acta* **256**, 328.

Simoni, R. D., and Postma, P. W. (1975). *Annu. Rev. Biochem.* **44**, 523.

Skulachev, V. P. (1971). *Curr. Top. Bioenerg.* **4**, 127.

Skulachev, V. P. (1974). *Dyn. Electron Transducing Membr., Proc. Symp., 1973* BBA Libr., Vol. 13, p. 243.

Slater, E. C., Rosing, J., and Mol, A. (1973). *Biochim. Biophys. Acta* **292**, 534.

Sone, N., Yoshida, M., Hirata, H., and Kagawa, Y. (1975). *J. Biol. Chem.* **250**, 7917.

Stiehl, H. H., and Witt, H. T. (1969). *Z. Naturforsch., Teil B* **24**, 1588.

Stricharz, G. R., and Chance, B. (1972). *Biochim. Biophys. Acta* **256**, 71.

Strotmann, H., and von Gösseln, C. (1972). *Z. Naturforsch., Teil B* **27**, 445.

Strotmann, H., Bickel, S., and Huchzermeyer, B. (1976). *FEBS Lett.* **61**, 135.

Telfer, A., and Evans, M. C. W. (1972). *Biochim. Biophys. Acta* **256**, 625.

Telfer, A., Barber, J., and Nicholson, J. (1975). *Biochim. Biophys. Acta* **396**, 301.

Thayer, W. S., and Hinkle, P. C. (1973). *J. Biol. Chem.* **248**, 5395.

Thayer, W. S., and Hinkle, P. C. (1975a). *J. Biol. Chem.* **250**, 5330.

Thayer, W. S., and Hinkle, P. C. (1975b). *J. Biol. Chem.* **250**, 5336.

Thore, A., Keister, D. L., Shavit, N., and San Pietro, A. T. (1968). *Biochemistry* **7**, 3499.

Tong, L. H. J., and Glesmann, M. C. (1964). *Photogr. Sci. Eng.* **8**, 319.

Trebst, A. (1964). *Z. Naturforsch., Teil B* **19**, 418.

Trebst, A. (1974). *Annu. Rev. Plant Physiol.* **25**, 423.

Trebst, A. (1976). *Z. Naturforsch., Teil C* **31**, 152.

Trebst, A., and Hauska, G. (1974). *Naturwissenschaften* **61**, 308.

Trebst, A., and Pistorius, E. (1965). *Z. Naturforsch., Teil B* **20**, 143.

Trebst, A., and Reimer, S. (1973a). *Biochim. Biophys. Acta* **305**, 129.

Trebst, A., and Reimer, S. (1973b). *Z. Naturforsch., Teil C* **28**, 710.

Trebst, A., and Reimer, S. (1973c). *Biochim. Biophys. Acta* **325**, 546.

Trebst, A., Reimer, S., and Hauska, G. (1975). *In* "Electron Transfer Chains and Oxidative Phosphorylation" (E. Quagliarello *et al.*, eds.), p. 343. Am. Elsevier, New York.

Trebst, A., Reimer, S., and Dallacker, F. (1976). *Plant. Sci. Lett.* **6**, 21.

Tyskiewics, E., and Roux, E. (1975). *Biochem. Biophys. Res. Commun.* **65**, 700.

Uribe, E. (1972). *Biochemistry* **11**, 4228.

Uribe, E., and Li, B. C. Y. (1973). *J. Bioenerg.* **4**, 435.

van Gorkom, H. J., Puller, M. P. J., Haveman, J., and den Haan, G. A. (1976). *Biochim. Biophys. Acta* **423**, 217.

Velthuys, B. R., and Amesz, J. (1974). *Biochim. Biophys. Acta* **333**, 85.

von Stedingk, L. V., and Baltscheffsky, H. (1966). *Arch. Biochem. Biophys.* **117**, 400.

Vredenberg, W. J., and Tonk, W. J. M. (1975). *Biochim. Biophys. Acta* **387**, 580.

Walker, N. A. (1975). *FEBS Lett.* **50**, 98.

Warden, J. T., Blankenship, R. E., and Sauer, K. (1976). *Biochim. Biophys. Acta* (in press).

Werdan, K., Heldt, H. W., and Milovancev, M. (1975). *Biochim. Biophys. Acta* **396**, 276.

Wessels, J. S. C. (1964). *Biochim. Biophys. Acta* **79**, 640.

West, J., and Packer, L. (1970). *J. Bioenerg.* **1**, 405.

West, K. R., and Wiskich, J. T. (1973). *Biochim. Biophys. Acta* **292**, 197.

Wikström, M. K. F. (1975). *In* "Electron Transfer Chains and Oxidative Phosphorylation" (E. Quagliarello *et al.*, eds.), p. 97. Am. Elsevier, New York.

Wikström, M. K. F., and Saari, H. T. (1976). *Mol. Cell. Biol.* (in press).

Williams, R. J. P. (1969). *Curr. Top. Bioenerg.* **3**, 79.

Williams, R. J. P. (1974). *Ann. N.Y. Acad. Sci.* **227**, 98.

Williams, R. J. P. (1975). *FEBS Lett.* **53**, 123.

Witt, H. T. (1967). *Fast. React. Primary Processes Chem. Kinet., Proc. Nobel Symp., 5th, 1967* p. 261.

Witt, H. T. (1971). *Q. Rev. Biophys.* **4**, 365.

Witt, H. T. (1975). *in* "Bioenergetics of Photosynthesis" (Govindjee, ed.), p. 493. Academic Press, New York.

Witt, H. T., and Zickler, A. (1973). *FEBS Lett.* **37**, 307.

Witt, H. T., and Zickler, A. (1974). *FEBS Lett.* **39**, 205.

Witt, H. T., Döring, G., Rumberg, B., Schmidt-Mende, P., Siggel, U., and Stiehl, H. H. (1966). *Brookhaven Symp. Biol.* **19**, 161.

Wood, P. M. (1974a). *FEBS Lett.* **44**, 22.

Wood, P. M. (1974b). *Biochim. Biophys. Acta* **357**, 370.

Wood, P. M., and Bendall, D. S. (1975). *In* "Electron Transfer Chains and Oxidative Phosphorylation" (E. Quagliarello *et al.*, eds.), p. 271. Am. Elsevier, New York.

Wraight, C. A., and Crofts, A. R. (1970). *Eur. J. Biochem.* **17**, 319.

Wraight, C. A., and Crofts, A. R. (1971). *Eur. J. Biochem.* **19**, 386.

Yamashita, T., and Butler, W. L. (1969). *Plant Physioi.* **44**, 435.

The Use of Ionophores and Channel Formers in the Study of the Function of Biological Membranes

A. Gómez-Puyou

A. Gómez-Puyou
Departamento de Biología Experimental,
Instituto de Biología,
Universidad de México,
México, D. F., México

C. Gómez-Lojero
Departamento de Bioquímica,
Centro de Investigaciones y Estudios Avanzados,
Instituto Politécnico Nacional,
México, D. F., México

I. Introduction

The purpose of this chapter is to describe experiments that relate to the effects and mechanism of action of molecules that upon incorporation into model and biological lipid bilayers increase the permeability of the membrane to ions. It is not possible to review all the information that is available, but it is expected that the data to be presented will help the reader to understand how biological membranes handle the transport of ions and how this relates to the phenomenon of energy conservation within a cell.

Since the vast majority of the experiments indicate that these molecules act similarly in biological and synthetic lipid membranes, it is assumed that these compounds operate in the lipid milieu of the membrane. Accordingly the interpretation of the experiments that have been carried out on the effect of these molecules in biological systems is based on their experimentally observed behavior in artificial lipid membranes. It is clear that a possible interaction of these compounds with a particular membrane enzyme cannot be rigorously excluded, but at the present there is no experiment that conclusively substantiates this possibility.

The current view is that biological membranes are a fluid mosaic composed of a sea of lipids arranged in a bilayer in which proteins either go across the lipid phase or are partially submerged in the membrane (for review, see Singer and Nicolson, 1972; Gitler, 1972; Edidin, 1974). The conclusion that the impermeability of the membrane to ions is determined by the existence of the lipid bilayer arose from the studies of Mueller et al. (1962) and Bangham et al. (1965), who showed that the membranes formed exclusively with lipids are highly impermeable to ions.

As hydrocarbons possess a low dielectric constant, the energy required to introduce an ion from an aqueous phase into a membrane would be several times the thermal energy of the ion. As a first approximation, the Born equation describes the work required to solubilize an ion in a lipid membrane. This equation takes into account the dielectric constant of the membrane and surrounding media and the radius and charge of the ion (for an authoritative paper, see Lauger and Neumeke, 1973). The equation excludes the nature of the ion and the interphase of the membrane.

A breakthrough in the understanding of how energy barriers that control ion permeability could be overcome arose when it was discovered that certain substances facilitated, in a very important form, the passage of ions across a membrane. Hotchkiss (1944) was the first to report an alteration of permeability by antibiotics. Nevertheless, many years elapsed until further studies with this type of compounds were conducted. Kinsky (1961) indicated that "polyenes exert their primarily fungicidal action by an alteration of permeability, probably due to direct action on the membrane of sensitive organisms." The work of Lampen *et al*. (1960, 1962) showed that polyenes bind mainly to the membrane and that they form complexes with cholesterol. McMurray and Begg (1959) reported that valinomycin uncoupled oxidative phosphorylation and, in 1964, Moore and Pressman published their classical paper on the valinomycin-mediated K^+ uptake in mitochondria. However, it was not until the action of these compounds was studied in synthetic membranes that their mode of action began to be elucidated (Mueller and Rudin, 1967). In the last few years the large amount of work that has been conducted on synthetic lipid bilayers has largely clarified the mechanism of action of most of these molecules; as a consequence, compounds that lower ion permeability have been used to explore the properties and structure of biological membranes. Today they are part of common day methodology in many laboratories engaged in the study of membranes.

According to their mechanism of action, compounds that facilitate ion transport may be divided into two categories. *Ionophores* are those molecules that increase ion permeability by carrying ions across lipid barriers as lipid-soluble complexes; implicit in this definition is the movement of the metal ion–ionophore complex across the membrane, and thus the term mobile carrier. In addition there are molecules that increase ion permeability by altering the structure of the membrane. These compounds combine with each other or with certain membrane lipids within the membrane, thereby disrupting the continuity of the bilayer creating an aqueous channel for the free diffusion of ions. These molecules are referred to as *channel formers*.

II. Ionophores

The ionophores have been divided into two classes. The *neutral* type of carriers, which are characterized by a closed ring structure without an ionizable group, and the *carboxylic* type of carriers, which are open molecules that possess an ionizable carboxylic group. The interaction of a cation with a neutral carrier results in a positively charged complex, while the complex in the carboxylic carriers is neutral. Nevertheless, there are certain exceptions to the latter rule. These will be described below.

A. NEUTRAL IONOPHORES

The structures of valinomycin, macrotetrolides, enniantins, antamanides, and polyethers are shown in the paper of Simon and Morf (1973).

After crystalline complexes of these compounds with alkali metal salts were isolated, the structure of these complexes was studied by X-ray analysis (Kilbourn *et al.*, 1967; Dobler *et al.*, 1969; Bright and Truter, 1970; Krigbaum *et al.*, 1972; Karle *et al.*, 1973). The structure of these complexes has also been studied in solutions of organic solvents by means of spectroscopic techniques (Shemyakin *et al.*, 1969; Prestegard and Chan, 1969; Haynes *et al.*, 1971; Ivanov *et al.*, 1971, 1973; Ohnishi *et al.*, 1972; Bystrov *et al.*, 1972). All the ionophores have oxygen groups oriented toward the interior of the molecule. The formation of the metal ion complex involves six of the oxygen groups of the carrier in the case of valinomycin and enniantins, eight with the macrotetrolides and ten with the crown polyethers.

Another characteristic of these ionophores is that they possess a lipophilic exterior (see Simon and 'Mòrf, 1973) that is essential for the solubilization of the ion complex in hydrophobic media.

An interesting relation between the structure of ionophores and their ability to translocate cations is encountered in the K^+ complexes of nonactin and enniantin. The former resembles a ball with the cation lying at the center (Kilbourn *et al.*, 1967) whilst the enniantin–K^+ complex is a disklike structure (Shemyakin *et al.*, 1969). In the enniantin complex, although the ion lies at the middle, the charge is uniformly distributed. The different structure of the complexes probably explains the greater ability of nonactin for carrying ions across a membrane (Mueller and Rudin, 1967; but see Ovchinnikov, 1974).

Another interesting correlation between the lipophilicity of a compound and its ability to transport ions is afforded by crown polyether XXXII which possesses two *t*-butyl groups that are absent in crown polyether XXXI; the former is about a 1000 times more effective in mediating ion transport. The latter property is in agreement with the partition coefficient of the metal-ion complex in water and hexane (McLaughlin and Eisenberg, 1976).

Each of these two examples illustrates how the Born energy required to take an ion across a membrane may be effectively reduced and how the partition coefficient of a complex reflects the ability of an ionophore to transport ions.

B. CARBOXYLIC IONOPHORES

The dominant feature in the structure of this type of carriers (see Simon and Morf, 1973), nigericin, monensin, dianemycin, X-537A, and A-23187 is a carboxylic group that is dissociated at pH around 7 (Pressman, 1973); also in contrast to the neutral carriers, these compounds are noncyclic molecules. These ionophores possess a variable number of oxygen groups (ether or keto); in addition A-23187 contains some nitrogen groups (Pfeiffer *et al.*, 1974).

Infrared and X-ray analysis showed that nigericin (Steinrauf *et al.*, 1968), dianemycin (Czerwinski and Steinrauf, 1971), monensin (Agtarap *et al.*, 1967), and X-537A (Johnson *et al.*, 1970; Mayer and Paul, 1971) have a cyclic conformation upon complexation with a cation. Pfeiffer *et al.* (1974) indicate that A-23187 may also adopt a cyclic structure. Nevertheless, Lutz *et al.* (1971) showed that complexation with a cation is not a requisite for cyclic formation in monensin. It is interesting to note that on the basis of X-ray analysis of nigericin and X-537A, Pressman and De Guzmán (1974) suggested that the particular orientation of the ligand oxygens in the complex could account for the lower selectivity of X-537A for monovalent cations. The ligand oxygens of nigericin are oriented toward the center of the molecules, whereas those of X-537A are directed slightly outward, thus requirements for the accommodation of a cation would be less demanding in X-537A. On the other hand, the high selectivity of A-23187 for divalent cations may be due to its nitrogen groups (Wong *et al.*, 1973).

C. COMPLEX FORMATION

The binding of an ion to an ionophore or complex formation requires the removal of the solvent molecules that surround the ion (Prestegard and Chan, 1969). Complex formation has been quantitatively determined in heterogeneous and homogeneous systems. In the heterogeneous system, the distribution of the cation in the presence of an ionophore is measured in a two-phase system composed of water and another solvent of low dielectric constant (Eisenman *et al.*, 1969; Frensdorff, 1971; Haynes and Pressman, 1974). In the homogeneous system, the association of the ion and ionophore is measured in a single solvent; this complexation can be followed with a wide variety of techniques (see Simon and Morf, 1973).

With these two methods, two important pieces of information have been obtained—i.e., the stoichiometry of the complex and its stability constant. From the latter the selectivity pattern of ionophores for cations may be established. Table I shows the selectivity pattern for cations of the most widely employed ionophores. The stoichiometry of the complex as it presumably exists in the membrane is also shown.

According to the data presented by Simon and Morf (1973), there is good agreement between the two methods. Nevertheless, differences that depend on the method employed have been encountered, but these

TABLE I
SOME PROPERTIES OF CARRIERS AND CHANNEL FORMERS

Agent	Proposed penetrating species[a]	Driving force for the flux of ions[a]	Expected action across membranes	Proposed mechanism of action	Examples	Selectivity pattern	References[b]
Neutral ionophore	$(IC)^+$ I	Electrochemical gradient of C^+	Modification of membrane potential	Electrophoretic mobile carrier	Valinomycin Macrotetrolides Beauvericin[c]	$Rb^+ > K^+ > Cs^+ > NH_4^+ > Na^+ \cong Li^+$ $NH_4^+ > K^+ > Rb^+ > Cs^+ > Na^+ > Li^+$ $Cs^+ \cong Rb^+ \cong K^+ \cong Na^+ > Li^+$	(1) (1) (2)
Carboxylic ionophores for monovalent cations	(I^-C^+) (IH)	Chemical gradients	Diminution of chemical gradients of protons and monovalent cations	Exchanger, mobile carrier	Nigericin[d] Monensin Dianemycin X-537A[d]	$K^+ \cong Rb^+ > Na^+ > Cs^+ \gg Li^+$ $Na^+ > K^+ \cong Rb^+ \gg Cs^+$ $Na^+ \cong K^+ \cong Rb^+ \cong Cs^+ > Li^+$ $Cs^+ \cong Rb^+ \cong K^+ \cong Na^+ \cong Li^+$ Ethanolamine > norepinephrine > epinephrine > isoproterenol	(3) (3) (3) (3) (10)
Uncoupling agents	(U^-) $(U_2H)^-$ (UH)	Electrochemical gradient of H^+	Dissipation of proton-motive force	Electrophoretic mobile carrier	Liposoluble weak acids (4, 8), i.e., DNP, FCCP, X-537A[d]		
Channel formers	Association of several monomers	Electrochemical gradients of C^+ and H^+	Dissipation of proton-motive force	Aqueous channels	Monazomycin[e] Alamethicin[e] Gramicidin	$H^+ > Cs^+ \cong Rb^+ \cong K^+ \cong Na^+ \cong Li^+$ $H^+ > Cs^+ \cong Rb^+ \cong K^+ \cong Na^+ \cong Li^+$ $H^+ \cong Cs^+ > Rb^+ > K^+ \cong Na^+ \cong Li^+$	(5) (3) (6)
Carboxylic ionophores for divalent cations	$(I_2^-\ C^{2+})$ (IH)	Chemical gradients	Diminution of chemical gradients of H^+ and divalent cations	Exchanger, mobile carrier	X-537A[f] A-23187	$Ba^{2+} > Ca^{2+} > Mn^{2+} > Sr^{2+} \gg Mg^{2+}$ $Mg^{2+} > Ca^{2+}$	

[a] I = ionophore; C^+ = monovalent cation; C^{2+} = divalent cation; H^+ = protons; U = uncoupler.

[b] (1) Szabo et al. (1973); (2) Ovchinnikov et al. (1971); (3) Pressman (1968); (4) Finkelstein (1970); (5) Mueller and Rudin (1969). Mueller and Finkelstein (1972a), Estrada-O. and Gómez-Lojero (1971); (6) Haydon and Hladky (1972); (7) Celis et al. (1974); (8) Reed and Lardy (1972); (10) Pressman and De Guzman (1974).

[c] Beauvericin binds Ca^{2+}, but not Mg^{2+} (Prince et al., 1974).

[d] At low concentrations they act as exchangers, at high concentrations as uncouplers. Nigericin may go across the membrane in the latter case as $(IH)_2$ C^+ (Toro et al. (1976).

[e] Voltage dependent (Mueller and Rudin, 1968, 1969).

[f] Monovalent cations are transported about 10 times more effectively than divalent cations in bulk phases by X-5237A in a concentration-dependent process (Pressman, 1973).

are of a quantitative nature; qualitatively either method gives essentially identical results. The differences have been ascribed to the energy barriers involved in the binding of a metal ion to the ionophore, which in turn depends on the cation–solvent and complex–solvent interactions. A discussion of this subject is beyond the scope of this review, but Krasne and Eisenman (1973) and Simon and Morf (1973) have made an excellent analysis of the problem.

In the study of ion complexation, it has become apparent that the homogeneous system has many advantages over the heterogeneous system. Indeed the elegant works of Eigen and Winkler (1970) and Grell et al. (1972) show that ionophores possess sufficient flexibility to allow a gradual fitting of the ion into the ionophore. This process occurs through conformational changes of the ionophore and a stepwise removal of solvent molecules that surround the ion. The overall advantage in this mechanism is the involvement of low activation energies and obviously fast reaction rates.

D.   EFFECTS ON BILAYERS

The experiments on the action of ionophores in black lipid membranes have established that ion translocation can occur either as an electrically active or as in an electrically silent process. Figure 1 illustrates the mechanisms through which ionophores may mediate cation transfer across a membrane.

The translocation of a cation by a neutral-type ionophore (Fig. 1A) will generate electrical current, since a charge is transferred to one side of the membrane. Accordingly some predictions of this model have been formulated and tested experimentally.

1. A 1:1 stoichiometry of the complex has been confirmed through measurements of conductance at various concentrations of the ionophore or of the cation (for macrotetrolides, see Szabo et al., 1969; for valinomycin, see Stark and Benz, 1971).

2. Ionophores that translocate cations form stable complexes in hydrophobic solvents in the presence of a lipophilic anion (Eisenman et al., 1969; Haynes and Pressman, 1974).

3. Ionophores translocate ions regardless of the thickness of the membrane (Tosteson, 1971; Simon and Morf, 1973).

4. Ionophores do not translocate cations in a frozen membrane (Krasne et al., 1971).

5. The specificity of an ionophore for translocating cations is identical or at least similar, to the binding characteristics of a cation to the ionophore. Measurements of bi-ionic potentials in the presence of a given pair of cations, as well as the measurement of conductance for a

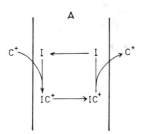

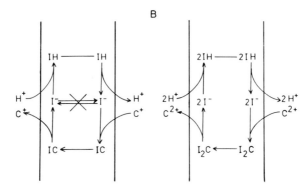

FIG. 1. Models of ionophore-mediated ion transport. I = ionophore; C^+ and C^{2+} = monovalent and divalent cation, respectively. (A) Transport by a neutral type ionophore. (B) Transfer of cations (monovalent or divalent) across a membrane via a carboxylic type ionophore. In (A), a positive charge is deposited on one side of the membrane, thus the process is electrically active. In (B), the ionophore mediates an exchange of positive charges, and movement of the negatively charged ionophore across the membrane is forbidden; this is an electrically silent process, but one in which pH differences across the membrane may be altered.

given metal-ion sequence have confirmed this prediction (Szabo *et al.*, 1973).

Szabo *et al.* (1973) pointed out that the latter postulation occurs and is valid only when the translocation is in the equilibrium domain, i.e., the reactions of complex formation are faster than diffusion of the complex across the membrane. Also it will be expected that the selectivity of an ionophore for a cation will change when the rate-limiting step is the dissociation of the complex (kinetic domain).

Figure 1B shows the translocation of a cation by a carboxylic type ionophore. This model has been made on the fundamental observation that this type of compound mediates ion transport, but does not induce conductance in bilayers; in other words carriers of this type move ions back and forth across a membrane, and thus the transport is electrically silent. As a corollary, it must be postulated that the free carrier does not diffuse across a membrane.

G. Szabo (personal communication) has designed a system to measure the action of this type of molecule without radioactive tracers; a membrane potential generated by a gradient of cations in the presence of neutral ionophores is collapsed by a carboxylic type ionophore as a consequence of the equilibration of the cation gradients.

Although the model of Fig. 1B may be applied to carriers such as nigericin, some experimental data with this ionophore (Toro *et al.*, 1976) as well as with A-23187 (Case *et al.*, 1974) and X-537A (Celis *et al.*, 1974) reveal deviations from this model. It has been observed that these ionophores at high concentrations induce conductance in bilayers. The mechanisms proposed to account for this behavior are at variance and depend on the ionophore involved. X-537A may go across the membrane as a dimer formed by a dissociated and a nondissociated species (Celis *et al.*, 1974), and this would account for the electrical properties of X-537A in black lipid membranes. Also a dimer of two nondissociated nigericin molecules with one potassium going across the membrane could explain the nigericin-induced conductance (Table I) (Toro *et al.*, 1976).

In the latter cases it is clear that more energy is required to take a charged species than a neutral complex across a membrane. Therefore a large number of cycles, electrically silent, should be operating in relation to the number of electrically active movements. Indeed Pressman (1973) showed that X-537A translocates one charge for every 10^4 exchange cycles.

III.   Channel Formers

A.   Experimental Basis

In addition to carrier-mediated transport, certain compounds, such as EIM [the excitability-inducing material of Mueller and Rudin (1963)], gramicidin, malonyl gramicidin, alamethicin, monazomycin, and the polyene antibiotics, facilitate transport through the formation of trans-membrane aqueous channels. There are several lines of evidence that support this conclusion.

1. The permeability of some nonelectrolytes diminishes with increase in their Stokes–Einstein radius (Finkelstein and Cass, 1968; Holz and Finkelstein, 1970).

2. Conductance in synthetic bilayers is proportional to the *n* power of the concentration of the compound; the reported values are 2 for gramicidin (Tosteson *et al.*, 1968), 6 for alamethicin (Mueller and Rudin,

1968), up to 12 for nystatin (Finkelstein and Cass, 1968), and 5 for monazomycin (Mueller and Finkelstein, 1972a), the exception being 1 for malonyl gramicidin, but see below. The simplest interpretation for this cooperative behavior is the self-association of several monomers with or without membrane lipids to yield a channel.

3. The induction of discrete conductance jumps in synthetic membranes by these compounds (Bean, 1973; Eisenberg *et al.*, 1973; Gordon and Haydon, 1972), which apparently depend on the formation and decay of individual pores.

4. The effect of nonactin and valinomycin in bilayers disappears upon "freezing" the membrane, while the action of gramicidin is not appreciably modified (Krasne *et al.*, 1971); the interpretation being that a channel former would not need to diffuse back and forth across a membrane, a process that is obligatory in a carrier.

B. ORGANIZATION OF CHANNELS

Models of how channel formers associate to form transmembranal structures have been proposed. The elucidation of the structure of EIM has presented unusual problems, thus it is not known how it interacts with a membrane (Bean, 1973).

1. Alamethicin

Alamethicin is a cyclic polypeptide with a known primary structure (Payne *et al.*, 1970). This compound induces conductance in bilayers through a process that is dependent on a high power of alamethicin concentration (Eisenberg *et al.*, 1973), and it also induces discrete conductance jumps in membranes (Gordon and Haydon, 1972; Eisenberg *et al.*, 1973). All these observations are consistent with the formation of a pore. In addition it has been observed that the action of alamethicin critically depends on the applied voltage (Mueller and Rudin, 1968; Eisenberg *et al.*, 1973). This is apparently a consequence of an increase in the number of holes that are formed, owing to a voltage-induced increase in the concentration of alamethicin molecules in the membrane. It is not clear how the alamethicin molecules aggregate to form a hole, although efforts have been made to answer this question (McMullen and Stirrup, 1971).

2. Gramicidin

Urry *et al.* (1971) and Urry (1971) have indicated that a channel may be formed by the arrangement of two molecules of gramicidin; this would result from H-bonding of the formyl groups of gramicidin in a head-to-head interaction [head-to-head π (LD) helical dimer]. Indeed the second-order dependence of conductance on the concentration of gramicidin turns into a first-order dependence with the malonyl dimer of gramicidin. Evidence indicating that the transmembrane channel is an ion-conducting dimer in equilibrium with the nonconducting monomer was presented by Bamberg and Lauger (1973). The channel probably contains some water (Myers and Haydon, 1972) and is less than 30 Å in length (Hladky and Haydon, 1972). According to crystallographic data, the cylinders are 27–32 Å in length (Veatch *et al.*, 1974). Although the models proposed imply the existence of an internal hole, there is no direct evidence that the gramicidin dimer has an internal cavity. In this respect it is relevant to indicate that, according to Bamberg and Lauger (1973), the transport of K^+ mediated by a single channel of gramicidin is three orders of magnitude higher than the turnover of a single valinomycin molecule. This observation indirectly implies a gramicidin-induced aqueous communication.

Aside from the Urry model, other models for the gramicidin dimer have been proposed (Veatch and Blout, 1974). On the basis of spectroscopic measurements, Veatch and Blout (1974) proposed a parallel β-double helix. Both the model of Urry and that of Veatch and Blout could explain channel formation; however, the data obtained with malonyl gramicidin cannot be interpreted with the Veatch and Blout model. It would seem that spectroscopic measurements of gramicidin in liposomes similar to those carried out by Veatch *et al.* (1974) would yield direct information on the structure of the gramicidin channel.

3. Monazomycin

Monazomycin is an antibiotic with an empirical formula $C_{62}H_{119}O_{20}N$ (Akasaki *et al.*, 1963). Mueller and Rudin (1969) found that the monazomycin-induced voltage dependence in bilayers was proportional to the fifth power of monazomycin concentration (Mueller and Finkelstein, 1972a). The mechanism through which molecules of monazomycin aggregate to form a channel is unknown, but Mueller and Finkelstein (1972a,b) made the important observation that an alteration of the surface potential may create an internal field which modulates monazomycin action.

4. Polyenes

The structure of amphotericin B is known. Apparently it orients perpendicular to the membrane with its amino and carboxyl groups in or near the water phase. It appears that several molecules are aligned in a turbinelike fashion forming a hole (Finkelstein and Holz, 1973; Andreoli, 1973). To account for the requirement of cholesterol in the action of amphotericin, it has been proposed that the amphotericin molecules are packed by cholesterol molecules on the outer part of the core.

IV.   Use of Ionophores for Monovalent Cations and Channel Formers in Mitochondria, Chloroplasts, and Chromatophores

Ionophores and channel formers facilitate passive movements of ions in biological and synthetic membranes. Figure 1A will predict that the net movement of ions mediated by the neutral type ionophores will be controlled by the electrochemical potential of the ion, whereas the net movement of ions mediated by the carboxylic ionophores, an electrically silent process (Fig. 1B), will be governed exclusively by the chemical gradient. Therefore the movement of ions across membranes as facilitated by ionophores has been successfully employed to evaluate qualitatively and quantitatively important parameters of membrane function. In particular, some of the basic postulates of the chemiosmotic hypothesis of oxidative and photosynthetic phosphorylation, as elaborated by Peter Mitchell (1968), have been tested by employing ionophores.

The fundamental points of the chemiosmotic hypothesis were stated by Mitchell (1961, 1968), and Greville (1969) made an excellent evaluation of the hypothesis. According to the chemiosmotic mechanism of oxidative and photosynthetic phosphorylation, the hydrogen and electron carriers of the respiratory chain are "looped" in such a way that oxidation–reduction processes are accompanied by the translocation of protons from one side of the membrane to the other. The resulting asymmetric distribution of protons generates an electrochemical potential difference of protons or proton-motive force. In electrical units, the proton-motive force $\Delta\mu_H$ is expressed

$$\Delta\mu_H = \Delta\psi - Z\Delta pH \tag{1}$$

where $Z = 2.3\ RT/F$ and $\Delta\psi$ is the membrane potential. Accordingly, $\Delta\mu_H$ is made up of the electrical component $\Delta\psi$ and an osmotic component ΔpH, where ΔpH is the pH difference between the two sides of the membrane.

In addition, Mitchell postulates that ATP synthetase is a reversible proton pump and that there are specialized systems for transport of ions that behave as secondary or passive mediators of anion and cation movements across the membrane that are controlled by the proton-motive force. Implicit in the chemiosmotic mechanism is the impermeability of the membrane to protons.

A.   Evaluation of $\Delta\psi$ and ΔpH

One of the basic questions of the chemiosmotic hypothesis is whether the observed ΔpH across a membrane can be ascribed to a Donnan potential resulting from the disequilibrium of K^+ across a membrane. If

ΔpH is not collapsed by valinomycin in a KCl medium, this possibility would be untenable. Mitchell and Moyle (1969a) measured ΔpH by monitoring extramitochondrial pH and the changes that it undergoes after lysis of the mitochondria. Padan and Rottenberg (1973) measured ΔpH from the distribution of DMO. In both cases, it was found that valinomycin plus K^+ increase the pH difference across the membrane. These observations indicate that ΔpH is not due to a disequilibrium of K^+ according to a Donnan potential. In chloroplasts valinomycin also does not collapse ΔpH (Rottenberg and Grunwald, 1972; Schuldinger *et al.*, 1972a).

Since an ionophore or a channel former may equilibrate a cation across the membrane according to the membrane potential, the $\Delta\psi$ term of Eq. (1) can be calculated from the distribution of a cation in the two sides of the membrane. Thus when a metal ion (C^+) reaches equilibrium:

$$\Delta\psi = -(2.3RT/F) \log C_{in}^+/C_{out}^+ \qquad (2)$$

In general there is good agreement on the reported values of $\Delta\psi$ in intact mitochondria incubated with valinomycin and K^+ (Mitchell and Moyle, 1969a; Rossi and Azzone, 1969; Padan and Rottenberg, 1973). Mitchell and Moyle (1969a) obtained higher values than Padan and Rottenberg (1973) probably because the former authors employed K^+-depleted mitochondria incubated with EGTA and higher concentrations of phosphate. In the presence of Ca^{2+}, the $\Delta\psi$ values for Rb^+ and K^+ are lower than in its absence (Mitchell and Moyle, 1969a; Rottenberg and Scarpa, 1974).

The membrane potential of bacteria (Harold and Papineau, 1972; Lombardi *et al.*, 1973; Bhattacharyya *et al.*, 1971; Maloney *et al.*, 1974), red blood cells (Hoffman and Laris, 1974), and tumor cells (De Cespedes and Christensen, 1974) has also been determined with the use of ionophores.

B.   INDUCTION OF ATP SYNTHESIS

According to Eq. (1), it would be theoretically possible to induce ATP synthesis through an artificially induced proton-motive force. The free energy necessary for driving ATP synthesis could be obtained through an increase in $\Delta\psi$, ΔpH, or both. Indeed Jaggendorf and Uribe (1966) found that chloroplasts incubated in the absence of light in an acidic medium, sythesized ATP if the pH of the mixture was rapidly raised. Clearly in those conditions ATP synthesis occurs mainly at the expense of the increase in the ΔpH term of Eq. (1). However, neutral ionophores, through their capacity to increase permeability to cations may generate a membrane potential of sufficient magnitude which would result in ATP synthesis upon induction of an electrical disequilibrium of protons.

Therefore it is of importance that the synthesis of ATP as driven by an acid-base transition in chloroplasts is importantly enhanced by promoting the influx of K^+ with valinomycin (Uribe, 1973). In agreement with these findings McCarty (1970) and Schuldinger et al. (1972b, 1973) reported that the low synthesis of ATP that occurs at suboptimal ΔpH values is significantly enhanced by superimposing a membrane potential as created by ionophores (either valinomycin plus K^+ or nonactin plus Na^+). Schuldinger et al. (1973) found a similar phenomenon with valinomycin plus K^+ in chromatophores.

Nevertheless, there are some differences between chromatophores and chloroplasts. Leiser and Gromet-Elhanan (1974, 1975) showed that in chromatophores an acid-base transitions similar to that described by Jaggendorf and Uribe (1966) in chloroplasts, did not induce formation of ATP, but Leiser and Gromet-Elhanan (1974) found that ATP was formed if valinomycin and K^+ were added in the base stage. In agreement with Mitchell (1968), these findings would indicate that the proton-motive force in chromatophores is composed of a large $\Delta\psi$ and a rather small ΔpH; an inverse situation prevails in chloroplasts, presumably owing to their high permeability to other ions.

In the postillumination period, a high concentration of K^+ in the presence of valinomycin enhances ATP synthesis in chloroplasts; this enhancement is also obtained with high concentrations of Na^+ and monactin (Schuldinger et al., 1973). In similar conditions, high concentrations of K^+ plus either valinomycin, monactin, or nonactin were effective in enhancing ATP formation in chromatophores (Gromet-Elhanan and Leiser, 1975). However, in the same system, Na^+ plus nonactin did not induce ATP synthesis in chromatophores (Gromet-Elhanan and Leiser, 1975); this is in contrast to their effect in chloroplasts. The reason for the discrepancy is not clear, but it should be explored in more detail owing to its potential importance.

In mitochondria with a polarity opposite to that of chloroplasts, a base to acid transition in the presence of valinomycin plus K^+ caused the synthesis of 0.5 nmole of ATP per milligram of protein (Reid et al., 1966). Better yields (2 nmoles/mg) were obtained in mitochondria incubated with rotenone upon induction of K^+ efflux by valinomycin (Cockrell et al., 1967). The synthesis of ATP induced by valinomycin increases to approximately 15 nmoles/mg if K^+ is allowed to accumulate prior to stopping electron flow with rotenone and inducing K^+ efflux by valinomycin (Rossi and Azzone, 1970).

Submitochondrial particles incubated at pH 5.0 with valinomycin synthesized ATP when they were rapidly changed to a pH 7.5 mixture that contained K^+ (Thayer and Hinkle, 1975a,b); the yield was about 2 nmoles/mg. It is certain that in all these conditions the creation of a conducting pathway for K^+ by valinomycin originates a $\Delta\psi$ which contributes in an important way to the formation of a proton-motive force of magnitude sufficient to drive the synthesis of ATP.

In accordance with these findings, the generation of a membrane potential by a valinomycin-induced release of intramitochondrial K^+ has been shown to produce influx of Ca^{2+} (Scarpa and Azzone, 1970). Conversely valinomycin in the presence of K^+ induces release of Ca^{2+} from mitochondria, undoubtedly by diminishing $\Delta\psi$ (Rottenberg and Scarpa, 1974).

Maloney *et al.* (1974) showed that ATP synthesis in *Streptococcus lactis* and *Escherichia coli* took place upon addition of valinomycin to cells incubated in a K^+-free medium. ATP synthesis was abolished by DCCD and external K^+; in addition, ATP formation did not occur in ATPase-negative mutants. Under their conditions of ATP formation a proton-motive force of about 200 mV was attained, of which 195 mV corresponded to $\Delta\psi$.

One of the most interesting conclusions that can be drawn from these experiments on ATP synthesis induced by an artificial proton-motive force in bacteria, chromatophores, chloroplasts, and mitochondria is that apparently a common principle of energy conservation exists throughout the biological world.

C.   UNCOUPLING ACTION

Henderson (1971) has made an excellent evaluation of the early work on the effect of ionophores and channel formers on oxidative and photosynthetic phosphorylation, therefore only a brief summary of this subject will be included here.

1. Mitochondria

In intact mitochondria in which the interior of the particle is negative, it would be expected that neutral ionophores, in the presence of a proper cation and a permeant anion, would induce cation influx down the electrical and chemical gradient, followed by extensive swelling, and uncoupling. In this respect, the evidence is overwhelming (see Henderson, 1971; Chance and Montal, 1971).

In submitochondrial particles in which the polarity of the membrane is inverted as a result of preparative procedures, neutral carriers plus cation would exert a different action. Indeed in these particles valinomycin plus K^+ diminished only to a small extent the P:O ratios (Papa *et al.*, 1969); also Montal *et al.* (1969) and Cockrell and Racker (1969) found that valinomycin plus K^+ induced a small stimulation of the oligomycin-inhibited respiration. In addition, a partial depression of the energy-requiring NAD-reduction by succinate was observed (Montal *et al.*, 1969). This set of findings is highly suggestive that the energy-conserving machinery of submitochondrial particles is affected by neutral ionophores, but to a smaller extent than that of intact mitochondria.

Papa *et al.* (1970a, 1972) showed that the respiration-driven proton uptake of submitochondrial particles incubated with oligomycin is stimulated by valinomycin and K^+. These authors also observed stimulation of the rate of oxidation of flavoproteins, ubiquinone and b cytochromes in an anaerobic to aerobic transition by valinomycin in the presence of K^+. As it had been shown by Cockrell and Racker (1969) that submitochondrial particles load K^+ in the absence of respiration and subsequently release it provided electron transport is initiated in the presence of valinomycin, it is possible that a discharge of K^+ from the particles induces a diminution in $\Delta\psi$ which would be compensated by an increase in ΔpH which would account for the findings of Papa *et al.* (1970a, 1972). Moreover, Papa *et al.* (1973) interpret their findings as evidence of the electrogenic nature of the respiration-driven proton translocation.

In the same manner, Hinkle *et al.* (1972) found that the rate of electron transport in vesicles reconstituted with phospholipids and cytochrome oxidase is stimulated about 2-fold by valinomycin and K^+. Nevertheless, the $^{32}P_i$-ATP exchange reaction of A particles reconstituted with F_1 and F_5 is not significantly inhibited by valinomycin and K^+ (Cockrell, 1973).

The basic concept of the chemiosmotic hypothesis implies that phosphorylation will be uncoupled when electrical differences and proton concentrations tend to equilibrium across the membrane. In mitochondria incubated with relatively low concentrations of nigericin and K^+, but in which the $K^+ - H^+$ exchange is maximal, no uncoupling of oxidative phosphorylation takes place (Lardy *et al.*, 1967; Graven *et al.*, 1966; Pressman *et al.*, 1967). The carboxylic ionophores for monovalent cations, dianemycin, and monensin also fail to uncouple oxidative phosphorylation (Estrada-O. *et al.*, 1967).

In submitochondrial particles, nigericin induces the expected exchange of protons for K^+, but it does not uncouple oxidative phosphorylation, nor does it modify the oligomycin-inhibited respiration (Montal *et al.*, 1969; Cockrell and Racker, 1969). Moreover, nigericin does not affect the rate of oxidation of the respiratory carriers in an anerobic–aerobic transition (Papa *et al.*, 1972). In phospholipase-treated mitochondria which behave like submitochondrial particles (Burstein *et al.*, 1971), nigericin does not uncouple oxidative phosphorylation, nor is the $^{32}P_i$ − ATP exchange reaction affected (Cockrell, 1973).

The inability of carboxylic ionophores for monovalent cations to act as uncouplers of oxidative phosphorylation is certainly due to the fact that they mediate an essentially neutral exchange of cations for protons, thereby leaving the $\Delta\psi$ term of Eq. (1) unchanged. Moreover these results indicate that in mitochondria the main component of the proton-motive force is $\Delta\psi$.

However, it is of interest that at high concentrations of both K^+ and nigericin, the ionophore induces uncoupling (Estrada-O. *et al.*, 1967; Ferguson *et al.*, 1971). As nigericin at high concentrations induces conductance in synthetic bilayers (Henderson, 1971; Toro *et al.*, 1976), it is probable that a mechanism similar to that depicted in Table I operates in those conditions in which nigericin uncouples oxidative phosphorylation.

2. Chloroplasts and Chromatophores

The study of the effect of ionophores in light-responsive membranes has established which is the main component of the proton-motive force in chloroplasts and chromatophores. Nigericin (Shavit and San Pietro, 1967; Packer, 1967) in the presence of cations is a potent uncoupler of photophosphorylation in chloroplasts. This indicates that the ΔpH term of Eq. (1) is the main component of the proton-motive force (Mitchell, 1968). The observation that chromatophores are less sensitive than chloroplasts to the uncoupling action of nigericin led also to the suggestion that the membrane potential provides the more important contribution of the proton gradient in these structures (Jackson *et al.*, 1968).

It has been proposed that millisecond delayed light emission of chloroplasts can be used to estimate the size of the electrical potential across the thylakoid membrane. This proposition rests on the observation that delayed light emission increases in the presence of valinomycin if a sudden gradient of K^+ is imposed (Barber, 1972). In addition Wraight and Crofts (1971) have interpreted the millisecond delayed fluorescence in terms of a mechanism that comprises the electrical and chemical components of a proton gradient of the type proposed by Mitchell. They have shown that the kinetics of the delayed light emission are altered in the presence of valinomycin, but that the steady state of the phenomenon is unaffected. These observations indicate a diminution of the membrane potential by valinomycin followed by an increase in ΔpH so as to attain a constant proton-motive force.

The membrane potential of chloroplasts has been measured by absorption changes at 515 nm which indicate electrical field. Witt (1974) showed that the relaxation time of the light-induced response measured at 515 nm is decreased in the presence of valinomycin and K^+. Junge and Schmid (1971) and Schmid and Junge (1975) used this nonelectrochemical method to measure the electrical properties of the thylakoid membrane in the presence of neutral ionophores (valinomycin and nonactin) and monovalent cations. They evaluated the current–voltage relationship, the dependence of current on the concentration of ionophore and cation, and the selectivity of the ionophores for monovalent cations in the thylakoid membrane. Their results provide some of the best experimental evidence for postulating that ionophores act in identical form in biological and artificial membranes.

There are some reports in the literature that indicate that in K^+-free media, valinomycin at rather high concentrations affects photosynthetic systems (Keister and Minton, 1970; Karlish and Avron, 1971; Telfer and Barber, 1974); the effects are inhibition of electron transport and uncoupling of photophosphorylation. In this respect it is important to recall that valinomycin is a surfactant (Shemyakin et al., 1969). Thus it is conceivable that some of the "anomalous" effects of valinomycin are due to a disruption in the continuity of the bilayer (increase in proton permeability) or to a disorganization of membrane components (electron carriers).

D. ACTION OF GRAMICIDIN

One of the most effective uncouplers of phosphorylation in both chloroplasts and chromatophores (Baltscheffsky and Baltscheffsky, 1964; Karlish and Avron, 1968), as well as in mitochondria and submitochondrial particles (Chappell and Crofts, 1965; Harris et al., 1967), is gramicidin. This compound increases the permeability of the membrane to protons and monovalent cations (Haydon and Hladky, 1972; Shavit et al., 1968). Therefore in a sense gramicidin mimics the action of the classical weak acid uncouplers, i.e., they short-circuit the proton-motive force, even though their mechanisms of action are entirely different.

Witt (1971) has made an interesting use of gramicidin. He titrated with this compound the relaxation time of the electrochromic change at 515 nm that occurs in chloroplasts upon illumination. His results are consistent with the concept that the functional unit in the electrical phenomenon is the membrane of one thylakoid.

E. ACTION OF ALAMETHICIN AND MONAZOMYCIN

It has been shown that alamethicin increases the macroscopic conductance of black lipid films in a voltage-dependent form; at voltages below 60 mV, the resistance of synthetic membranes is not significantly modified by alamethicin (Mueller and Rudin, 1968). Taking advantage of this property of alamethicin, Zickler *et al.* (1975) used the compound to measure the transmembrane voltage of the thylakoid; under a saturating single flash they estimated a transmembrane potential of 100 mV.

Another interesting molecule that behaves like alamethicin is monazomycin, except that with the latter, the potential must be negative on the compartment opposite to that which contains the antibiotic (Mueller and Rudin, 1969). Estrada-O. and Gómez-Lojero (1971) found that monazomycin uncouples phosphorylation in intact mitochondria, but that it does not affect the oligomycin-inhibited respiration of the inverted submitochondrial particles. Moreover C. Gómez-Lojero (unpublished data) found that the respiration of submitochondrial particles prepared in the presence of monazomycin fails to respond to oligomycin.

F.   EVALUATION OF ANION TRANSLOCATION

The basic characteristics of anion translocation in mitochondria have been discussed in detail by Williamson (1976). In this section only those experiments on the effect of ionophores on anion transport will be described.

The transport of metabolites across the mitochondrial membrane is an obligatory step in the overall process of oxidative phosphorylation. Over the past years, important evidence has accumulated which indicates that the translocation of anionic substrates occurs via specific translocators. Figure 2 shows the anion translocators that have been postulated to operate in the mitochondria.

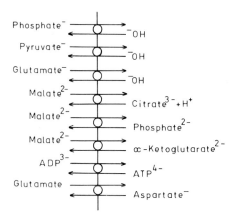

FIG. 2. Proposed anion translocators of mitochondria.

It should be pointed out that the deposition of protons on the other side of the mitochondrion as a consequence of electron flow creates an internal negative potential which tends to inhibit anion influx. However, the difficulty may be overcome if the entrance of a particular anion occurs through an exchange with an internal anion. In Fig. 2, it may be observed that three of the translocators operate as hydroxyl-anion antiporters; it is important to note that this type of translocation may also be expressed as a symport of the anion with a proton. The citrate–malate exchange is a special case, but it essentially involves the translocation of a proton in the direction of the flux of citrate.

Since the translocation of these anions involves proton movements, their inwardly directed transport would depend on the magnitude of ΔpH across the membrane. Also it will be expected that the distribution of anion across the membrane will be determined by the proton concentrations on the two sides of the membrane.

Graven et al. (1966) made the interesting observation that with certain substrates, nigericin inhibited mitochondrial respiration. In addition it was observed that valinomycin in a K^+- free media inhibited uncoupler stimulated respiration and ATPase activity (Gómez-Puyou et al., 1969a). The common parameter between these two observations is the diminution of ΔpH across the membrane, either through an exchange of external protons for internal K^+ in the experiments of Graven et al. (1966) or through a valinomycin-induced efflux of internal K^+ in the latter experiments. In relation to these observations, Mitchell and Moyle (1969b) found that nigericin promoted the uptake of phosphate in the presence of a concentration of K^+ higher than that encountered in the inner side of the mitochondrion. At these concentrations of external K^+, nigericin promotes an exchange of external K^+ for internal protons that would tend to increase ΔpH and thus promote the influx of phosphate.

The studies of Quagliariello and Palmieri (1970) and Palmieri and Quagliariello (1970) showed that the intramitochondrial/extramitochondrial distribution ratio of acetate, malate, and phosphate diminished as the external pH was increased. The high ratios obtained at the lower pH were decreased by nigericin and increased by nonactin, simultaneous to corresponding changes in ΔpH.

In the same way, Papa et al. (1970b) found that valinomycin plus K^+ (which induces a decrease in $\Delta\psi$ and an enhancement of ΔpH) augmented the uptake of phosphate, malate, citrate, and α-ketoglutarate. Under similar conditions, the uptake of pyruvate is also facilitated (Papa et al., 1971). Formation of α-ketoglutarate from cis-aconitate is also increased by valinomycin and K^+; Sluse et al. (1971) showed that this was due to an increase in the influx of cis-aconitate into the mitochondria. These studies together with those of Quagliariello *et al.* (1971), in which anion influx was measured in the presence of electron transport which increases ΔpH, provide important evidence that indicates that anion influx is controlled by the magnitude of ΔpH. Indeed, in an interesting analysis Rottenberg (1973) found a good correlation between the succinate distribution ratio and ΔpH as varied with valinomycin plus K^+ (plus or minus phosphate).

Papa *et al.* (1970b) showed that in the absence of K^+, nigericin promoted the exchange of internal citrate for external malate. This was taken as evidence for a neutral exchange of citrate^{2-} for malate^{2-} (see Fig. 2) through a process that involves the ejection of a proton in the direction of citrate translocation; the acidification of the interior by the nigericin-mediated exchange of external protons for internal K^+ being responsible for the stimulating action in citrate efflux. As expected from this model, valinomycin had no effect on the reaction. McGivan and Klingenberg (1971) reached similar conclusions without the use of ionophores.

The carrier for adenine nucleotides is the most studied of the mitochondrial translocators (Klingenberg, 1970; Vignais *et al.*, 1973). Klingenberg (1970) postulated that the exchange of ATP^{4-} for ADP^{3-} is partially compensated by proton movements in the direction of ATP flux and is thus electroneutral. However, the exchange of external ADP^{3-} for internal ATP^{4-} will tend to diminish the existing interior negative potential. Therefore it would seem that, depending on the conditions, the exchange may be electroneutral or partially electrogenic.

In this respect, it has been shown that valinomycin-facilitated inwardly directed K^+ movements enhance the influx of ATP into the mitochondria (Gómez-Puyou *et al.*, 1972) and that nigericin at low K^+ concentrations inhibits the valinomycin-stimulated ATPase activity (Estrada-O. *et al.*, 1967). Therefore it is likely that both a membrane potential and a pH gradient influence the transport of adenine nucleotides. Nevertheless, it would seem that the membrane potential predominates since higher ATP/ADP ratios are detected on the outer than on the inner side of the mitochondria (Heldt *et al.*, 1972; Slater *et al.*, 1973).

LaNoue and Tischler (1974) propose that the glutamate–aspartate translocator is electrogenic (see Fig. 2). In this respect the data on the effect of nigericin and valinomycin on the efflux of aspartate are of interest (LaNoue *et al.*, 1974). In mitochondria incubated with 150 mM K^+, nigericin does not modify the efflux of aspartate, but under similar conditions, valinomycin which induces a marked diminution of $\Delta\psi$ inhibited the efflux. As valinomycin in the absence of K^+ promoted the efflux of aspartate, it was inferred that aspartate efflux is controlled by the magnitude of $\Delta\psi$.

V. Ionophores for Divalent Cations in Biological Membranes

A. ACTION ON MITOCHONDRIA AND CHLOROPLASTS

1. Phosphorylation

Reed (1972) and Reed and Lardy (1972) showed that in the presence of EDTA, A-23187 induces an important and rapid decrease of the intramitochondrial concentration of Ca^{2+} and Mg^{2+}. In the absence of chelating agents, Binet and Volfin (1973) also observed A-23187-induced release of Mg^{2+}.

A-23187 uncouples oxidative phosphorylation (Reed and Lardy, 1972) through a process that is reversed by EGTA and potentiated by Ca^{2+} (Wong *et al.*, 1973). This uncoupling action is most probably due to an A-23187-induced cyclic movement of Ca^{2+}, since La^{3+} and ruthenium red, two inhibitors of Ca^{2+} transport (Vainio *et al.*, 1970; Lehninger and Carafoli, 1971; Moore, 1971), prevent the uncoupling action of A-23187.

In addition it has been reported that A-23187 inhibits the valinomycin-, dinactin-, and 2,4-dinitrophenol-stimulated ATPase activities of mitochondria (Reed and Lardy, 1972; Wong *et al.*, 1973). This action of A-23187 is most probably due to the decrease in the Mg^{2+} content of the mitochondria, which results in low ATPase activity. Thus it is interesting that extremely low rates of ATPase activity suffice to maintain good phosphorylation rates; according to the data of Reed and Lardy (1972), good phosphorylation rates operate in conditions in which ATPase activity is diminished by more than 80%.

X-537A was shown by Estrada-O. *et al.* (1974) to inhibit the oxidation of glutamate, pyruvate, α-ketoglutarate, and citrate through a process that is sensitive to pH variations and cation concentrations. In agreement with these findings, Lin and Kun (1973a,b) found inhibition of glutamate and isocitrate oxidation which had been stimulated by ADP and uncouplers; however, contrary to Estrada-O. *et al.* (1974) they ascribed X-537A action to an effect on NADP reduction. Estrada-O. *et al.* (1974) also reported that the oxidation of β-hydroxybutyrate and succinate was not affected by X-537A; moreover, with these substrates, high concentrations of the ionophore-induced uncoupling. Interestingly, the authors showed that X-537A in the presence of Ca^{2+} releases oligomycin-inhibited respiration in submitochondrial particles. In view of the high concentrations of X-537A required to release oligomycin-inhibited respiration, it is possible that X-537A behaves as an exchanger of protons for Ca^{2+}, but also as a lipophilic anion (see Table I) which is accumulated in the inverted particles, thereby inducing uncoupling. In this respect, the behavior of X-537A would resemble the uncoupling action of nigericin plus K^+ in the presence of tetraphenylboron (Chance and Montal, 1971).

In chloroplasts, Andreo and Vallejos (1974) found that A-23187 and X-537A (Vallejos et al., 1975) uncouple photophosphorylation in the presence of divalent cations. The authors propose that the uncoupling action of A-23187 is due to its ability to translocate protons.

An interesting use of A-23187 has been made in chloroplasts; Hind et al. (1974) proposed that Mg^{2+} acts as a counterion in the light-induced uptake of protons across the thylakoid. In an illustrative dissection of the process with various ionophores, Barber et al. (1974) found that, in the absence of added cations, fluorescence quenching was inhibited by A-23187 [a Ca^{2+}–H^+ and Mg^{2+}–H^+ exchanger (Reed and Lardy, 1972); and see Fig. 1]. Nigericin or valinomycin plus uncoupler did not reproduce the effect of A-23187, nor did beauvericin, which is known to bind Ca^{2+}, but not Mg^{2+} (Prince et al., 1974). On these grounds, Barber et al. (1974) concluded that Mg^{2+} is the counterion in the light-induced proton uptake in chloroplasts. This is of interest because Mg^{2+} is also involved in the regulation of CO_2 fixation (Walker, 1973) and in the distribution of light energy to the two photosystems (Murata, 1969).

2. Ca^{2+} Transport

The reaction of Ca^{2+} with mitochondria has been extensively studied (Lehninger et al., 1967). It is now accepted that Ca^{2+} uptake is an energy-linked process, and apparently there is a specific carrier for Ca^{2+} (Reynafarje and Lehninger, 1969) which is inhibited by ruthenium red (Moore, 1971; Vasington et al., 1972) and La^{3+} (Mela, 1968). Its kinetic behavior has been studied by Vinogradov and Scarpa (1973).

Since mitochondria prefer to utilize their energy to accumulate Ca^{2+} than to phosphorylate ADP (Rossi and Lehninger, 1964), Ca^{2+} uptake by the mitochondria would appear to be one of the most fundamental processes of cell physiology. Also it would be expected that if mitochondria exert a regulatory role of intracellular Ca^{2+} levels some of the Ca^{2+} accumulated would be released. However, this has been observed under the action of uncouplers or respiratory inhibitors, agents which under normal conditions are not in contact with mitochondria. Of importance is the finding of Carafoli (1974) on the release of mitochondrial Ca^{2+} by Na^+, but again, in certain instances, Na^+ may act as an uncoupling agent (Gómez-Puyou et al., 1969b).

In any case, whether Ca^{2+} release from mitochondria is related to the regulation of cellular processes is an open question. Accordingly, it is of interest that release of Ca^{2+} can be induced by A-23187. Reed and Lardy (1972) showed that mitochondria lose a substantial amount of their endogenous Ca^{2+} (and Mg^{2+}) upon expose to A-23187, provided EGTA was included in the incubation mixture. A-23187 also induces inhibition of Ca^{2+} uptake (Sordahl, 1974; Rottenber and Scarpa, 1974). However, this does not seem to be due to inhibition of Ca^{2+} uptake, but rather to acceleration of Ca^{2+} efflux as induced by A-23187 (Sordahl, 1974). Indeed, ruthenium red, the inhibitor of Ca^{2+} uptake, induces a slow release of accumulated Ca^{2+}, and A-23187 induces an extremely rapid efflux (Sordahl, 1974); of interest is the observation that release of accumulated Ca^{2+} by A-23187 does not require EGTA.

Rottenberg and Scarpa (1974) also observed that, within a certain concentration range, A-23187 and X-537A did not inhibit Ca^{2+} uptake by mitochondria. The authors suggest that, at limiting concentration of ionophore, Ca^{2+} efflux is compensated by uptake; however, their experiments were carried out in the presence of Mg^{2+}, which may complex with the ionophores. In this respect, Sordahl (1974) reported that A-23187-mediated efflux of Ca^{2+} is retarded by Mg^{2+}, and this in turn is reverted by increasing the concentration of the ionophores.

Nigericin plus K^+ enhances Ca^{2+} uptake, while under similar conditions valinomycin depresses the process (Rottenberg and Scarpa, 1974). The results are interpreted as a diminution and enhancement of $\Delta\psi$ by valinomycin and nigericin, respectively.

Similar to their effects on mitochondria, A-23187 and X-537A inhibit Ca^{2+} uptake in sarcoplasmic reticulum as a consequence of an increase in the release of Ca^{2+} (Caswell and Pressman, 1972; Scarpa and Inesi, 1972; Scarpa et al., 1972; Entman et al., 1972a,b). In a reconstituted system, X-537A and A-23187 also inhibit Ca^{2+} uptake (Racker, 1972). In this particular process, A-23187 is much more effective than X-537A, presumably owing to its greater ability to complex divalent cations in the membrane–water interphase (Caswell and Pressman, 1972). The release of Ca^{2+} induced by these two ionophores is accompanied by a high ATPase activity; this would be expected in vesicles that continuously release Ca^{2+} that is accumulated in an energy-dependent process.

Case et al. (1974) determined the fluorescence properties of A-23187 in biological membranes. As they point out, it is conceivable that some of the intrinsic properties of membranes may be explored with this compound.

B. CARBOXYLIC ANTIBIOTICS FOR DIVALENT CATIONS IN THE STUDY OF THE REGULATION OF METABOLIC PROCESSES

Ionophores have been a very powerful tool in the study of the properties of mitochondria, chloroplasts, and chromatophores. Also they have been used with success to study the transfer of metabolites across membranes. In the last two years, ionophores, in particular those that transfer Ca^{2+} across membranes, have been extensively used to trigger certain metabolic process that in some way seem to depend on the flux of Ca^{2+} across a membrane. Table II shows some of the cellular

TABLE II

EFFECT OF A-23187 AND X-537A ON CELLULAR PROCESSES

Biological system	Ionophore	Effect
Neurohypophysis	X-537A	Induction of vasopressin release (Nakazato and Douglas, 1974)
Retina	X-537A	Induction of dark current (Hagins and Yoshikami, 1974)
Retina	X-537A and A-23187	Induction of release of taurine, a possible neurotransmitter (Pasantes-Morales et al., 1974; Salceda and Pasantes-Morales, 1975).
Diaphragm	X-537A	Increased resting tension and contracture (Levy et al., 1973; but see Devore and Nastuk, 1975)
Skeletal muscle	X-537A	Reduction of the resting potential and its amplitude. Devore and Nastuk (1975) indicate that the phenomenon is due to movements of Na^+ as mediated by the ionophore
Heart	X-537A	Increase in frequency and amplitude of beat (Pressman, 1973)
Aortic ring	X-537A and A-23187	Induction of contraction (Pressman, 1973)
Adrenals	A-23187	Induction of release of catecholamines (García et al., 1975)
Salivary glands	A-23187	Stimulation of fluid secretion (Prince et al., 1973) and induction of protein secretion, glycogen breakdown, and incorporation of $^{32}P_i$ into proteins (Rossignol et al., 1974)
Parotid slices	A-23187	Induction of K^+ release (simulation of epinephrine action) (Selinger et al., 1974).
Pancreatic islets	A-23187	Stimulation of insulin release and increase in the level of cyclic adenosine 3':5'-monophosphate in the absence of glucose (Karl et al., 1975)
Thyroid	A-23187	Inhibition of thyrothropic hormone action on hexose monophosphate pathway and binding of iodine to protein (Grenier et al., 1974)
Cultured pancreatic cells	A-23187	Induction of insulin release in the absence of glucose (Wollheim et al., 1975)
Pancreatic slices	A-23187	Induction of amylase secretion (Eimerl et al., 1974)
Mast cell	A-23187 and X-537A	Induction of histamine secretion (Cochrane and Douglas, 1974; Foreman et al., 1973)
Yeasts	A-23187	Inhibition of cell division (Dufus and Patterson, 1974)
Sea urchin eggs	A-23187	Induction of parthenogenesis (Chambers et al., 1974)
Dogs	X-537A	Increase in cardiac contractility (De Guzman and Pressman, 1974)

functions that are affected by perturbing the permeability of the membrane to Ca^{2+} by either X-537A or A-23187. Although in some of the experiments shown in Table II it is not clear whether ionophore-mediated Ca^{2+} movements are exclusively responsible for the induction of a process (Levy et al., 1973; Devore and Nastuk, 1975), it is remarkable that these ionophores can affect such a wide variety of biological systems. On the other hand, it may not be too surprising, since Ca^{2+} controls a very high number of metabolic processes.

The principal significance of the data in Table II is the demonstration of the capacity of Ca^{2+} to trigger, under many conditions, a response that is specific to a particular cell. Moreover, if the experimental data of Table II are examined, it becomes apparent that the flux of Ca^{2+} across a membrane is the critical factor in the modification of a metabolic pathway. This transfer of Ca^{2+} across a membrane, however, may induce modifications in the level of intracellular Ca^{2+}. Therefore it is logical to conclude that the factor responsible for a given cellular response is the transport of Ca^{2+} across the membrane which may bring a change in the intracellular level of Ca^{2+}. In any case, a modification of cellular permeability to Ca^{2+} seems to be the initial step in the alteration of many metabolic pathways in a wide variety of biological systems, which certainly suggests a common underlying mechanism.

Undoubtedly, much more of future research will be directed to elucidate which are the events involved in the initiation of metabolic processes as induced by sudden fluxes of Ca^{2+} across the membrane of particular cells. Because of the ability of certain ionophores to modify Ca^{2+} fluxes, it may be predicted that compounds of this type will be extensively employed.

VI.   Isolation and Characterization of Ionophores from Animal Membranes

Present evidence indicates that cellular membranes possess specialized molecules or systems that facilitate the transfer of ions across the lipid barrier. The challenge for membrane biologists in the coming years is to isolate and characterize the molecules or systems responsible of translocation. To this purpose important efforts are conducted in mitochondria as well as in other biological membranes.

In the mitochondrial membrane an exchange of Na^+ for H^+ was postulated by Mitchell and Moyle (1967) on the basis of a faster decay of extramitochondrial pH as induced by an oxygen pulse in media that contained Na^+ than in mixtures containing K^+. In agreement with this conclusion are the data obtained with antibiotics with a broad selectivity spectra. Gramicidin, monazomycin, and beauvericin induce to a greater extent oxygen uptake in media that contained Na^+ than in those that contain K^+ (Harris *et al.*, 1967; Estrada-O. and Gómez-Lojero, 1971; Estrada-O. *et al.*, 1972). As these three compounds increase the permeability of the membrane to Na^+ (see Table I for their selectivity pattern and their mechanism), the intrinsic exchange of internal Na^+ for external protons would induce a short-circuit of protons across the membrane which will be responsible for the larger oxygen uptake in Na^+ media.

Furthermore Douglas and Cockrell (1974) compared swelling of rat liver mitochondria and ion uptake in submitochondrial particles and found that Na^+ was more effective by a ratio of 50:1. Papa *et al.* (1973) presented evidence for a Na^+-H^+ antiport in submitochondrial particles, and Izzard and Tedeschi (1973) reported transport of Na^+ in the presence of phosphate.

With respect to the transport of K^+ in mitochondria, Brierley *et al.* (1971, 1973) showed that with *p*-chloromercuriphenylsulfonate an AT-Pase activity of heart mitochondria that is critically dependent on K^+ becomes apparent. Further studies by Brierley (1976) have shown that mitochondria swell extensively in potassium acetate provided electron transport is established. Also in mitochondria incubated with EDTA, significant release (Packer *et al.*, 1966; Azzi and Azzone, 1967; Settlemire *et al.*, 1968; Gómez-Puyou *et al.*, 1970) and uptake (Barrera and Gómez-Puyou, 1975) of K^+ take place. Moreover, Tl^+ in limiting amounts inhibits the release and the uptake of K^+ by mitochondria (Barrera and Gómez-Puyou, 1975).

Therefore the data available are strongly indicative that mitochondria possess carrier systems for Na^+ and K^+, it is also apparent that the Na^+ system functions at a faster rate.

With respect to the isolation of carriers from the mitochondrial membrane, Blondin and co-workers (Blondin *et al.*, 1971; Blondin, 1974; Southard *et al.*, 1974) reported the isolation of a low-molecular-weight compound that induces mitochondrial swelling in KCl and NaCl Media; these researchers claim to have isolated an ionophore. Unfortunately, the method of assay is very unspecific and more precise means of monitoring ion translocation are required before accepting their important conclusion. Indeed the material of Blondin and co-workers may correspond to a nonspecific action of compounds such as fatty acids. In this respect, it must be noted that Wojtczak (1974) showed that fatty acids increase the permeability of mitochondria to monovalent cations; moreover, myristate extracts K^+ into organic solvents.

From tryptic digests of electroplax membranes Shamoo and co-workers (Shamoo and Albers, 1973; Shamoo *et al.*, 1974; Blumenthal and Shamoo, 1974; Shamoo and Myers, 1974) reported the isolation of a compound of molecular weight between 1400 and 6000. This compound can be incorporated into synthetic membranes with a resulting increase in the conductance. On the basis of the discrete current fluctuations that were observed in membranes treated with this compound, it was proposed that the compound could form a pore that spanned across the bilayer. Shamoo and co-workers claim that it may be a functional part of the $(Na^+ + K^+)$ ATPase of the electroplax. Nevertheless, it is not evident that the material of Shamoo and co-workers is the functional ionophore of the intact biological membrane.

Also Shamoo and MacLennan (1974) reported that a proteolipid extracted from sarcoplasmic reticulum induced a significant, but short-lasting, increase in the conductance of synthetic bilayers. In addition a succinylated Ca–ATPase preparation increased conductance upon its incorporation in bilayers; the process is highly specific for Ca^{2+} and inhibited by Na^+. Since Racker (1972) has reconstituted Ca^{2+} transport in vesicles with Ca–ATPase from sarcoplasmic reticulum, it may be inferred that the Ca^{2+} translocation in sarcoplasmic reticulum is related to the Ca^{2+}-stimulated ATPase.

However, in more recent work, Racker and Eytan (1975) observed a lack of correlation of various Ca^{2+}-activated ATPase preparations with their ability to transport Ca^{2+} in reconstituted vesicles. This observation led to the isolation of a heat-stable factor that enhanced Ca^{2+} transport in systems reconstituted with a Ca–ATPase fraction that was rather inactive with respect to its transport properties. Also, it is interesting that this factor alone induced efflux of Ca^{2+} from Ca^{2+}-loaded liposomes. The data are highly consistent with the idea that the factor may be an ionophore.

It should be emphasized that regardless of extensive efforts, no low-molecular-weight carrier or channel former has been conclusively isolated from mitochondria or other animal membranes. In principle, a valinomycin or nigericin type of molecule should be easily extractable from membranes; the failure to do so casts doubts that low molecular weight compounds with characteristics similar to those of these ionophores exist in animal membranes. More probably, and in the light of the findings of Shamoo and of Racker, it appears that in animal membranes ionophores or channel formers are part of a complex lipoprotein structure, either as prosthetic groups or as integral part of the enzyme.

Therefore difficulties are envisaged in the extraction, isolation, and characterization of ionophores from biological membranes. The extraction of proteins from membranes offers particular problems. In addition to detergents, other types of extraction procedures, such as solubilization of proteolipids in hydrophobic solvents after ion-pair formation should be explored in detail. Indeed it has been possible to extract functional membrane proteins as ion-pair into organic solvents (Gitler and Montal, 1972); however, with this procedure carriers, but not channel formers, could be isolated.

It is also recognized that the method of assay of a carrier may prove ambiguous. Cockrell (1974) made an interesting summary of the K^+/Na^+ selectivity ratio of nigericin as assayed in various system. The ratio was highly dependent on the experimental system employed. Thus it is probable that the ionophores or channel formers that are isolated will present characteristics that will depend on whether the compound is in the free or integrated state. We have also learned that in some cases the action of a compound in increasing ion permeability is voltage dependent. Apparently the effect of voltage is to increase the concentration of the compound in the membrane (Mueller and Rudin, 1968). This may mean that perhaps we should look for ion-conducting substances in the extramembranal solutions.

VII.   Antibiotics as Models of Channels or Carriers in Biological Membranes

There are essentially two possibilities through which ions are transported across a membrane: either the ions combine with specialized carriers or they pass through an aqueous channel. Although in the light of the studies in artificial membranes, it would seem rather easy to demonstrate which of the two mechanisms is involved in a given process, the reality is that it is very difficult to discriminate between the two alternatives. Moreover, some observations indicate that there are important differences between model systems and those that exist in biological membranes. Armstrong (1975) reported that the K^+ channels of the squid axon are sensitive to alkylammonium ions only if they are on the internal side of the membrane; however, the alkylammonium ion can be removed by external K^+. These findings are consistent with a channel mechanism, but it was also shown that this pore is highly selective on the outside, but not on the inside. So far no channel with these characteristics has been described in model systems.

Notwithstanding these difficulties and on the basis of the data obtained on ionophores and channel formers in artificial membranes, it should be theoretically possible to distinguish between a channel and a carrier mechanism in biological membranes. A carrier requires a fluid milieu whereas a channel-mediated mechanism would be independent of the fluidity of the membrane (Krasne *et al.*, 1971). In addition it may be expected that the rates of ion transport through a channel would be significantly higher than those facilitated by a carrier.

Harold and Barda (1967) presented data that confirm the former principle. These authors showed that the displacement of $^{86}Rb^+$ from *Streptococcus faecalis* is essentially complete in 5 minutes at 0°C provided gramicidin is included in the system. On the contrary, the displacement of $^{86}Rb^+$ in the presence of valinomycin occurs slowly at 0°C and very rapidly at 27°C. It should be recalled that the exchange of Rb^+ is independent of metabolic energy.

Racker and Hinkle (1974) measured the proton translocating activity of rhodopsin incorporated into phospholipid vesicles and the effect of nigericin and gramicidin at various temperatures. Nigericin did not inhibit proton translocation at the low temperatures, whereas gramicidin inhibited the process at all the temperatures studied. This would be consistent with the idea that a mobile carrier, but not a channel former, requires a fluid environment. Furthermore Racker and Hinkle (1974) found that the initial rates of rhodopsin-mediated proton translocation are unaffected by low temperatures. Moreover, proton uptake by the vesicles was increased at the low temperatures as a consequence of a slower decay of the proton gradient. The conclusion of these experiments was that rhodopsin acts as a proton pump via a channel. Unfortunately, the intimate mechanism of proton translocation with rhodopsin is still an unsolved mystery.

With respect to the rates of ion translocation in biological membranes, important evidence has come from studies with nerve. Armstrong (1975) calculated transport rates of 10^6 ions per second from measurements of Na^+ conductance in relation to tetrodotoxin binding sites, and the mobile carrier valinomycin transports 10^4 ions per second (Lauger, 1972). These values provide circumstantial evidence for the existence of Na^+ channels in nerve.

Although predictions can be made on the transport mechanisms that operate in biological membranes, a full understanding may have to wait until the structures responsible for ion translocation are isolated and incorporated into synthetic membranes. With the present methodology, it seems that this is the only approach. Nevertheless, the knowledge that has been obtained from ionophores, channel formers, and artificial membranes will undoubtedly smooth the road for future experimentation.

VIII. Conclusions

Ionophores and channel formers have been powerful tools in the study of membrane function. In particular, a significant number of the basic concepts of the chemiosmotic hypothesis on energy coupling have been successfully tested with ionophores; furthermore, it is clear that ATP synthesis can be driven by a proton-motive force of sufficient magnitude.

With respect to the transfer of ions across biological membranes, it would seem that research should be strongly directed to isolate the natural compounds that mediate ion transport. It is evident that the experimental data that have been obtained with model ionophores and channel formers will facilitate future studies with the natural ion-transporting molecules.

REFERENCES

Agtarap, A., Chamberlin, J. W., Pinkerton, M., and Steinrauf, L. K. (1967). *J. Am. Chem. Soc.* **89,** 5737–5739.

Akasaki, K., Karasawa, K., Watanabe, M., Yonehara, H., and Umezawa, H. (1963). *J. Antibiot., Ser. A* **16,** 127–131.

Andreo, C. S., and Vallejos, R. H. (1974). *FEBS Lett.* **46,** 343–346.

Andreoli, T. E. (1973). *Kidney Int.* **4,** 337–345.

Armstrong, C. M. (1975). *Biophys. J.* **15,** 932–933.

Azzi, A., and Azzone, G. F. (1967). *Biochim. Biophys. Acta* **131,** 468–478.

Baltscheffsky, H., and Baltscheffsky, M. (1964). *Abstr. Int. Congr. Biochem., 6th, 1964,* Vol. 10, p. 773.

Bamberg, E., and Lauger, P. (1973). *J. Membr. Biol.* **11,** 177–194.

Bangham, A. D., Standish, M. N., and Watkins, J. C. (1965). *J. Mol. Biol.* **13,** 238–252.

Barber, J. (1972). *FEBS Lett.* **20,** 251–254.

Barber, J., Mills, J., and Nicolson, J. (1974). *FEBS Lett.* **49,** 106–110.

Barrera, H., and Gómez-Puyou, A. (1975). *J. Biol. Chem.* **250,** 5370–5374.

Bean, R. C. (1973). *In* "Membranes: A Series of Advances" (G. Eisenman, ed.), Vol. 2, pp. 409–477. Dekker, New York.

Bhattacharyya, P., Epstein, W., and Silver, S. (1971). *Proc. Natl. Acad. Sci. U.S.A.* **68,** 1488–1492.

Binet, A., and Volfin, P. (1975). *FEBS Lett.* **49,** 400–403.

Blondin, G. A. (1974). *Biochem. Biophys. Res. Commun.* **56,** 97–105.

Blondin, G. A., De Castro, A. F., and Senior, A. E. (1971). *Biochem. Biophys. Res. Commun.* **43,** 28–35.

Blumenthal, R., and Shamoo, A. E. (1974). *J. Membr. Biol.* **19,** 141–162.

Brierley, G. P. (1976). *In* "Mitochondria: Bioenergetics, Biogenesis, and Membrane Structure" (L. Packer and A. Gómez-Puyou, eds.), pp. 3–20. Academic Press, New York.

Brierley, G. P., Scott, K. M., and Jurkowitz, M. (1971). *J. Biol. Chem.* **246,** 2241–2251.

Brierley, G. P., Jurkowitz, M., and Scott, K. M. (1973). *Arch. Biochem. Biophys.* **159,** 742–756.

Bright, D., and Truter, M. R. (1970). *Nature (London)* **225,** 176–177.

Burstein, C., Loyter, A., and Racker, E. (1971). *J. Biol. Chem.* **246,** 4075–4082.

Bystrov, V. F., Ivanov, V. T., Kozmin, S. A., Mikhaleva, I. I., Khalilulina, K. K., Ovhinnikov, Y. A., Fedin, E. I., and Petrovskii, P. V. (1972). *FEBS Lett.* **21,** 34–38.

Carafoli, E. (1974). *Recent Adv. Stud. Card. Struct. Metab.* **4,** 393–406.

Case, G. D., Vanderkooi, J. M., and Scarpa, A. (1974). *Arch. Biochem. Biophys.* **162,** 174–185.

Caswell, A. H., and Pressman, B. C. (1972). *Biochem. Biophys. Res. Commun.* **49**, 292–298.

Celis, H., Estrada-O., S., and Montal, M. (1974). *J. Membr. Biol.* **18**, 187–199.

Chambers, E. L., Pressman, B. C., and Rose, B. (1974). *Biochem. Biophys. Res. Commun.* **60**, 126–132.

Chance, B., and Montal, M. (1971). *Curr. Top. Membr. Transp.* **2**, 99–156.

Chappell, J. B., and Crofts, A. R. (1965). *Biochem. J.* **95**, 393–402.

Cochrane, D. E., and Douglas, W. W. (1974). *Proc. Natl. Acad. Sci. U.S.A.* **71**, 408–412.

Cockrell, R. S. (1973). *J. Biol. Chem.* **248**, 6828–6833.

Cockrell, R. S. (1974). *J. Biol. Chem.* **249**, 5464–5471.

Cockrell, R. S., and Racker, E. (1969). *Biochem. Biophys. Res. Commun.* **35**, 414–419.

Cockrell, R. S., Harris, E. J., and Pressman, B. C. (1967). *Nature (London)* **215**, 1487–1488.

Czerwinski, E. W., and Steinrauf, L. K. (1971). *Biochem. Biophys. Res. Commun.* **45**, 1284–1287.

De Cespedes, C., and Christensen, H. M. (1974). *Biochim. Biophys. Acta* **339**, 139–145.

De Guzmán, N. T., and Pressman, B. C. (1974). *Circulation* **44**, 1072–1077.

Devore, D. I., and Nastuk, W. L. (1975). *Nature (London)* **253**, 644–646.

Dobler, M., Dunitz, J. D., and Krajewski, J. (1969). *J. Mol. Biol.* **42**, 603–606.

Douglas, M. G., and Cockrell, R. S. (1974). *J. Biol. Chem.* **249**, 5464–5471.

Dufus, J. H., and Patterson, L. J. (1974). *Nature (London)* **251**, 626–627.

Edidin, M. (1974). *Annu. Rev. Biophys. Bioeng.* **3**, 179–201.

Eigen, M., and Winkler, R. (1970). *In* "The Neurosciences: Second Study Program" (F. D. Schmitt, ed.), Vol. II, pp. 685–696. Rockefeller Univ. Press, New York.

Eimerl, S., Savion, N., Heichal, O., and Selinger, Z. (1974). *J. Biol. Chem.* **249**, 3991–3993.

Eisenberg, M., Hall, J. E., and Mead, C. A. (1973). *J. Membr. Biol.* **14**, 143–176.

Eisenman, G., Ciani, S. M., and Szabo, G. (1969). *J. Membr. Biol.* **1**, 294–345.

Entman, M. L., Allen, J. C., Bornet, E. P., Gillette, P. C., Wallick, E. T., and Schwartz, A. (1972a). *J. Mol. Cell. Cardiol.* **4**, 681–687.

Entman, M. L., Gillette, P. C., Wallick, E. T., Pressman, B. C., and Schwartz, A. (1972b). *Biochem. Biophys. Res. Commun.* **48**, 847–853.

Estrada-O., S., and Gómez-Lojero, C. (1971). *Biochemistry* **10**, 1598–1603.

Estrada-O., S., Graven, S. N., and Lardy, H. A. (1967). *J. Biol. Chem.* **242**, 2925–2932.

Estrada-O., S., Gómez-Lojero, C., and Montal, M. (1972). *Bioenergetics* **3**, 417–428.

Estrada-O., S., Celis, H., Calderón, E., Gallo, G., and Montal, M. (1974). *J. Membr. Biol.* **18**, 201–218.

Ferguson, S. M. F., Estrada-O., S., and Lardy, H. A. (1971). *J. Biol. Chem.* **246**, 5645–5652.

Finkelstein, A. (1970). *Biochim. Biophys. Acta* **205**, 1–6.

Finkelstein, A., and Cass, A. (1968). *J. Gen. Physiol.* **52**, 1455–1457.

Finkelstein, A., and Holz, R. (1973). *In* "Membranes: A Series of Advances" (G. Eisenman, ed.), Vol. 2, pp. 377–408. Dekker, New York.

Foreman, J. C., Gomperts, B. D., and Monger, J. L. (1973). *Proc. 538th Meet. Biochem. Soc.* Vol. 1, pp. 853–854.

Frensdorff, H. K. (1971). *J. Am. Chem. Soc.* **93**, 600–606.

García, A. G., Kirpekar, S. M., and Prat, J. C. (1975). *J. Physiol. (London)* **244**, 253–262.

Gitler, C. (1972). *Annu. Rev. Biophys. Bioeng.* **1**, 51–92.

Gitler, C., and Montal, M. (1972). *Biochem. Biophys. Res. Commun.* **47**, 1486–1491.

Gómez-Puyou, A., Sandoval, F., Tuena, M., Chavez, E., and Peña, A. (1969a). *Arch. Biochem. Biophys.* **129**, 329–336.

Gómez-Puyou, A., Sandoval, F., Peña, A., Chavez, E., and Tuena, M. (1969a). *J. Biol. Chem.* **244**, 5339–5345.

Gómez-Puyou, A., Sandoval, F., Chávez, E., and Tuena, M. (1970). *J. Biol. Chem.* **245**, 5239–5245.

Gómez-Puyou, A., Sandoval, F., Chávez, E., Freites, D., and Tuena de Gómez-Puyou, M. (1972). *Arch. Biochem. Biophys.* **153**, 215–225.

Gordon, L. G. M., and Haydon, D. A. (1972). *Biochim. Biophys. Acta* **255**, 1014–1018.

Graven, S. N., Estrada-O., S., and Lardy, H. A. (1966). *Proc. Natl. Acad. Sci. U.S.A.* **56**, 654–658.

Grell, E., Funk, T., and Eggers, F. (1972). *In* "Molecular Mechanisms of Antibiotic Action on Protein Synthesis and Membranes (E. Muños, F. García, and D. Vazquez, eds.), pp. 646–685. Elsevier, Amsterdam.

Grenier, G., Van Sande, J., Glick, D., and Dumont, J. E. (1974). *FEBS Lett.* **49**, 96–99.

Greville, G. D. (1969). *Curr. Top. Bioenerget.* **3**, 1–78.

Gromet-Elhanan, Z., and Leiser, M. (1975). *J. Biol. Chem.* **250**, 90–93.

Hagins, W. A., and Yoshikami, S. (1974). *Exp. Eye Res.* **18**, 299–305.

Harold, F. M., and Baarda, J. R. (1967). *J. Bacteriol.* **94**, 53–60.

Harold, F. M., and Papineau, D. (1972). *J. Membr. Biol.* **8**, 27–44.

Harris, E. J., Hofer, M. P., and Pressman, B. C. (1967). *Biochemistry* **6**, 1348–1360.

Haydon, D. A., and Hladky, S. B. (1972). *Q. Rev. Biophys.* **5**, 187–282.

Haynes, D. H., and Pressman, B. C. (1974). *J. Membr. Biol.* **18**, 1–21.

Haynes, D. H., Pressman, B. C., and Kowalsky, A. (1971). *Biochemistry* **10**, 852–860.

Heldt, H. W., Klingenberg, M., and Milovancev, M. (1972). *Eur. J. Biochem.* **30**, 434–440.

Henderson, P. J. F. (1971). *Annu. Rev. Microbiol.* **25**, 393–428.

Hind, G., Nakatani, H. Y., and Izawa, S. (1974). *Proc. Natl. Acad. Sci. U.S.A.* **71**, 1484–1488.

Hinkle, P. C., Kim, J. J., and Racker, E., (1972). *J. Biol. Chem.* **247**, 1338–1339.

Hladky, S. B., and Haydon, D. A. (1972). *Biochim. Biophys. Acta* **274**, 294–312.

Hoffman, F. M., and Laris, P. C. (1974). *J. Physiol. (London)* **239**, 519–552.

Holz, R., and Finkelstein, A. (1970). *J. Gen. Physiol.* **56**, 125–145.

Hotchkiss, R. D. (1944). *Adv. Enzymol.* **4**, 153–199.

Ivanov, V. T., Miroshnikov, A. I., Abdullaev, N. D., Senyavina, L. B., Arkhipova, S. P., Uvarova, N. N., Khalilulina, K. K., Bystrov, V. F., and Ovchinnikov, Y. A. (1971). *Biochem. Biophys. Res. Commun.* **42**, 654–663.

Ivanov, V. T., Kogan, G. A., Tulchinsky, V. M., Miroshnikov, A. V., Mikhalyova, I. I., Eustratov, A. V., Zenkin, A. A., Kostetsky, P. V., Ovchinnikov, Y. A., and Lokshin, B. V. (1973). *FEBS Lett.* **30**, 199–204.

Izzard, S., and Tedeschi, H. (1973). *Arch. Biochem. Biophys.* **154**, 527–539.

Jackson, J. B., Crofts, A. R., and von Stedingk, L. V. (1968). *Eur. J. Biochem.* **6**, 41–54.

Jagendorf, A. T., and Uribe, E. (1966). *Proc. Natl. Acad. Sci. U.S.A.* **55**, 170–177.

Johnson, S. M., Herrin, J., Liu, S. J., and Paul, I. C. (1970). *J. Am. Chem. Soc.* **92**, 4408–4413.

Junge, W., and Schmid, R. (1971). *J. Membr. Biol.* **4**, 179–192.

Karl, R. C., Zawalich, W. S., Ferrendeli, J. A., and Matschinsky, F. M. (1975). *J. Biol. Chem.* **250**, 4575–4579.

Karle, I. L., Karle, J., Wieland, T., Burgermeister, W., Faulstich, H., and Witkop, B. (1973). *Proc. Natl. Acad. Sci. U.S.A.* **70**, 1836–1840.

Karlish, J. D., and Avron, M. (1971). *Eur. J. Biochem.* **20**, 51–57.

Karlish, S. J., and Avron, M. (1968). *FEBS Lett.* **1**, 21–24.

Keister, D. L., and Minton, N. J. (1970). *Bioenergetics* **1**, 367–377.

Kilbourn, B. T., Dunitz, J. D., Pioda, L. A. R., and Simon, W. (1967). *J. Mol. Biol.* **30**, 559–563.

Kinsky, S. C. (1961). *J. Bacteriol.* **82**, 889–897.

Klingenberg, M. (1970). *Essays Biochem.* **6**, 119–159.

Krasne, S., and Eisenman, G. (1973). *In* Membranes: A Series of Advances (G. Eisenman, ed.), Vol. 2, pp. 277–328. Dekker, New York.

Krasne, S., Eisenman, G., and Szabo, G. (1971). *Science* **174**, 412–415.

Krigbaum, W. R., Kuegler, F. R., and Oelschlaeger, H. (1972). *Biochemistry* **11**, 4548–4552.

Lampen, J. O., Arnow, P. M., and Safferman, R. S. (1960). *J. Bacteriol.* **80**, 200–206.

Lampen, J. O., Arnow, P. M., Borowska, Z., and Laskin, A. I. (1962). *J. Bacteriol.* **84**, 1152–1160.

LaNoue, K. F., and Tischler, M. E. (1974). *J. Biol. Chem.* **249**, 7522–7528.

LaNoue, K. F., Bryla, J., and Bassett, D. J. P. (1974). *J. Biol. Chem.* **249**, 7514–7521.

Lardy, H. A., Graven, S. N., and Estrada-O., S. (1967). *Fed. Proc., Fed. Am. Soc. Exp. Biol.* **26**, 1355–1360.

Lauger, P. (1972). *Science* **178**, 24–30.

Lauger, P., and Neumeke, B. (1973). *In* "Membranes: A Series of Advances" (G. Eisenman, ed.), Vol. 2, pp. 1–59. Dekker, New York.

Lehninger, A. L., and Carafoli, E. (1971). *Arch. Biochem. Biophys.* **143**, 506–515.

Lehninger, A. L., Carafoli, E., and Rossi, C. S. (1967). *Adv. Enzymol.* **29**, 259–320.

Leiser, M., and Gromet-Elhanan, Z. (1974). *FEBS Lett.* **43**, 267–270.

Leiser, M., and Gromet-Elhanan, Z. (1975). *J. Biol. Chem.* **250**, 84–89.

Levy, J. V., Cohen, J. A., and Inesi, G. (1973). *Nature (London)* **242**, 461–463.

Lin, D. C., and Kun, E. (1973a). *Proc. Natl. Acad. Sci. U.S.A.* **70**, 3450–3453.

Lin, D. C., and Kun, E. (1973b). *Biochem. Biophys. Res. Commun.* **50**, 820–825.

Lombardi, F. G., Reeves, J. P., and Kaback, H. R. (1973). *J. Biol. Chem.* **248**, 3551–3565.

Lutz, W. K., Winkler, F. W., and Dunitz, J. P. (1971). *Helv. Chim. Acta* **54**, 1103–1108.

McCarty, R. E. (1970). *FEBS Lett.* **9**, 313–316.

McGivan, J. D., and Klingenberg, M. (1971). *Eur. J. Biochem.* **20**, 392–399.

McLaughlin, S., and Eisenman, M. (1976). *Annu. Rev. Biophys. Bioeng.* **4**, 335–366.

McMullen, A. I., and Stirrup, J. A. (1971). *Biochim. Biophys. Acta* **241**, 807–814.

McMurray, W. C., and Begg, R. W. (1959). *Arch. Biochem. Biophys.* **84**, 546–548.

Maloney, P. G., Kashket, E. R., and Wilson, T. H. (1974). *Proc. Natl. Acad. Sci. U.S.A.* **71**, 3896–3900.

Mayer, C. A., and Paul, I. C. (1971). *Chem. Commun.* p. 181.

Mela, L. (1968). *Arch. Biochem. Biophys.* **123**, 286–293.

Mitchell, P. (1961). *Nature (London)* **191**, 144–148.

Mitchell, P. (1968). "Chemiosmotic Coupling and Energy Transduction." Glynn Res., Bodmin, Cornwall, England.

Mitchell, P., and Moyle, J. (1967). *Biochem. J.* **105**, 1147–1162.

Mitchell, P., and Moyle, J. (1969a). *Eur. J. Biochem.* **7**, 471–484.

Mitchell, P., and Moyle, J. (1969b). *Eur. J. Biochem.* **9**, 149–155.

Montal, M., Chance, B., Lee, C. P., and Azzi, A. (1969). *Biochem. Biophys. Res. Commun.* **34**, 104–110.

Montal, M., Chance, B., and Lee, C. P. (1970a). *J. Membr. Biol.* **2**, 201–234.

Montal, M., Nishimura, M., and Chance, B. (1970b). *Biochim. Biophys. Acta* **223**, 183–188.

Moore, C. L. (1971). *Biochem. Biophys. Res. Commun.* **42**, 298–305.

Moore, C. L., and Pressman, B. C. (1964). *Biochem. Biophys. Res. Commun.* **15**, 562–567.

Mueller, P., and Rudin, D. O. (1963). *J. Theor. Biol.* **4,** 268–280.

Mueller, P., and Rudin, D. O. (1967). *Biochem. Biophys. Res. Commun.* **26,** 398–404.

Mueller, P., and Rudin, D. O. (1968). *Nature (London)* **217,** 713–719.

Mueller, P., and Rudin, D. O. (1969). *Curr. Top. Bioenerg.* **3,** 157–249.

Mueller, P., Rudin, D. O., Tien, H. T., and Wescott, W. C. (1962). *Circulation* **26,** 1167–1172.

Mueller, R. V., and Finkelstein, A. (1972a). *J. Gen. Physiol.* **60,** 263–284.

Mueller, R. V., and Finkelstein, A. (1972b). *J. Gen. Physiol.* **60,** 285–306.

Murata, N. (1969). *Biochim. Biophys. Acta* **189,** 171–181.

Myers, V. B., and Haydon, D. A. (1972). *Biochim. Biophys. Acta* **274,** 313–322.

Nakazato, Y., and Douglas, W. W. (1974). *Nature (London)* **249,** 479–481.

Ohnishi, M., Fedarko, M. C., and Baldeschwieler, J. D. (1972). *Biochem. Biophys. Res. Commun.* **46,** 312–320.

Ovchinnikov, Y. A. (1974). *FEBS Lett.* **44,** 1–21.

Ovchinnikov, Y. A., Ivanov, V. T., and Mikhaleva, I. (1971). *Tetrahedron Lett.* **2,** 159–162.

Packer, L. (1967). *Biochem. Biophys. Res. Commun.* **38,** 1022–1027.

Packer, L., Utsumi, K., and Mustafa, M. G. (1966). *Arch. Biochem. Biophys.* **117,** 381–393.

Padan, E., and Rottenberg, H. (1973). *Eur. J. Biochem.* **40,** 431–437.

Palmieri, F., and Quagliariello, E. (1970). *Eur. J. Biochem.* **17,** 230–238.

Papa, S., Tager, J. M., Guerrieri, F., and Quagliariello, E. (1969). *Biochim. Biophys. Acta* **172,** 184–186.

Papa, S., Guerrieri, F., Rossi Bernardi, L., and Tager, J. M. (1970a). *Biochim. Biophys. Acta* **179,** 100–103.

Papa, S., Lofrumento, N. F., Quagliariello, E., Meijer, A. J., and Tager, J. M. (1970b). *Bioenergetics* **1,** 287–307.

Papa, S., Francavilla, G., Paradies, G., and Meduri, B. (1971). *FEBS Lett.* **12,** 285–288.

Papa, S., Scarpa, A., Lee, C. P., and Chance, B. (1972). *Biochemistry* **11,** 3091–3098.

Papa, S., Guerrieri, F., Simone, S., Lorusso, M., and Larosa, D. (1973). *Biochim. Biophys. Acta* **292,** 20–38.

Pasantes-Morales, H., Salceda, R., and Gómez-Puyou, A. (1974). *Biochem. Biophys. Res. Commun.* **58,** 847–853.

Payne, J. W., Jakes, R., and Hartley, B. S. (1970). *Biochem. J.* **117,** 757–766.

Pfeiffer, D. R., Reed, P. W., and Lardy, H. A. (1974). *Biochemistry* **13,** 4007–4014.

Pressman, B. C. (1968). *Fed. Proc., Fed. Am. Soc. Exp. Biol.* **27,** 1283–1288.

Pressman, B. C. (1973). *Fed. Proc., Fed. Am. Soc. Exp. Biol.* **32,** 1698–1703.

Pressman, B. C., and De Guzmán, N. T. (1974). *Ann. N. Y. Acad. Sci.* **227,** 380–391.

Pressman, B. C., Harris, E. J., Jaggers, W. S., and Johnson, J. H. (1967). *Proc. Natl. Acad. Sci. U.S.A.* **58,** 1949–1956.

Prestegard, J. H., and Chan, S. I. (1969). *Biochemistry* **10,** 3921–3927.

Prince, R., Crofts, A. R., and Steinrauf, L. K. (1974). *Biochem. Biophys. Res. Commun.* **59,** 567–603.

Prince, W. T., Rasmussen, H., and Berridge, M. J. (1973). *Biochim. Biophys. Acta* **329,** 98–107.

Quagliariello, E., and Palmieri, F. (1970). *FEBS Lett.* **13,** 253–257.

Quagliariello, E., Genchi, G., and Palmieri, F. (1971). *FEBS Lett.* **13,** 253–257.

Racker, E. (1972). *J. Biol. Chem.* **247,** 8198–8200.

Racker, E., and Eytan, E. (1975). *J. Biol. Chem.* **250,** 7533–7534.

Racker, E., and Hinkle, P. C. (1974). *J. Membr. Biol.* **17,** 181–188.

Reed, P. W. (1972). *Fed. Proc., Fed. Am. Soc. Exp. Biol.* **31,** 432.

Reed, P. W., and Lardy, H. A. (1972). *J. Biol. Chem.* **247**, 6970–6977.

Reid, R. A., Moyle, J., and Mitchell, P. (1966). *Nature (London)* **212**, 257–258.

Reynafarje, B., and Lehninger, A. L. (1969). *J. Biol. Chem.* **244**, 584–593.

Rossi, C. S., and Lehninger, A. L. (1964). *J. Biol. Chem.* **239**, 3971–3980.

Rossi, E., and Azzone, G. F. (1969). *Eur. J. Biochem.* **7**, 418–426.

Rossi, E., and Azzone, G. F. (1970). *Eur. J. Biochem.* **12**, 319–327.

Rossignol, B., Herman, G., Chambaut, A. M., and Keryer, G. (1974). *FEBS Lett.* **43**, 241–246.

Rottenberg, H. (1973). *J. Membr. Biol.* **11**, 117–137.

Rottenberg, H., and Grunwald, T. (1972). *Eur. J. Biochem.* **25**, 71–74.

Rottenberg, H., and Scarpa, A. (1974). *Biochemistry* **13**, 4811–4817.

Salceda, R., and Pasantes-Morales, H. (1975). *Brain Res.* **96**, 206–211.

Scarpa, A., and Azzone, G. F. (1970). *Eur. J. Biochem.* **12**, 328–335.

Scarpa, A., and Inesi, G. (1972). *FEBS Lett.* **22**, 273–276.

Scarpa, A., Baldassare, J., and Inesi, G. (1972). *J. Gen. Physiol.* **60**, 735–749.

Schmid, R., and Junge, W. (1975). *Biochim. Biophys. Acta* **394**, 76–92.

Schuldinger, S., Rottenberg, H., and Avron, M. (1972a). *Eur. J. Biochem.* **12**, 64–70.

Schuldinger, S., Rottenberg, H., and Avron, M. (1972b). *FEBS Lett.* **28**, 173–176.

Schuldinger, S., Rottenberg, H., and Avron, M. (1973). *Eur. J. Biochem.* **39**, 455–462.

Selinger, Z., Eimerl, S., and Schramm, M. (1974). *Proc. Natl. Acad. Sci. U.S.A.* **71**, 128–131.

Settlemire, C. T., Hunter, G. R., and Brierley, G. P. (1968). *Biochim. Biophys. Acta* **162**, 487–499.

Shamoo, A. E., and Albers, R. W. (1973). *Proc. Natl. Acad. Sci. U.S.A.* **70**, 1191–1194.

Shamoo, A. E., and MacLennan, D. H. (1974). *Proc. Natl. Acad. Sci. U.S.A.* **71**, 3522–3526.

Shamoo, A. E., and Myers, M. (1974). *J. Membr. Biol.* **19**, 163–178.

Shamoo, A. E., Myers, M. M., Blumenthal, R., and Albers, R. W. (1974). *J. Membr. Biol.* **19**, 129–140.

Shavit, N., and San Pietro, A. (1967). *Biochem. Biophys. Res. Commun.* **28**, 277–283.

Shavit, N., Dilley, R. A., and San Pietro, A. (1968). *Biochemistry* **7**, 2356–2363.

Shemyakin, M. M., Ovchinnikov, Y. A., Ivanov, V. T., Antonov, V. K., Vinogradova, E. I., Malenkov, G. G., Eustratov, A. V., Laine, I. A., Melnik, E. I., and Ryabova, I. D. (1969). *J. Membr. Biol.* **1**, 402–430.

Simon, W., and Morf, W. E. (1973). In "Membranes: A Series of Advances" (G. Eisenmen, ed.), Vol. 2, pp. 329–375. Dekker, New York.

Singer, S. J., and Nicolson, G. L. (1972). *Science* **175**, 720–731.

Slater, E. C., Rosing, J., and Mol, A. (1973). *Biochim. Biophys. Acta* **292**, 534–553.

Sluse, F. E., Meijer, A. J., and Tager, J. M. (1971). *FEBS Lett.* **18**, 149–153.

Sordahl, L. A. (1974). *Arch. Biochem. Biophys.* **167**, 104–115.

Southard, J. H., Blondin, G. A., and Green, D. A. (1974). *J. Biol. Chem.* **249**, 678–681.

Stark, G., and Benz, R. (1971). *J. Membr. Biol.* **5**, 133–153.

Steinrauf, L. K., Pinkerton, M., and Chamberlin, J. W. (1968). *Biochem. Biophys. Res. Commun.* **33**, 29–31.

Szabo, G., Eisenman, G., and Ciani, S. (1969). *J. Membr. Biol.* **1**, 346–382.

Szabo, G., Eisenman, G., Laprade, R., Ciani, S. M., and Krasne, S. (1973). In "Membranes: A Series of Advances" (G. Eisenman, ed.), Vol. 2, pp. 179–277. Dekker, New York.

Telfer, A., and Barber, J. (1974). *Biochim. Biophys. Acta* **333**, 343–352.

Thayer, W. S., and Hinkle, P. C. (1975a). *J. Biol. Chem.* **250**, 5330–5335.

Thayer, W. S., and Hinkle, P. C. (1975b). *J. Biol. Chem.* **250**, 5336–5342.

Toro, M., Gómez-Lojero, C., Montal, M., and Estrada-O., S. (1976). *Bioenergetics* **8**, 19–26.

Tosteson, D. C. (1971). *Proc. Int. Congr. Microbiol. 10th, 1970.* pp. 191–200.

Tosteson, D. C., Andreoli, T. E., Tieffenberg, M., and Cook, P. (1968). *J. Gen. Physiol.* **52**, Part 2, 3735–3746.

Uribe, E. G. (1973). *FEBS Lett.* **36**, 143–147.

Urry, D. W. (1971). *Proc. Natl. Acad. Sci. U.S.A.* **68**, 672–676.

Urry, D. W., Goodall, M. C., Glickson, J. D., and Myers, D. F. (1971). *Proc. Natl. Acad. Sci. U.S.A.* **68**, 1907 and 1911.

Vainio, H., Mela, L., and Chance, B. (1970). *Eur. J. Biochem.* **12**, 387–391.

Vallejos, R. H., Andreo, C. S., and Ravizzini, R. A. (1975). *FEBS Lett.* **50**, 245–249.

Vasington, F. D., Gazzotti, P., Tiozzo, R., and Carafoli, E. (1972). *Biochim. Biophys. Acta* **256**, 43–54.

Veatch, R. W., and Blout, E. R. (1974). *Biochemistry* **13**, 5257–5264.

Veatch, R. W., Fossel, E. T., and Blout, E. R. (1974). *Biochemistry* **13**, 5249–5256.

Vignais, P. V., Vignais, P. M., Lauquin, G., and Morel, F. (1973). *Biochimie* **55**, 763–778.

Vinogradov, A., and Scarpa, A. (1973). *J. Biol. Chem.* **248**, 5527–5531.

Walker, D. A. (1973). *New Phytol.* **72**, 209–235.

Williamson, J. R. (1976). *In* "Mitochondria: Bioenergetics, Biogenesis, and Membrane Function" (L. Packer and A. Gómez-Puyou, eds.), pp. 79–107. Academic Press, New York.

Witt, H. T. (1971). *Q. Revs. Biophys.* **4**, 365–477.

Witt, H. T. (1974). *In* "Perspectives in Membrane Biology" (S. Estrada-O. and C. Gitler, eds.), pp. 413–421. Academic Press, New York.

Wojtczak, L. (1974). *FEBS Lett.* **44**, 25–30.

Wollheim, C. B., Blondel, B., Trueheart, P., Renold, A. E., and Sharp, R. W. G. (1975). *J. Biol. Chem.* **250**, 1354–1360.

Wong, D. T., Wilkinson, J. R., Hamill, R. L., and Horng, J. S. (1973). *Arch. Biochem. Biophys.* **156**, 578–585.

Wraight, C. A., and Crofts, A. R. (1971). *Eur. J. Biochem.* **19**, 386–397.

Zickler, A., Boheim, G., and Witt, H. T. (1975). *Abstr. Int. Biophys. Congr., 5th, 1975.* p. 55.

Mitochondrial Calcium Transport

Fyfe L. Bygrave
Department of Biochemistry,
Faculty of Science,
The Australian National University,
Canberra, Australia

I. Introduction

Considerable progress has been made in the past two decades toward understanding the role of inorganic ions in the function and control of biochemical reactions. Consequently, it is not surprising to find in the literature a large number of reports that implicate these ions, especially calcium (Ca^{2+}), as an important component of numerous specific regulatory mechanisms in cell metabolism. Clearly any form of metabolic control involving the ionic environment must also involve movements of ions and the concomitant development and utilization of ionic concentration gradients. What is emerging is an increasing awareness that the mitochondrial Ca^{2+} transport system is a primary mechanism used by cells to modify the intracellular distribution of Ca^{2+}. Such modification can be shown in turn to be linked to transient or permanent changes in the cell metabolic network.

A study of mitochondrial Ca^{2+} transport therefore not only bears directly on the specific molecular details of metabolite transport across the mitochondrial inner membrane, but also on the general question of how such transport is geared to coordinating metabolic events sensitive to this ion, that occur inside and outside the mitochondria. This article will concentrate on the first of these two aspects of mitochondrial Ca^{2+} transport. The second aspect is the subject of a forthcoming review (Bygrave, 1977).

The topic of mitochondrial Ca^{2+} transport in past reviews has been both embedded in the more general question of ion movements in mitochondria (Harris et al., 1966; Lehninger et al., 1967; Pullman and Schatz, 1967; Cereijo-Santalo, 1970; Pressman, 1970; Chance and Montal, 1971; Henderson, 1971; Moore, 1972; Azzone and Massari, 1973) and considered independently of other ions (Lehninger, 1970; Lehninger and Carafoli, 1970; Carafoli, 1973, 1974, 1975a). The present review focuses attention on an overall critical and detailed analysis of the mechanism of the process. It is timely because, as will become evident, there is a need now to critically evaluate the large body of information amassed on the topic in the last few years.

The review considers the details of the carrier system responsible for transporting Ca^{2+} across the inner membrane of mitochondria. These are discussed as far as possible in molecular terms. Particular emphasis is placed on the inherent difficulties associated with the technology involved in analyzing the various aspects of mitochondrial Ca^{2+} transport and the solutions that have been devised to overcome some of them. It is then shown briefly how Ca^{2+} and the mitochondrial Ca^{2+} transport system are integral components of the cellular metabolic network.

Finally, some recently described biosystems are discussed that provide a new dimension to the study of the molecular biology of Ca^{2+} transport in mitochondria.

II. Phases in the Development of the Study of Mitochondrial Calcium Transport

Although the primary aim of this review is to consider the current status of mitochondrial Ca^{2+} transport, it is profitable initially to place it in perspective by recalling briefly the more outstanding events that have influenced research in this subject. Chronologically, the development of knowledge on the topic falls into three quite distinct phases.

Among the earliest reports on Ca^{2+} accumulation by mitochondria was that of Slater and Cleland (1953). However, these authors suggested that the observations made were of little biological consequence since they took place at 0°C. Somewhat earlier it was shown that Ca^{2+} could stimulate ATPase activity in intact mitochondria (Potter, 1947; Siekevitz and Potter, 1953; Potter et al., 1953) and that the ion could uncouple phosphorylation from respiration (Lehninger, 1949). Later, reports appeared indicating that Ca^{2+} and other divalent cations could be accumulated by isolated mitochondria against a concentration gradient in an energy-dependent process (see, e.g., Bartley and Amoore, 1958).

In the early 1960s, the second phase in the development, a number of scientists provided a large body of evidence that related Ca^{2+} movements, first, to the mechanism of energy transduction in mitochondria, and second, to the gross morphological changes that mitochondria undergo when presented with large concentrations of Ca^{2+}. Notable contributions to this work were made by DeLuca and Engstrom (1961), Vasington and Murphy (1962), and Saris (1963) and by the groups of Brierley (see Brierley et al., 1964), Chance (see Chance, 1965), Chappell (see Chappell and Crofts, 1966), Lehninger and Carafoli (see Lehninger et al., 1967), and Mitchell (see Mitchell and Moyle, 1969a). The excellent and most comprehensive review of Lehninger et al. (1967) covers most of the studies undertaken in these two phases (see also the review of Pullman and Schatz, 1967).

The third phase began at the end of the 1960s and extends to the present. The principal advances that have been made in this phase include: the concept of a carrier responsible for transporting Ca^{2+} (Mela, 1968a; Reynafarje and Lehninger, 1969) and, in an extension of this concept, the various attempts to isolate such a carrier (see Carafoli and Sottocasa, 1974); the discovery of specific inhibitors of Ca^{2+} transport (Mela, 1968a; Moore, 1971); the development and use of techniques to measure initial rates of Ca^{2+} transport (Mela and Chance, 1968; Bygrave et al., 1971a; Scarpa, 1974; Reed and Bygrave, 1975a); the attempts to identify the "driving force" for mitochondrial Ca^{2+} transport with the components of the proton electrochemical gradient (Scarpa and Azzone, 1970; Selwyn et al., 1970; Reed and Bygrave, 1974c; Rottenberg and Scarpa, 1974); and the discovery of biosystems in which the "activity" of mitochondrial Ca^{2+} transport can be shown to change according to physiological circumstances (Thorne and Bygrave, 1974b; Bygrave et al., 1975; Dorman et al., 1975). It is the contributions that have been made in this last phase that will now be considered in detail.

III. An Analysis of the Calcium Transport System

An analysis of any biological transport system like that of a classical enzyme (see Dixon and Webb, 1964) ideally should initially involve kinetic measurements in order to define particular criteria that might be expected to be met in any molecule that is subsequently isolated and considered to represent the system in situ. These considerations seem to have been rigorously applied in the study of the translocation of adenine nucleotides (see Klingenberg, 1970), of inorganic phosphate (Coty and Pedersen, 1974), and of some substrate anions (Palmieri et al., 1972; Sluse et al., 1973), but not in that of Ca^{2+} transport.

The failure to analyze the Ca^{2+} transport system initially from kinetic measurements probably stems from a combination of circumstances. First, the early work on Ca^{2+} transport revealed a close relation between its mechanism of operation and that of energy transduction in mitochondria (see Chance, 1965; Lehninger et al., 1967; Greville, 1969). Consequently, much of that work was oriented toward examining the interactions between Ca^{2+} movements, ATPase activity and respiratory activity (see also Rossi and Lehninger, 1964). It was not until toward the end of the last decade that the mechanism of Ca^{2+} transport across the mitochondrial membrane(s) was suggested to involve a distinct carrier (see Section III,E). Then, at the beginning of the present decade and soon after the success achieved in isolating transport binding-proteins from bacteria by "osmotic-shock" techniques (see Heppel, 1971), there arose a desire to isolate with similar techniques a protein from mitochondria that functionally represented the Ca^{2+} carrier (see Section III,K).

Yet it is only in the last two years that any detailed and systematic kinetic analysis of the carrier was initiated. It has been argued that a kinetic analysis is a necessary prerequisite to the development of any rational model for the Ca^{2+} carrier (Reed and Bygrave, 1974b, 1975a).

A. The Experimental Difficulties of Quantitatively Analyzing the System

Any quantitative analysis (kinetic or otherwise) of the Ca^{2+} transport system in mitochondria is potentially susceptible to a variety of experimental difficulties. First, the rate of the process is sufficiently rapid as to necessitate the use of techniques with high-time resolution. Although some have been used since the late 1960s (see below), they all have suffered from the further and most important problem of failing to distinguish between "transported" and "nontransported" or externally bound Ca^{2+}.

Scheme 1 illustrates the various pools in and around mitochondria that are accessible to Ca^{2+}. We shall assume for the moment the existence of a specific carrier and its location in the inner membrane. The evidence relating to this is presented below. Clearly, only that Ca^{2+} present *within* the matrix space (IF or IB) is Ca^{2+} that has been *transported* by mitochondria. All the remaining Ca^{2+} is that located on sites external to the carrier molecules in the inner membrane. The important, and even critical, point to appreciate is that most if not all of the Ca^{2+} on these latter sites bears little *direct* relation to the mitochondrial Ca^{2+} transport system, but, on the other hand, it does represent a potential source of interference of its measurement.

1. The Methods for Measuring Mitochondrial Calcium Transport

It is fruitful and pertinent at this juncture to consider the wide range of techniques that have been used to measure transport of Ca^{2+} by mitochondria. These are listed in Table I together with comments on the principle involved in the application of the technique, its particular attributes, and, finally, what the author sees as the potential limitations to the individual technique. Those that have been used most widely are

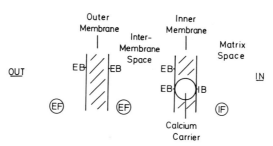

SCHEME 1. E, External; I, internal; B, bound; F, free. Pools in mitochondria available to Ca^{2+}. From Reed and Bygrave (1974c).

TABLE I

TECHNIQUES USED FOR THE MEASUREMENT OF MITOCHONDRIAL CALCIUM TRANSPORT

Technique	Principle	Particular attribute	Potential limitation	References
Spectrophotometry	The changes in absorbance at specific wavelengths are recorded when Ca^{2+} associates or dissociates from a metallochromic indicator located external to the mitochondria. The most commonly used indicator is murexide (ammonium purpurate) whose E_{540} $(-E_{507}$ to minimize nonspecific absorbance) decreases as Ca^{2+} becomes bound to it. Recently a photoprotein (aequorin) isolated from jelly fish has also been used (Ashley and Caldwell, 1974).	Combination of dual-wavelength spectrophotometry and stopped flow for rapid mixing enable the measurement of rapid rates of Ca^{2+} transport by mitochondria. It is possible to add amounts of Ca^{2+} to reaction mixtures such that negligible dilution of the system occurs. The indicator mixes very rapidly with the Ca^{2+}, and the high extinction coefficients make the system very sensitive to changes in Ca^{2+} concentration. A range of divalent cations can be readily examined.	1. Lowest concentration of Ca^{2+} that can be used in initial rate measurements is approx. 10 μM (Scarpa, 1974). However, lower concentrations of Ca^{2+} may be employed if murexide is substituted for arsenazo III (see Vallieres et al., 1975). 2. Possible interference from nonspecific binding of Ca^{2+} to external surface of inner membrane especially when employing low concentrations of Ca^{2+}. This is reportedly prevented by having Mg^{2+} present also in the incubation mixture (Scarpa, 1974). But Mg^{2+} in turn inhibits Ca^{2+} transport in heart mitochondria (Sordahl, 1975; Jacobus et al., 1975). 3. Not conclusively established as to the physical location of the murexide nor to what extent it combines to the inner membrane.	Mela and Chance (1968), Chance (1972), Scarpa (1972, 1974), Ashley and Caldwell (1974), Jacobus et al. (1975), Sordahl et al. (1975), Vallieres et al. (1975).

Potentiometry	The signals produced when a specific Ca^{2+} electrode monitors changes in Ca^{2+} concentration in the bulk phase are continuously recorded.	The system of Madeira (1975) is reportedly very sensitive and simple, permitting the measurement of rapid rates of Ca^{2+} transport even at very low concentrations of the ion.	According to Mela and Chance (1968) it is located in the aqueous phase outside the mitochondria. Some Ca^{2+} electrodes have slow responses to changes in Ca^{2+} concentration (Pressman, 1967). These are useful therefore only for measuring overall reactions, not for initial rates of changes (but see Madeira, 1975).	Truesdell and Pommer (1963), Johnson and Pressman (1968), Pressman (1967), Moore (1969), Madeira (1975)
Radioassay	Radioactive calcium ($^{45}Ca^{2+}$) is used to monitor movement of the ion into or out of mitochondria. Separation of mitochondria from the medium is achieved by rapid filtration or centrifugation; the mitochondria-free supernatant or the mitochondria themselves can then be assayed for the presence of $^{45}Ca^{2+}$. The usefulness of this method has been greatly extended by the application of the "EGTA-ruthenium red quench" technique (Reed and Bygrave, 1974b, 1975b) and improved buffers to give known concentrations of "free" calcium (Reed and Bygrave, 1975b).	By adopting the recent improvements to the technique, it is now possible to accurately measure initial rates of Ca^{2+} transport and especially to discriminate transported Ca^{2+} from that bound externally. The system allows great flexibility in incubation conditions, and only very small quantities of biological material need to be used. The transport of very low levels ($1 \mu m$) of "free" Ca^{2+} can be determined very accurately. Moreover, no complex equipment is required.	The new technique has few limitations. 1. The major one perhaps is the time resolution (about 5 seconds with unsophisticated equipment). This can be increased by employing a rapid-mixing device. 2. One should be aware of *possible* interference from exchange of radiocalcium with endogenous calcium. 3. The technique is clearly limited to radioions.	Lehninger and Carafoli (1967), Reed and Bygrave (1974b, 1975a,b)

(Continued)

TABLE I (*Continued*)

Technique	Principle	Particular attribute	Potential limitation	References
Anion penetration (swelling)	Use is made of the original technique of Chappell (1968) to suspend mitochondria in isoosmotic solutions of salts. When both the cation and anion are permeable, the solution is osmotically inactive and the mitochondria swell. The following anions are especially useful: isethionate (non-penetrant), acetate (electrically neutral movement as acetic acid or on acetate/OH^- antiporter producing pH across the membrane), chloride (crosses the membrane slowly by electrogenic uniport), thiocyanate (as for chloride, but rapidly).	The Ca^{2+} carrier can be studied readily in the absence of an energy source. Information on the penetration properties of cations can be obtained as well as that on the involvement of the electrochemical gradient on Ca^{2+} transport.	1. Information of only a qualitative nature can be obtained with this technique. 2. Very high (unphysiological) concentrations of both anions and cations are required. 3. Because of the dual requirement for anions and cations, it is not possible to study Ca^{2+} transport in the presence of only low concentrations of anions.	Chappell and Haarhoff (1967), Chappell (1968), Mitchell and Moyle (1969b), Selwyn et al. (1970), Chappell et al. (1972).
Fluorometry	Changes are recorded in fluorescence intensity at specific excitation (400 nm) and emission (520 nm) wavelengths when Ca^{2+} interacts with	Since the intensity of the fluorescence spectrum is a function of the polarity of the environment, information on the location of the cation in the	1. Knowledge is lacking on the precise location of the probe in the membrane and whether or not it can itself be translocated across the membranes. It is known,	Schatz (1969), Caswell and Hutchinson (1971a,b), Caswell (1972), Docktor and Magnuson (1973, 1974), Schuster and Olson (1974a)

Method	Principle	Advantages	Disadvantages	References
	chlortetracycline. The fluorescence is enhanced when the probe chelates diamagnetic cations like Ca^{2+} or Mg^{2+}. The fluorescence of the chelate is polarity-dependent, being greater in nonpolar environments such as that within a membrane. In these events also the calcium chelate has a conformation (and thus fluorescence) different from that of the magnesium chelate. In this way it is possible to distinguish between the Ca^{2+} and Mg^{2+} bound to the membrane.	membrane might be possible to obtain.	for example, that bacteria can actively transport chlortetracycline (Docktor and Magnuson, 1973, 1974) and that the compound is a potent inhibitor of mitochondrial protein synthesis—a process that occurs on the matrix side of the inner membrane (see Schatz, 1969). 2. It is not known how the probe–Ca^{2+} complex behaves when incubation conditions, such as ionic strength, pH, and temperature, are altered.	Saris (1963), Chance (1965), Chappell and Crofts (1965), Bielawski and Lehninger (1966), Thorne and Bygrave (1973).
Calcium-stimulated ATPase activity or calcium-stimulated respiration	Continuously record ATPase activity by H^+ ejection or oxygen uptake following the addition of Ca^{2+} to the reaction medium.	It is possible to quickly obtain many data on the gross effects of Ca^{2+} on mitochondria as well as considerable information on the Ca^{2+} carrier. This can be achieved with relatively unsophisticated equipment.	1. Limited to a substrate- or ATP-supported Ca^{2+} transport study. 2. Information concerning the Ca^{2+} carrier may be obtained only indirectly. 3. Quite high concentrations of mitochondria are usually required in order to make the measurements.	

(Continued)

TABLE I (*Continued*)

Technique	Principle	Particular attribute	Potential limitation	References
Magnetic resonance	Paramagnetic analogs of Ca^{2+} (e.g., Mn^{2+} and certain lanthanides) are analyzed by electron paramagnetic resonance (EPR) or nuclear magnetic resonance (NMR) techniques. The interaction of the ion with specific ligands within the mitochondria induce specific spectral characteristics that can be analyzed.	Much information can be obtained that is not so readily available by other techniques. These include the nature of the chemical bonding and state of hydration of the ion. This in turn provides information on the nature of the environment inside the mitochondria where the ion is located and the degree to which the transported ion is ionized.	1. The time needed for scanning can lead to a redistribution of the ion both within and without the mitochondria. 2. The paramagnetic analogs may not interact exactly in the same way as Ca^{2+} with the Ca^{2+} transport system.	Chappell *et al.* (1963), Gunter and Puskin (1972), Puskin and Gunter (1972), Gunter *et al.* (1975), Case (1975)
Flame spectro-photometry	The sample is "burned" in a flame that excites the element. The excitation spectrum can be read at a particular wavelength, usually against a standard curve using an appropriate spectrophotometer. In a recent modification, a new burner allows higher temperatures to be used enabling a greater degree of excitation of the element.	The modified burner and instrumentation allows not only Ca^{2+}, but also other cations to be analyzed at picogram levels contained in microliter volumes. Minimal interference occurs from coexisting anions and cations in the modified system.	No severe limitations of the technique are readily apparent.	Haljamae and Wood (1971)

the radioassay [without the ethyleneglycolbis(aminoether)-N,N'-tetraacetic acid (EGTA) quench] and the spectroscopic technique employing the metal chelator murexide. In very few reports has more than one technique been applied in the same study. Thus a direct comparison between these two techniques has yet to be made. In the author's view this would be a most profitable exercise since it would probably reveal explanations for some of the conflicting results obtained in different laboratories (see below). One notable instance where, in a single study, different results were obtained according to the method used to measure transport, is that of Schuster and Olson (1974a). These workers examined Ca^{2+} and Mg^{2+} transport by beef heart mitochondria using both the fluorometric and radio techniques. With the fluorometric technique, added phosphate was interpreted as inhibiting the transport of the ions into the mitochondria whereas with the radioassay, the phosphate enhanced ion transport (as would be expected from the large volume of information on the subject, see Lehninger et al., 1967). This illustrates the dangers inherent in experiments involving a "probe."

In the bulk of the experiments carried out in our laboratory, the radioassay has been employed. Because of our concern that the techniques to measure mitochondrial Ca^{2+} transport have not always been sufficiently rigorous as to quantitatively reflect the true activity of the process, we have devised a much improved radioassay for making such measurements. Since the assay is relatively new and has many attributes, it is profitable to discuss it here at some length.

2. A Solution to the Problem

The problem of low-affinity binding and its possible interference in kinetic measurements can be overcome in at least two ways. In the first, it is theoretically possible to add to the incubation system a compound or compounds that inhibit low-affinity (non-carrier-linked) external binding but which do not affect the carrier. Potentially suitable compounds would include K^+, Na^+, Mg^{2+} (Scarpa and Azzone, 1968; Azzone et al., 1969; Vainio et al., 1970) and local anesthetics (Mela, 1968b; Scarpa and Azzone, 1968), all of which readily bind to phospholipids. Indeed Mg^{2+} has been employed in reaction mixtures for just this purpose (Rottenberg and Scarpa, 1974; Scarpa, 1974).

However, this approach has quite severe limitations since any compound which inhibits external binding will do so competitively with respect to Ca^{2+}. Thus estimates of the V_{max}, for example, will still include the binding contribution (Reed, 1974).

The second approach has proved to be much more successful. Use has been made (Reed and Bygrave, 1974b) of knowledge that EGTA, which is a powerful chelator of Ca^{2+} (Schmid and Reilly, 1957; Sillen and Martell, 1964), is not accessible to the inner membrane matrix space of mitochondria. Evidence in support of this latter point comes from the following observations: (a) The mitochondrial spaces accessible to ^{14}C-labeled sucrose and ^{14}C-labeled ethylenediamine tetraacetic acid (EDTA) are identical (Harris and Van Dam, 1968). (b) The Mn^{2+} accumulated by mitochondria is inaccessible to EGTA (Chappell *et al.*, 1963; Chappell and Crofts, 1965) and to EDTA (Puskin and Gunter, 1973). (c) Mitochondrial swelling does not occur in isoosmotic solutions of NH_4-EGTA or NH_4-EDTA (Reed, 1974). As well, EGTA appears not to have any deleterious effects on mitochondria (Settlemire *et al.*, 1968).

Scheme 2 illustrates how EGTA has been used both to quench the transport of Ca^{2+} and to remove all the Ca^{2+} (external "free" and external "bound") not transported. Details of the procedure can be seen elsewhere (Reed and Bygrave, 1974b, 1975b).

One important practical attribute of the technique apart from its obvious simplicity is that it provides a means of unequivocally discriminating between the following three pools of Ca^{2+}: internal (i.e., transported), externally bound, or "free" (Reed and Bygrave, 1975b). Moreover, it can be calculated (Fig. 1) that treatment of the mitochondria with a 10-fold, or greater, excess of EGTA (above Ca^{2+}) should completely inhibit both transport and external binding of Ca^{2+}, assuming

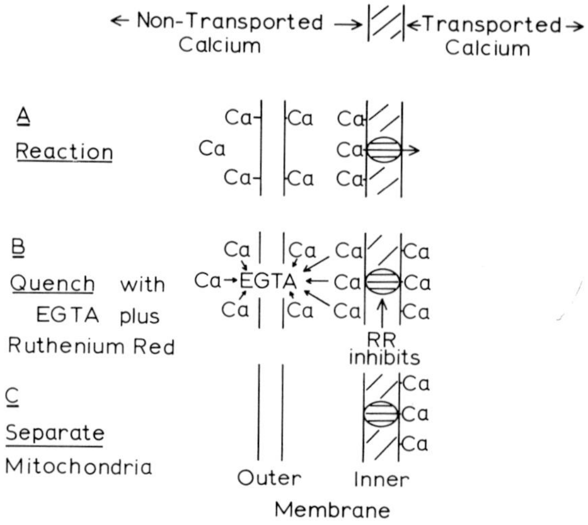

SCHEME 2. Sequence of steps involved in measuring mitochondrial Ca^{2+} transport by the ethyleneglycolbis(aminoether)-*N,N'*-tetraacetic acid (EGTA)-ruthenium red technique.

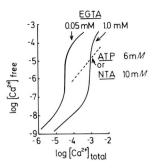

FIG. 1. Chelation of Ca^{2+} by ethyleneglycolbis(aminoether)-N,N'-tetraacetic acid (EGTA), ATP, and nitrilotriacetic acid (NTA). From Reed and Bygrave (1975b).

surface binding to be rapidly and completely reversible (Reed and Bygrave, 1974b).

The external application of EGTA as described can induce an efflux of Ca^{2+} from the mitochondria, since there is good evidence that carrier-mediated transport of Ca^{2+} reflects the establishment of a steady-state distribution dependent on the activity of Ca^{2+} in the internal and external spaces (see Section III,G). This efflux can be prevented by including ruthenium red in the quench medium (Reed and Bygrave, 1974b) (see Scheme 2).

The final point that needs to be made regarding the new technique, relates to the choice of buffer to be used, especially when low concentrations of "free" Ca^{2+} are employed. As will be shown below, the apparent K_m of the carrier system for Ca^{2+} is about 10^{-6} M, so a suitable buffer should generate stable concentrations of "free" Ca^{2+} in this range. Ca-EGTA buffers are clearly not suitable as at pH 7.4 a linear slope between "free" and total Ca^{2+} concentration exists only when the free concentration is less than 10^{-8} M (Fig. 1). When free Ca^{2+} is in the range of 10^{-6} M, it changes 50 times as rapidly as does the total concentration. We have employed ATP and more recently nitrilotri-acetic acid (NTA), both of which buffer in the region 10^{-6} M to 10^{-4} M "free" Ca^{2+} (Fig. 1). Of these, the latter is preferable as it is relatively inert (Reed and Bygrave, 1975b) whereas ATP can be transported and metabolized by the mitochondria although this can be overcome by using appropriate inhibitors (Bygrave et al., 1971a; Spencer and By-grave, 1972, 1973). The available evidence would suggest that the concentrations of EGTA employed in these studies, have little effect on the general properties of the mitochondrial membranes. Full details of the technology involved and suggested protocols for measuring Ca^{2+} transport are described elsewhere (Reed and Bygrave, 1974b, 1975b).

B. Evidence for the Location of the Calcium Carrier in the Inner Mitochondrial Membrane

Klingenberg (1970) has summarized the evidence indicating the highly permeable nature of the outer membrane of mitochondria to most metabolites and quite high molecular weight (ca. 10,000) compounds. Thus the transport systems that facilitate the rapid uptake of hydrophilic compounds into the matrix space are by implication generally associated with the inner membrane. There is now much evidence to support this view (Klingenberg, 1970). The particular evidence that consolidates this fact as regards the Ca^{2+} transport system is the following: (a) Mitoplasts (i.e., mitochondria devoid of the outer membrane) are able to transport Ca^{2+} with properties that are similar to those of intact mitochondria (Pedersen and Coty, 1972). (b) Ca^{2+} transport in mitochondria is driven electrophoretically by the proton electrochemical gradient that exists *across* the inner membrane (see Section III,G). (c) EGTA and EDTA, both of which do not penetrate the inner membrane, have no direct access to that Ca^{2+} which has been transported into the matrix space (Chappell *et al.*, 1963; Puskin and Gunter, 1973; Reed and Bygrave, 1974b).

C. The Affinity for Calcium

Prior to the employment of initial rate measurements to obtain quantitative information on the affinity of mitochondrial calcium transport for Ca^{2+}, there were indications from several earlier reports that the affinity was quite high, in fact possibly higher than that of ADP for the ATP synthetase in intact mitochondria. Thus Chance (1956, 1959, 1965) and Rossi and Lehninger (1964) reported that quite low concentrations of the ion could stimulate respiration. As well, the latter authors made the important observation that phosphorylating mitochondria provided with a mixture of ADP and Ca^{2+} will transport the Ca^{2+} prior to phosphorylating the ADP. Other evidence that provided some indication of the high affinity of mitochondria for Ca^{2+} was the experiment of Carafoli and Azzi (1972) in which the ability of varying concentrations of Ca^{2+} to stimulate the oxidation of reduced cytochrome *b* was measured. The authors obtained a value for the K_m of approximately 2 μM.

Detailed quantitative information on the affinity of the transport system for Ca^{2+} based on well-defined kinetic measurements was first obtained in 1971 by Bygrave *et al.* (1971a). Using a radioassay (Table I), they measured the initial rate of Ca^{2+} transport with ATP as a Ca^{2+} "sink" to lower the free concentration of the ion. The concentration of total Ca^{2+} was varied over a set range, and the "free" Ca^{2+} concentrations were computed from known values of the stability constants for Ca-ATP (see Fig. 2).

This experiment provides three important pieces of information concerning the mitochondrial Ca^{2+} transport system. It shows, first, that the system has a very high affinity for "free" Ca^{2+}; the K_m is 2–4 μM; second, the plot always exhibits saturation kinetics; and third, the curve is always sigmoidal, not hyperbolic. Moreover, analyses of the data by Hill plots revealed that the value of the Hill coefficient approaches 2 (Bygrave *et al.*, 1971a,b; Spencer and Bygrave, 1973; Reed and Bygrave, 1975a). Each of these fundamental properties of the Ca^{2+} transport system are seen also when nitrilotriacetic acid (see Table I) is used in place of ATP and when the EGTA-quench technique is applied to the measurement (Fig. 2). As well, these features have been seen in mitochondria from insect flight muscle (Bygrave *et al.*, 1975) and from ascites tumor cells (Thorne and Bygrave, 1975).

The sigmoidal nature of the curve relating initial velocity to Ca^{2+} concentration has since been confirmed by Scarpa and co-workers (Scarpa and Graziotti, 1973; Vinogradov and Scarpa, 1973; Scarpa, 1974; Vallieres *et al.*, 1975) using the murexide technique to measure initial rates of Ca^{2+} transport. On the other hand, these workers have consistently obtained considerably higher values for the K_m (50–60 μM) than those obtained in the author's laboratory. It seems possible that the measurements made with the murexide technique, especially at very low concentrations of Ca^{2+}, are susceptible to the nonspecific external

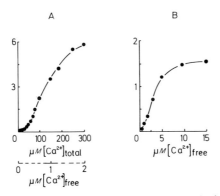

FIG. 2. Basic features of mitochondrial Ca^{2+} transport obtained from initial rate measurements. (A) With ATP as a Ca^{2+} "sink" (Bygrave *et al.*, 1971a). (B) With nitrilotriacetic acid to control the "free" Ca^{2+} concentration (Reed and Bygrave, 1975a). Initial rates (ordinates) nanomoles of calcium per milligram of protein: (A) in 10 seconds at 25°C; (B) in 5 seconds at 0°C.

binding of Ca^{2+} as discussed previously in this review (Section III,A). Scarpa (1974) has recently reported that a concentration of 10 μM Ca^{2+} is about the lowest measurable with accuracy by murexide in fast reaction kinetics. Moreover, the high K_m values reported by this group are difficult to reconcile with the observation that Ca^{2+} is transported by mitochondria in preference to phosphorylating ADP when each are present at similar concentrations; the K_m for the latter is less than 25 μM (Bygrave and Lehninger, 1967; Pfaff et al., 1969).

D. THE SPECIFICITY FOR METAL IONS

It is now clear that not one but a number of metal ions can be transported across the inner membrane of those species of mitochondria that are able to transport Ca^{2+}. However, not all these ions are transported at identical rates.

Mg^{2+}. Mitochondria in general do not accumulate Mg^{2+} (Chappell et al., 1963; Klingenberg, 1963; Pressman and Park, 1963; Sallis et al., 1963; Carafoli et al., 1964; Carafoli, 1965a; Selwyn et al., 1970; Thorne and Bygrave, 1973; Reed and Bygrave, 1974a).

Presumably Mg^{2+} present in mitochondria (Thiers and Vallee, 1957; Bogucka and Wojtczak, 1971) is taken up by passive movement of the ion across the inner membrane and/or by engulfing processes during the biogenesis of the organelle, perhaps chelated to a nucleotide or lipoprotein. On the other hand, it has been shown that mitochondria isolated from heart readily accumulate the ion-utilizing mechanisms similar to those that exist in liver mitochondria (Brierley et al., 1963, 1964, 1970).

Mn^{2+}. The study of Bartley and Amoore (1958) clearly established that Mn^{2+} could be accumulated by rat liver mitochondria, and Chappell et al. (1962) observed that Mn^{2+} could stimulate respiration in rat liver mitochondria. The ability of mitochondria to transport Mn^{2+} has since been confirmed by indirect (Carafoli, 1965a) and direct techniques (Chappell et al., 1963; Vainio et al., 1970; Gunter and Puskin, 1972; Case, 1975; Gunter et al., 1975). As a paramagnetic ion, it has been used extensively in magnetic resonance studies of bivalent ion transport in mitochondria (see Table I).

Ba^{2+} and Sr^{2+}. Several groups have established that Ba^{2+} and Sr^{2+} are accumulated by rat liver mitochondria. Carafoli (1965a,b) established that each of the ions could stimulate respiration and used direct techniques to measure Sr^{2+} transport. Selwyn et al. (1970) used the swelling technique to show that these ions were readily accessible to the matrix space of mitochondria. Vainio et al. (1970) used dual-wavelength spectroscopy and murexide and arrived at similar conclusions. The reports from each of these groups contain data that establish the following specificity pattern for bivalent ion transport in rat liver mitochondria: $Ca^{2+} > Sr^{2+} > Mn^{2+} > Ba^{2+}$.

La^{3+}. As discussed elsewhere in this review (Section III,E) La^{3+} is a potent inhibitor of mitochondrial Ca^{2+} transport. Despite this, however, it was known some years ago that the inhibition by La^{3+} of Ca^{2+} transport could be released with time (Mela, 1968a,b, 1969b; Lehninger and Carafoli, 1971), suggesting that the ion might be transported into the mitochondria. Later, Reed and Bygrave (1974a) showed unequivocally, using a variety of experimental techniques, that La^{3+} is indeed transported into mitochondria in a process similar in many respects to that of Ca^{2+} transport. More recently, Case (1975), using NMR techniques, has confirmed the conclusions of Reed and Bygrave (1974a) regarding the permeability of rat liver mitochondria to La^{3+}.

Fe^{2+}. In recent years Romslo and co-workers (Flatmark and Romslo, 1975; Romslo, 1975; Romslo and Flatmark, 1975) have examined in detail the transport of Fe^{2+} by rat liver mitochondria. Their studies indicate that the ion is transported across the inner membrane of mitochondria utilizing a carrier mechanism similar to that used in Ca^{2+} transport, but having an absolute requirement for reducing equivalents from the respiratory chain (Flatmark and Romslo, 1975). The ion appears to move across the membrane in the ferrous state.

In summary, the above information provides evidence that the following ions are able to be transported into rat liver mitochondria: Ca^{2+}, Sr^{2+}, Ba^{2+}, Mn^{2+}, La^{3+}, Fe^{2+}. Mg^{2+} is not transported by these mitochondria, but is transported by heart mitochondria.

Are all the ions mentioned above transported into mitochondria on the same or physically separate carrier systems? While there is little evidence to support the latter alternative, the following considerations would strongly argue that all the ions are transported on the same carrier. The inhibition of Ca^{2+} transport by La^{3+} (see Section III,E) and that of Sr^{2+} by Ca^{2+} (Carafoli, 1965a), is competitive. Chance and Mela (1966) also have argued that Mn^{2+} is accumulated by mitochondria in much the same way as is Ca^{2+}. Moreover, the general properties of accumulation of the individual ions are strikingly similar in respect to their requirements for energy, stimulation by permeant anions, and ability to stimulate substrate-supported respiration.

E. Inhibition by Lanthanum and Rare-Earth Cations

The inhibition by a specific compound of the movement of a molecule across a biological membrane constitutes important evidence for the involvement of a specific carrier (Stein, 1967). The finding of Mela (1967, 1968a,b) that La^{3+} inhibited a number of Ca^{2+}-associated responses in mitochondria was thus most significant. The pertinent observations made were that only 0.1–2 nmoles of La^{3+} per milligram of protein were needed to half-maximally inhibit the response to Ca^{2+}-, Mn^{2+}-, and Sr^{2+}-stimulated processes; the inhibition by La^{3+} was transient, disappearing in several minutes. In further reports (Mela, 1969a; Mela and Chance, 1969; Vainio *et al.*, 1970) it was shown, using the murexide technique, that Ca^{2+} transport itself was inhibited by La^{3+} as well as by other rare-earth cations (Pr^{3+}, Ce^{3+}, Ce^{4+}). In these experiments a La^{3+} concentration of 0.05–0.07 nmoles per milligram of protein was found to be sufficient to specifically inhibit Ca^{2+} transport. Moreover, the inhibition by La^{3+} was described (Mela, 1969a) as being noncompetitive.

In an analysis of Ca^{2+} transport driven by K^+ efflux, Scarpa and Azzone (1970) showed that in contrast to the conclusions of Mela (1969a), the inhibition of Ca^{2+} transport by La^{3+} was competitive, with half-maximal inhibition occurring at 50 ng ions per milligram of protein. The competitive inhibitory nature of the rare-earth cations on Ca^{2+} transport has been observed also by Selwyn *et al.* (1970) and more recently by Reed and Bygrave (1974b).

Several features of the inhibitory effect of La^{3+} on mitochondrial Ca^{2+} transport are such that they can complicate the quantitative measurement of the effects of the inhibitor. First, and as already mentioned, the inhibitory effect of La^{3+} is transient, reflecting its transport into the mitochondria (Reed and Bygrave, 1974a). Second, because of its high charge density, La^{3+} will bind to many of the components of the reaction mixture and thus falsify the concentration of La^{3+} in the medium. Third, it is clear that the lanthanides are very potent inhibitors and must be considered as "tightly bound" inhibitors. The kinetic data obtained should therefore be analyzed according to treatments specifically designed for this class of inhibitors (Strauss and Goldstein, 1943; Morrison, 1969; Henderson, 1972).

The information in Fig. 3A summarizes the salient features of the inhibitory effect of La^{3+} on the initial rate of Ca^{2+} transport by rat liver mitochondria. In the experiment shown, the initial rate of Ca^{2+} transport was determined at two concentrations of La^{3+} (for further details, see Reed and Bygrave, 1974b). The extrapolated lines intersect above the abscissa showing competitive inhibition (Dixon and Webb, 1964). The apparent K_i is 2×10^{-8} M, a value very similar to that obtained also by Mela (1969a) and Scarpa and Azzone (1970). Finally, an estimate of the concentration of La^{3+} binding sites can be made from these data; it has an approximate upper limit of 2×10^{-9} M or 0.001 nmoles per milligram of protein.

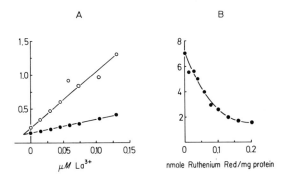

FIG. 3. Inhibition by La^{3+} and ruthenium red of initial rate of Ca^{2+} transport in rat liver mitochondria. (A) $\bigcirc$, 45 μM Ca^{2+}; $\bullet$, 185 μM Ca^{2+}. Ordinates: (A) 1/initial rate and (B) initial rate, nanomoles of calcium per milligram of protein in 5 seconds. From Reed and Bygrave (1974b).

F. INHIBITION BY RUTHENIUM RED

Moore in 1971 first observed that mitochondrial Ca^{2+} transport was sensitive to ruthenium red. The concentration of the dye required for half-maximal inhibition was approximately 4 nmoles per milligram of protein. Because it was considered that the dye reacted specifically with mucopolysaccharides (but see Luft, 1971), Moore concluded that such a compound must lie at the active center of the sites of the transport process.

Moore's findings were confirmed and extended by Vasington et al. (1972), who showed that a variety of Ca^{2+}-dependent mitochondrial activities including high- and low-affinity Ca^{2+} binding, were inhibited by ruthenium red in the concentration range 3–6 nmoles per milligram of protein. These workers found also that the compound did not inhibit the release of Ca^{2+} from mitochondria as measured indirectly by mitochondrial swelling and proton ejection. In a later report Rossi et al. (1973) showed, however, that if ruthenium red is added to mitochondria while they are accumulating Ca^{2+}, then a rapid release of the Ca^{2+} results. Once all the Ca^{2+} has been transported into the mitochondria, ruthenium red apparently no longer has any inhibitory effect.

The failure of ruthenium red to prevent the release of Ca^{2+} from mitochondria was seen by Stucki and Ineichen (1974). As well, they made the potentially interesting observation that the ability of ruthenium red to inhibit mitochondrial Ca^{2+} transport is related to the rate at which this process is occurring. On the other hand, Reed and Bygrave (1974c) have found that ruthenium red can inhibit the efflux of Ca^{2+} from mitochondria induced by EGTA.

In attempts to define further the interaction of ruthenium red with the Ca^{2+} carrier, Reed and Bygrave (1974b) examined the influence of the compound on the initial rate of Ca^{2+} transport. In this work, care was taken to ensure the purity of the ruthenium red used. The data in Fig. 3B, taken from this work, show that a concentration of only about 0.16 nmole per milligram of protein brings about almost complete inhibition of the initial rate of Ca^{2+} transport; the value for the K_i is approximately 0.05 nmole per milligram of protein. Similar values were also obtained with mitochondria from blow-fly flight muscle (Bygrave et al., 1975) and from ascites tumor cells (Thorne and Bygrave, 1975). The derived plots of the data treated in the form for "tightly bound" inhibitors (see Reed and Bygrave, 1974b), show the concentration of ruthenium binding sites as 0.08 nmole per milligram of protein. Most important, the inhibition by ruthenium red is noncompetitive ($K_i \simeq 3 \times 10^{-8}$ M) in contrast to the competitive inhibition by La^{3+}. The possible relation of ruthenium red inhibition to conformational changes in the Ca^{2+} carrier is considered below (Section III,I,2). Another compound that reacts with mucopoly-saccharides (hexamine cobaltichloride), has been shown also to specifi-cally inhibit mitochondrial Ca^{2+} transport (Tashmukhmedov et al., 1972).

It was pointed out earlier that studies with La^{3+} are potentially subject to a number of complications. The same is true for studies with ruthenium red. In the first place the compound needs to be purified prior to its use (Fletcher et al., 1961; Reed and Bygrave, 1974b). Thus the values for the K_i obtained with the pure recrystallized material (Reed and Bygrave, 1974b) are very much lower than those obtained with the crude preparations (Moore, 1971; Vasington et al., 1972). Second, the compound is prone to oxidation under mildly acid conditions, and it absorbs strongly to glass, quartz, etc., thus raising the possibility of its being "carried over" between successive incubations (Reed and By-grave, 1974b).

A comparison of the known inhibitory effects of La^{3+} and ruthenium red on mitochondrial Ca^{2+} transport is shown in Table II. It should be evident to the reader that these compounds and their analogs provide a powerful tool for analyzing the carrier mechanism. Already the value of ruthenium red has been demonstrated in the technique of measuring mitochondrial Ca^{2+} transport (Reed and Bygrave, 1975a, 1975b). The further identification of a colorless ruthenium complex inhibitory to Ca^{2+} transport (Reed and Bygrave, 1974d; see also Shamoo et al., 1975) should be more useful than ruthenium red in determining the relation between noncompetitive carrier inhibition and energy transduction in mitochondria. The use of the lanthanides will be especially fruitful, since

TABLE II

COMPARISON OF PROPERTIES OF LANTHANUM AND RUTHENIUM RED INHIBITION OF
MITOCHONDRIAL CALCIUM TRANSPORT[a]

Property	Lanthanum	Ruthenium red
Number of binding sites (pmoles/mg protein)	1	80
Nature of inhibition	Competitive	Noncompetitive
Inhibition released with time	Yes	No
Possible binding ligand	Acidic oxygen atom (phosphate, carboxylate?)	Potentially numerous (mucopolysaccharides, glycoprotein, phospholipid)

[a] References are listed in the text.

their interaction with the carrier can be analyzed both by fluorometric and spectroscopic techniques (Williams, 1970).

G. THE PRIMARY SOURCE OF ENERGY

Ever since the early experiments of DeLuca and Engstrom (1961), Vasington and Murphy (1962), Saris (1963), and Brierley *et al.* (1964), it has been evident that the nature of the driving force for Ca^{2+} transport is intimately associated with the underlying mechanism of energy transduction in mitochondria. Specific inhibitors and uncouplers of oxidative phosphorylation were used in this and later work to establish that Ca^{2+} transport could be supported by the energy of ATP hydrolysis (Fanberg and Gergely, 1965; Bielawski and Lehninger, 1966; Haugaard *et al.*, 1969; Tjioe *et al.*, 1970; Spencer and Bygrave, 1973), of respiration (Chance, 1956, 1965; Rossi and Lehninger, 1964), or of valinomycin-induced K^+ efflux in respiration-inhibited mitochondria (Scarpa and Azzone, 1970). These findings in turn implied that a common form of energy existed in mitochondria which was able to drive Ca^{2+} transport.

The potentially complicated nature of the interrelation between these three forms of energy—redox, phosphate group transfer, and electrochemical—is shown in Scheme 3. It is not profitable to discuss here the current status of the various theories of oxidative phosphorylation and the physicochemical nature of the partial events involved in the overall process, since numerous articles and symposia have been devoted to this question (see, for example, Mitchell, 1966, 1967; Greville, 1969; Racker, 1970; Skulachev, 1971; Green, 1974; Boyer, 1975; Boyer *et al.*, 1975). What does seem clear is that a reasonably strong argument can be

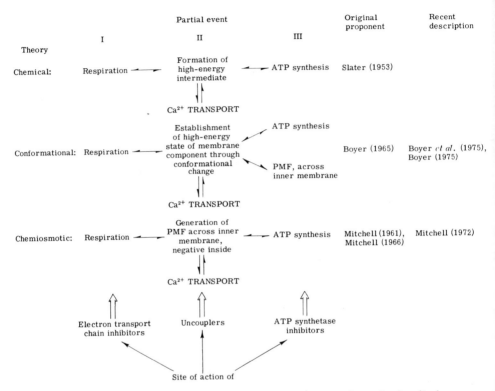

SCHEME 3. Description of the principal theories of energy transformation in mitochondria. PMF is the proton electrochemical gradient: $\Delta pH + \Delta\psi$ (membrane potential).

made establishing the direct involvement of the energy of the electrical component of the proton electrochemical gradient across the inner mitochondrial membrane in the translocation of Ca^{2+}. This argument will be developed now.

In his original enunciation of the chemiosmotic hypothesis, Mitchell (1961) proposed that the primary function of the electron transport chain was to generate what is now described as a proton electrochemical gradient across the inner membrane negative on the inside (see also Lundegårdh, 1945; Davies and Ogston, 1950; Robertson, 1960, 1968). Later Mitchell (1966) envisaged that charged molecules (including Ca^{2+} ions) would move across this membrane on an array of specific transporter systems located in this membrane essentially in response to this gradient. Indeed considerable evidence for the existence of such transporter systems in mitochondria has since accumulated (see Chappell, 1968; Klingenberg, 1970). A great deal of evidence indicates too that most anions distribute themselves across the inner membrane in response to the proton gradient (Quagliariello and Palmieri, 1970; McGivan and Klingenberg, 1971).

While few today would dispute the existence of a proton electrochemical gradient across the inner mitochondrial membrane (negative on the inside), several important quantitative aspects of it are currently the subject of much debate. Experiments of Mitchell and Moyle (1969a) yielded values for this gradient of 230 mV, negative inside; the major contributory component to this was the membrane potential ($\Delta\psi$). These findings were questioned by Rottenberg (1970) and Padan and Rottenberg (1973), who obtained lower values for the proton motive force, but recently the findings have been corroborated by Nicholls (1974), using a technique based on the distribution of Rb^+, acetate, and methylamine. What is important in the present context, however, is that in all these studies the membrane potential comprised at least 50% of the total proton motive force.

Although it has been argued that Ca^{2+} transport in mitochondria is an electrophoretic process driven by the membrane potential (see, for example, Lehninger, 1970; Pressman, 1970; Chance and Montal, 1971; Skulachev, 1971, 1972; Rottenberg, 1973), until recently few direct experiments have been undertaken to test this potentially most important aspect of mitochondrial Ca^{2+} transport. In the past few years, however, data in several laboratories have shed considerable light on this question.

Selwyn et al. (1970) used the passive swelling technique (Table I) to demonstrate that the transport of Ca^{2+} into the matrix space of mitochondria can occur independently of respiratory activity. They concluded that Ca^{2+} transport occurs either electrophoretically on a Ca^{2+} uniporter or as a K^+/Ca^{2+} exchange, i.e., independently of a mechanism involving a high-energy intermediate of oxidative phosphorylation. In the same year, Scarpa and Azzone (1970) showed that the influx of Ca^{2+} could be coupled to the efflux of K^+ in the presence of valinomycin in respiration-inhibited mitochondria. Later, Rottenberg and Scarpa (1974) provided evidence that, in the presence of valinomycin, $^{86}Rb^+$ distributes itself across the membrane in a way that correlates with the distribution of Ca^{2+}. In this work, however, respiration was not inhibited.

During 1974 three groups independently reported that Ca^{2+} could be transported by mitochondria in the absence of energy derived from respiration (Åkerman et al., 1974; Reed and Bygrave, 1974c; Southard and Green, 1974). Reed and Bygrave (1974c) used the impermeability of the inner membrane to EGTA (see Table I and Scheme 2) as a topological criterion for distinguishing between external binding (which potentially makes a major contribution to that "transported") and carrier-mediated transport. Reed and Bygrave (1974c) showed that the carrier could transport $^{45}Ca^{2+}$ to the internal phase (see Scheme 1) after treatment of the mitochondria with inhibitors of electron transport or with the uncoupler carbonyl cyanide m-chlorophenyl hydrazone (CCCP).

The evidence supporting the assumption that this Ca^{2+} represents that transported by the Ca^{2+} carrier included the inaccessibility of it to EGTA, its increase with time, its sensitivity to La^{3+} and ruthenium red in both the forward and reverse directions. The information in Table III summarizes the known properties of the Ca^{2+} transport system in mitochondria in which the generation of a transmembrane proton gradient from respiration is inhibited. A comparison of this information with that in Table I reveals several fundamental points relevant to the mechanism of mitochondrial Ca^{2+} transport.

First, many of the properties of the carrier system are qualitatively unchanged when the *proton* gradient is inoperative or collapsed. Second, since the rate of Ca^{2+} transport also is not significantly decreased under

TABLE III

PROPERTIES OF THE CALCIUM TRANSPORT SYSTEM IN RESPIRATION-INHIBITED MITOCHONDRIA

Property	Reference
1. Transported Ca^{2+} is inaccessible to EGTA	Reed and Bygrave (1974c)
2. Ca^{2+} saturates in mitochondria at about 20–50 ng of ions/mg protein	Reed and Bygrave (1974c), Scarpa and Azzone (1970)
3. Ca^{2+} in mitochondria increases with time	Reed and Bygrave (1974c), Scarpa and Azzone (1970)
4. Initial rate of Ca^{2+} transport of the order 5 ng of ions/ mg protein per second[a]	Scarpa and Azzone (1970)
5. Influx and efflux inhibited by low concentrations of ruthenium red and La^{3+}	Reed and Bygrave (1974c), Scarpa and Azzone (1970)
6. Influx inhibited by Pr^{3+}	Selwyn *et al.* (1970)
7. Transport inhibited by uncouplers of oxidative phosphorylation	Reed and Bygrave (1974c), Scarpa and Azzone (1970)
8. Stoichiometric exchange of Ca^{2+} and K^+ occurs	Scarpa and Azzone (1970), Selwyn *et al.* (1970)

Conclusions: a. There is no obligatory coupling of transmembrane Ca^{2+} transport to proton gradient
 b. The carrier transports Ca^{2+} electrophoretically across the inner membrane in response to the membrane potential

[a] Some external (i.e., EGTA-sensitive) binding could make this value an overestimate.

these conditions, there seems to be little reason to doubt that the primary driving force for Ca^{2+} transport is the electrical component of the proton electrochemical gradient. Third, the conclusions drawn here have obvious implications for the stoichiometry of Ca^{2+} to proton and Ca^{2+} to oxygen ratios and the interpretation of the values obtained, since Ca^{2+} movements can occur across the inner membrane without any concomitant respiration-generated movement of protons. For a recent appraisal of the problem of such stoichiometry, see Brand and Lehninger (1975).

A fourth point arising from the information in Table III is that respiration-inhibited mitochondria can be profitably exploited in future studies on the mechanism of mitochondrial Ca^{2+} transport. Indeed these mitochondria represent the least complex viable system yet described and would be ideally suited for such studies. A detailed examination of their properties should reveal basic information about the molecular details of the transport system. It would be of considerable interest to determine, for example, how permeant anions (which distribute themselves across the membrane in response to the proton gradient) and other metabolites (see Section IV) influence Ca^{2+} transport in this system. It would be profitable to study also the quantitative relation between the membrane potential and Ca^{2+} gradients in respiration-inhibited mitochondria.

The points that have been considered above are not meant to imply that the proton gradient does *not* influence Ca^{2+} transport. Since the membrane potential is generated by the electrogenic translocation of protons across the inner membrane (Mitchell, 1966; see also Henderson 1971), it logically follows that membrane-potential-driven Ca^{2+} transport will have a limited *capacity* in respiration-inhibited mitochondria. Thus it is quite conceivable that the proton gradient may act to *control* Ca^{2+} transport *driven* by the membrane potential. Apart from its obvious role in generating the membrane potential, the proton gradient may also influence Ca^{2+} transport in a number of ways including the following: (a) by altering the distribution of anions across the inner membrane that are known to influence Ca^{2+} transport (see Section IV and Lehninger, 1974); (b) by altering the internal alkalinity, which in turn will increase or diminish the availability of internal anionic sites for transported Ca^{2+}; (c) by inducing specific conformational changes in the Ca^{2+} carrier (see Section III,I and Boyer, 1975); (d) by altering the permeability of the inner membrane to Ca^{2+}; and (e) by influencing the release of Ca^{2+} from mitochondria. In this way the membrane potential is seen as the fundamental driving force for Ca^{2+} transport, but the rate and capacity of the process are modifiable by the proton gradient.

H. The Binding Components of the Mitochondrial Calcium Transport System

The operation of biological transport systems can be considered mechanistically in terms of the following components: *binding* of the substrate to the carrier, *translocation* of the bound substrate on the carrier from one side of the membrane to the other, *release* of the substrate from the carrier at the membrane surface, and finally, the *restoration* of the carrier to its initial state in preparation for the binding of a second molecule.

The binding of Ca^{2+} to the Ca^{2+} carrier clearly might be expected to constitute an obligatory step in its overall transport from the intermembrane space to the matrix space. Information on the concentration and dissociation constant of carrier-specific binding sites is essential for a complete analysis of the Ca^{2+} carrier. This information provides as well some of the criteria that must be met by any isolated protein or molecule regarded to be the carrier (see Table V).

Attempts to measure carrier-specific Ca^{2+} binding were reported by Lehninger *et al.* (1969), Reynafarje and Lehninger (1969), and Carafoli and Lehninger (1971). The work, carried out with rat liver mitochondria, revealed a class of high-affinity binding sites with properties very similar to those of the Ca^{2+} transport system itself; this energy-independent, high-affinity binding was equated with carrier-specific binding.

The conclusions drawn by these workers were questioned by Mela and Chance (1969) mainly because the number of high-affinity binding sites, reported as being between 0.6 and 8 nmoles per milligram of protein (Lehninger, 1969; Reynafarje and Lehninger, 1969; Carafoli and Lehninger, 1971), did not fit with the small number of binding sites revealed from La^{3+} inhibition data (Mela and Chance, 1969). In an analysis of La^{3+} and ruthenium red inhibition of mitochondrial Ca^{2+} transport, Reed and Bygrave (1974b) later observed that these compounds inhibit by binding at sites numbering less than 0.1 nmole per milligram of protein. Moreover, in reevaluating the significance of energy-independent Ca^{2+} binding by rat liver mitochondria, Reed and Bygrave (1974c) drew attention to the fact that the striking sensitivity of the high-affinity Ca^{2+} binding to the proton-conducting uncouplers 2,4-DNP and CCCP (Reynafarje and Lehninger, 1969) suggested that the site of such "binding" is not the Ca^{2+} carrier. Since the carrier had been shown to operate independently of metabolism (see Section III,G), binding to the carrier would be expected to be insensitive to uncoupling agents.

Reed and Bygrave (1974c) reexamined the energy-independent binding of Ca^{2+} to rat liver mitochondria using as mentioned above, the impermeability of the inner membrane to EGTA (see Section III,A) as a topological criterion for distinguishing between carrier-mediated transport and external binding. It could be demonstrated that the "high-affinity, energy-independent" binding reported by Reynafarje and Lehninger (1969) represented Ca^{2+} that had been transported to the internal space of the mitochondria. Conclusions similar to those of Reed and Bygrave (1974c) were reached independently by Åkerman et al. (1974) and by Southard and Green (1974). Thus the "energy-independent, high-affinity binding" of Ca^{2+} was shown to reflect limited active transport of the ion into the mitochondria. This provides a trivial explanation for the close similarity between Ca^{2+} transport and high-affinity, energy-independent binding. The argument that such binding represents a component of the transport system (Reynafarje and Lehninger, 1969; Carafoli and Lehninger, 1971; Carafoli, 1973, 1974, 1975a) is thus no longer valid.

In considering further the question of carrier-specific mitochondrial Ca^{2+} binding, Reed and Bygrave (1974c) have drawn attention to the difficulties (perhaps even the impossibility) of measuring such binding with present technology. There seems to be no way at present of obtaining accurate data for the concentration of "free" and "bound" Ca^{2+} at the very low levels required for such measurements.

Low-Affinity Binding Sites

It has been known for some years that mitochondria will bind Ca^{2+} in the absence of energy to a group of sites located on both the outer and inner membranes classed as "low-affinity" binding sites (Chappell et al., 1963; Rossi et al., 1967; Scarpa and Azzi, 1968; Scarpa and Azzone, 1968; Lehninger, 1969; Reynafarje and Lehninger, 1969; Carafoli and Lehninger, 1971). The sensitivity of the bound Ca^{2+} at these sites to Na^+, K^+ and local anesthetics (Mela, 1968b; Scarpa and Azzone, 1968; Vainio et al., 1970; Reed and Bygrave, 1974c) suggest that the binding sites are the polar head groups of membrane phospholipids. While early estimates of the number and affinity gave values of 30 nmoles per milligram protein and $K_d \simeq 100~\mu M$, respectively (see references above), the recent study of Reed and Bygrave (1974c), in which EGTA was employed to distinguish between internal and external Ca^{2+} (see Scheme 1), showed that these values are overestimates. In this work the low-affinity sites were shown to bind 15 nmoles of Ca^{2+} per milligram of protein with a K_d of approximately 20–25 μM. The role of these low-affinity Ca^{2+}-binding sites is not known, but it seems that they are not directly involved in the transport of Ca^{2+} across the inner membrane.

I. Approaches to the Study of the Physicochemical Features of the Carrier Molecule

Information recently obtained from several lines of work now enable at least some initial judgment to be made of the molecular properties of the mitochondrial Ca^{2+} carrier. Since much of the information is only preliminary, the present discussion will be aimed at providing an overall view rather than any detailed interpretation of the available data.

The relevant information pertaining to the physicochemical nature of the carrier can be gleaned from a consideration of the chemistry of Ca^{2+} itself and of the compounds that inhibit Ca^{2+} transport, by an analysis of appropriate data obtained from initial rate measurements, from a direct analysis of the interaction of the ion with the carrier, and by investigating the physicochemical properties of any molecule isolated from the membrane of mitochondria and *proved* to represent the carrier molecule *in situ*.

1. Types of Information

a. *Chemical Information.* The literature already contains much information providing clues as to the principal binding groups for Ca^{2+}; these are oxyanions, such as carboxylates, phosphates, and sulfonates (see Williams, 1970, 1974). In model complexes the binding strength of Ca^{2+} can be shown to be related to the number of carboxylates, a factor that probably forms the basis of the variable binding character of Ca^{2+} with some proteins (Williams, 1974). However, the binding of Ca^{2+} is not always simply related to the number of anionic groups available. For example, Ca^{2+} binds to EGTA with much greater affinity than it does to EDTA (Schmid and Reilley, 1957; Sillen and Martell, 1964), yet both compounds have an identical number (4) of carboxyl groups (see Appendix). Nor is binding strength related simply to the number of charged groups, although this may be so in some instances. Williams (1974) has pointed out that additional factors, such as the dielectric strength of the medium and the structure and strength of the hydrogen bonding to the water molecules and the other ligands may be important. These arise from second sphere, not just from coordination sphere, interactions. These latter points are relevant not only to the interaction of Ca^{2+} itself with ligands (especially those on the Ca^{2+} carrier) but as well to the related question of the cation specificity of the carrier.

b. *Kinetic Information.* Despite the potential wealth of information that can be gained from a systematic kinetic analysis of mitochondrial Ca^{2+} transport of factors relating to the physicochemical nature of the process, only one report of such a study has appeared in the literature at the time of writing. Cleland (1970) has pointed out that the effect of pH on the first-order and zero-order rate constants derived from the Michaelis–Menten equation (V/K_m and V, respectively) can provide information on both the active-site residues involved in the binding of substrate and in the rate-limiting step of its transformation.

In their kinetic study of the Ca^{2+} carrier, Reed and Bygrave (1975a) carried out such an experiment and observed that the plot of log V/K_m versus pH, asymptoted to a slope of one at low pH and to a slope of zero at high pH; the two asymptotes intersected at pH 7.8. The data indicated that a group or groups involved in the initial binding of Ca^{2+} to the carrier has a pK_a of 7.5 and is active in the dissociated state (Cleland, 1970).

Two other items of information were obtained from this study that provide clues on the identity of the carrier-binding site; the first is the high affinity for Ca^{2+} (the steady-state dissociation is of the order of 4 μM; see Section III,C); and the second, the high relative affinity of the site for divalent cations $Ca^{2+} > Sr^{2+} > Mn^{2+} > Ba^{2+} \gg Mg^{2+}$ (see Section III,D). Reed and Bygrave (1975a) pointed out that such high affinity and specificity are met only by a Ca^{2+}-binding site involving chelation by ionized oxygen atoms (Williams, 1970). However, no single functional group appears to have the desired properties (see Sillen *et al.*, 1971). Those compounds that best approximate the requirements are the multidentate ligands of the EDTA/EGTA type, where the cation is chelated by 3 carboxyl groups in close proximity to a tertiary nitrogen. Reed and Bygrave (1975a) have tentatively proposed that the binding site for the mitochondrial Ca^{2+} carrier involves (possibly) three carboxy-late residues in close proximity to a tertiary nitrogen, which has a pK_a near 7, e.g., of the imidazole ring in a histidine residue on or the primary amine of an N-terminal.

c. Magnetic Resonance Studies. In his study of the Ca^{2+} carrier in rat liver mitochondria employing magnetic resonance techniques, Case (1975) provided evidence that the carrier does not recognize Mn^{2+} on the basis of charge, since the complexes $MnHPO_4$ and MnC_2O_4 have none and yet can bind to the carrier. Case also reported that binding (of Mn^{2+}) was unaffected by the presence of permeant anions, such as phosphate and acetate. This was consistent with the earlier EPR data of Puskin and Gunter (1973), which showed that acetate does not displace the coordination H_2O from $Mn(H_2O)_6^{2+}$. This is good evidence that the anion enters mitochondria by a separate pathway. Other information gained from Case's study that is relevant to the present discussion was that the correlation time for carrier-bound Mn^{2+} is much too short to represent the motion of a spherical Mn^{2+}–protein complex in the membrane. Rather it was considered to be more consistent with a model where Mn^{2+} is bound to a small, freely swinging appendage similar in size to that of the ionophore A23187.

d. *The Isolated Carrier.* Little concrete information of a physico-chemical nature can be provided as yet from the Ca^{2+} carrier isolated from the mitochondria. As pointed out elsewhere in this review (see Section III,K), the identity of the molecules already isolated has yet to be firmly established. It is evident, however, that, if such success is achieved, it will constitute a major step toward providing a better understanding of the molecular details of mitochondrial Ca^{2+} transport.

2. Evidence for Interacting Binding Sites and Conformational Changes in the Carrier Molecule

In 1971 Bygrave *et al.* (1971a) reported that Ca^{2+} transport by isolated rat liver mitochondria exhibited the phenomenon of "cooperativity"; that is, when initial rates of Ca^{2+} transport are measured as a function of Ca^{2+} concentration, a sigmoidal curve results. This observation, which since has been confirmed in several laboratories, is now seen as a fundamental property of the carrier system in a range of mitochondrial species (Bygrave *et al.*, 1971a; 1975; Spencer and Bygrave, 1973; Scarpa and Grazziotti, 1973; Vinogradov and Scarpa, 1973; Reed and Bygrave, 1975a; Thorne and Bygrave, 1975). Of additional interest was the finding that the Hill plot derived from the primary data, gives a value for the Hill coefficient approaching two (Bygrave *et al.*, 1971a; see also references quoted above).

Cooperative interactions involving not Ca^{2+} alone, but Ca^{2+} and Mn^{2+}, have been observed by Chance and Mela (1966) and by Ernster and Nordenbrand (1967). The relation of that phenomenon to the one described above is not clear at this time.

Sigmoidal curves are usually interpreted in terms of a positive homotropic cooperativity between substrate-binding sites (Koshland, 1970), and in most cases of a cooperative enzyme, the Hill coefficient calculated from substrate-velocity data has given an accurate estimate for the maximum number of interacting binding sites. Thus it might be inferred that the mitochondrial Ca^{2+} carrier has a minimum of two interacting binding sites for Ca^{2+}. That the interaction of Ca^{2+} with biomembranes can induce structural (conformational) changes is now quite well established (Träuble and Eibl, 1974; Chapman, 1975; Jacobson and Papahadjopoulos, 1975).

Besides possessing two interacting binding sites for Ca^{2+}, the carrier is reversible and the EGTA-induced efflux can be inhibited by ruthenium red (Reed and Bygrave, 1974b, 1975a) a feature which also is consistent with a mechanism of Ca^{2+} transport involving conformational changes in the carrier protein.

A further item of evidence suggesting that the carrier undergoes conformational changes during its operation is that the ability of ruthenium red to inhibit Ca^{2+} transport depends upon the rate at which the Ca^{2+} is being transported across the inner membrane (Stucki and Ineichen, 1974); the greater the rate of Ca^{2+} transport initially, the higher was the affinity of the carrier for the inhibitor.

Of added interest to these findings are those of Wohlrab (1975), who examined the ability of ruthenium red to inhibit Ca^{2+} transport in mitochondria from flight muscle of the blow fly at different stages of development. He observed that the concentration of ruthenium red required to inhibit Ca^{2+} transport in young mitochondria (2 hours post emergence) was considerably greater than that required to inhibit in mature mitochondria (8 days post emergence). The ability of these mitochondria to transport Ca^{2+} changes markedly with development (see Section V), being greatest at emergence.

Evidence for conformational changes from magnetic resonance data has been mentioned already.

All these findings taken together provide evidence that the Ca^{2+} carrier undergoes some form of conformational change in the course of transporting Ca^{2+} from one side of the inner mitochondrial membrane to the other. The changes are such that they influence the ability of the carrier itself to transport Ca^{2+} and the ability of the specific inhibitor, ruthenium red, to bind to the carrier molecule. Further studies of these effects should provide informative insights into the mechanism of this aspect of mitochondrial Ca^{2+} transport.

J.   CALCIUM TRANSPORT IN SUBMITOCHONDRIAL PREPARATIONS

A number of groups have reported that Ca^{2+} can be accumulated by a range of submitochondrial preparations (see Table IV). Several experimental features appear to be common to all of the studies: First, a permeant anion was required in the incubation mixture; this was usually met with inorganic phosphate. Second, very high concentrations of Ca^{2+} (1–4 mM) were employed. Third, the initial rate of Ca^{2+} transport was not measured in any of the studies. Moreover, it is not possible to ascertain whether the measurements made in these studies reflected external nonspecific binding or transport of the ion or a combination of both. Some of the reports indicated an absolute requirement for ATP or ADP whereas others did not.

TABLE IV

CALCIUM "UPTAKE" IN VARIOUS SUBMITOCHONDRIAL PREPARATIONS[a]

Nature of preparation	Authors	Comments
Digitonin fragments prepared by treating mitochondria with digitonin	Vasington (1963)	Showed Ca^{2+} uptake was dependent on energy and respiration
Water-washed mitochondria	Vasington and Greenawalt (1964, 1968), Greenawalt et al. (1965)	These preparations have lost their ability to synthesize ATP, yet can take up large amounts of Ca^{2+}
Particles prepared either by sonic oscillation or digitonin treatment	Loyter et al. (1969), Christiansen et al. (1969)	Ca^{2+} uptake demonstrated. Absolute requirement for succinate and ATP shown. It is argued that Ca^{2+} transport takes place when membrane vesicles are inverted. High concentrations of Ca^{2+} required
Inner membrane vesicles prepared by controlled treatment of mitochondria with Lubrol	Chan et al. (1970), Pederson and Coty (1972)	Ca^{2+} uptake found to be dependent on added phosphate and a respiratory substrate. ATP alone could not support uptake, which was ruthenium red and mercurial-sensitive

[a] The term "uptake" is used as it is not possible to distinguish *transport* from *binding* in any of these studies (see Section III,A).

In summary, it seems difficult to make a judgment as to what the measurements made in these experiments with submitochondrial preparations really reflect. In some of the preparations, for example, it is possible that the treatment of the native mitochondria unmasked additional nonspecific binding sites for Ca^{2+}. It would be of value to reexamine some of these systems in the light of recent information on mitochondrial Ca^{2+} transport, especially that relating to the techniques that now permit discrimination between nonspecific, external binding and transport (Reed and Bygrave, 1974b).

K. THE ISOLATION OF CALCIUM-BINDING PROTEINS FROM MITOCHONDRIA

Efforts in several laboratories to isolate the Ca^{2+} carrier from mitochondria were initiated about 5 years ago, soon after it became apparent from studies with La^{3+} in particular (Mela, 1968a) and from those on high-affinity Ca^{2+} binding (Reynafarje and Lehninger, 1969, but see Section III,H) that such a carrier most likely exists.

The information pertaining to these studies is collated in Table V. Initial isolation procedures involved the osmotic-shock treatment of mitochondria in a manner similar to its application in the bacterial system (see Heppel, 1971). Other work has involved an analysis not only of the soluble (intermembrane) fraction of mitochondria, but also of the outer and inner membranes themselves. This work has led to the suggestion that the Ca^{2+} carrier is perhaps a glycoprotein (see Carafoli and Sottocasa, 1974, for a review).

Any studies of this nature that involve the isolation of a component from such a complex membrane system as found in mitochondria and the subsequent identification of the isolated component with that existing *in situ*, is clearly fraught with numerous hazards. Among the most obvious of these is not knowing whether the properties of the component change during its isolation from the membrane.

A list of basic criteria that might be considered as the minimum requirements to be met in attempting to identify any component isolated from the mitochondrial membrane that is purported to represent the Ca^{2+} carrier *in situ* would include the following:

1. The ability of the mitochondria to transport Ca^{2+} should diminish as the carrier is removed from the membrane.

2. The addition of the isolated carrier to the carrier-deficient mitochondria should restore the ability to transport Ca^{2+}.

3. Similarly to item 2, the addition of the isolated carrier to lipid vesicles might be expected to induce Ca^{2+} transport *provided* the specific phospholipid requirements of the carrier are known and met.

4. The properties of the isolated carrier (e.g., affinity and specificity for Ca^{2+}, sensitivity to lanthanides and ruthenium red) should be similar to those of the native system unless any alteration to the carrier in the course of its isolation can be shown to account for changes in these properties.

Additional, less stringent, features include items 5 and 6.

5. The concentration of the carrier in the membrane changes according to developmental and/or hormonal circumstances (see Section V).

6. The carrier might be expected to be located and distributed heterogeneously in the (inner) membrane (Werner and Neupert, 1972), with the highest concentration in that part where the outer and inner membranes are in close juxtaposition.

Until recently, few if any of the above criteria had been met with the isolated Ca^{2+}-binding protein. The difficulty with the "number of high-affinity binding sites" argument (Carafoli and Sottocasa, 1974) is the possibility that the values quoted are a gross overestimation of the actual

TABLE V

ANALYSIS OF CALCIUM-BINDING PROTEINS ISOLATED FROM MITOCHONDRIA

Reference	Isolation procedure	Reported physicochemical behavior	Comments
Lehminger (1971)	Osmotic-shock treatment	Soluble, heat-labile, binds Ca^{2+} with high affinity; MW > 150,000 inhibited by Sr^{2+}, La^{3+}, Mn^{2+}, but not Mg^{2+}	Technique used for Ca^{2+} binding subject to nonspecific binding (see Reed, 1972)
Gomez-Puyou et al. (1972)	Ammonium sulfate precipitation of soluble fraction from osmotic-shocked rat liver mitochondria	Insoluble in aqueous media; inactivated by dialysis; MW 67,000; high affinity for Ca^{2+} (K_D, 0.75-4 μM) with biphasic Scatchard plot; contains phospholipid and carbohydrate	Information on La^{3+} and ruthenium red sensitivity is lacking
Sottocasa et al. (1971), Sottocasa et al. (1972)	Soluble protein from ox liver mitochondria obtained by swelling in hypotonic buffer and purified by polyacrylamide gel electrophoresis	Acidic glycoproteins present in outer and inner membranes as well as in intermembrane space, all with similar properties; MW values vary from 42,000 to 33,000	Very high concentrations of ruthenium red (25 μM) induce only about 50% inhibition of Ca^{2+} binding
Carafoli and Sottocasa (1974)	Membrane fractions treated with chaotropic agents	One mole of glycoprotein binds approx. 3 moles of Ca^{2+} with high affinity; biphasic Scatchard plot; binding inhibited by La^{3+} and ruthenium red	The glycoprotein is found in yeast mitochondria, which apparently do not transport Ca^{2+} (Carafoli et al., 1970)

Reference			
Prestipino et al. (1974)	—	Electrical resistance of lecithin bilayers increases on addition of glycoprotein to medium	No net movement of Ca^{2+} across the bilayer occurs; lecithin may not be the natural phospholipid of the carrier in the mitochondrial membrane (cf. Spencer et al., 1976)
Sandri et al. (1976)	—	Ca^{2+}-binding protein is shown to move between mitochondrial compartments; Ca^{2+} transport occurs when the glycoprotein is bound to the membranes	See text
Blondin (1974)	Tryptic digestion of mercurial-treated, lipid-depleted heart mitochondria extracted with butanol:acetic acid:water	Properties of ionophore are similar to those of A23187 and X537A; it exhibits cation–proton exchange and induces the transfer of Mg^{2+} and Ca^{2+} across the mitochondrial (inner) membrane	See text

number (see Mela and Chance, 1969; Reed and Bygrave, 1974b). Also, some of the techniques employed to measure quantitatively the binding of Ca^{2+} to the isolated protein are open to criticism (Reed, 1972). Thus it may well be that fewer sites are actually present than those estimated from Ca^{2+} binding data alone. Furthermore, it appears from some of the reports (see Table V) that very high concentrations of La^{3+} and ruthenium red are required to inhibit Ca^{2+} binding in the isolated protein (cf. Sections III,E and F).

The apparent ubiquitous occurrence in the mitochondria of the glycoprotein (i.e., in the inner and outer membranes as well as the intermembrane space (Sottocasa et al., 1971), is difficult to reconcile with the overwhelming evidence supporting the specific location of the Ca^{2+} transport system in the inner membrane of mitochondria (see Section III,B). In recent reports from Sottocasa's laboratory, the suggestion as been made that the glycoprotein may behave as a mobile Ca^{2+} carrier which can readily associate and dissociate with the mitochondrial membrane. Evidence supporting this suggestion emanates from the observation that the extent of glycoprotein binding to the membrane(s) is dependent upon the existence of Ca^{2+} in the medium and is increased by Ca^{2+} transport. As well the detachment of the glycoprotein from the inner membrane of Ca^{2+}-loaded mitochondria, prevents the release of Ca^{2+} from the mitochondria (Sandri et al., 1976). If the findings can be upheld, then it would appear as though at least the first of the criteria listed above might have been satisfied.

Calcium Ionophores of Microbiological and Mitochondrial Origin

Ionophores, as their name implies, act by facilitating the movement of ions across artificial and biomembranes including the inner membrane of mitochondria. Two ionophores of microbiological origin have been found that will chelate Ca^{2+} and induce "exchange diffusion" type of cation transport across the mitochondrial membrane (for a recent review, see McLaughlan and Eisenberg, 1975). These are X537A and A23187 (see the Appendix for the formulas). Each is a carboxylic antibiotic.

The first, X537A, has a broad specificity for metal ions, being able to chelate Mg^{2+}, Ca^{2+}, Sr^{2+}, Ba^{2+}, and monovalent ions such as Rb^+ and Cs^+. Of these, Ba^{2+} chelates to the antibiotic with greatest affinity (Pressman, 1973). Two molecules of antibiotic are thought to form a complex with a single divalent cation.

The second of the two carboxylic antibiotics, A23187, is potentially more useful in studies with biomembranes because of its ion specificity. The ionophore is able to facilitate the transport of Mg^{2+} and Ca^{2+}, but not that of the monovalent ions. Again two molecules of antibiotic chelate to one of the divalent ions to give a neutral complex (but see Case *et al.*, 1974; Pfieffer *et al.*, 1974; Hunt, 1975). The available evidence would suggest that the ionophore catalyzes an electroneutral exchange of protons for cations (Reed and Lardy, 1972; McLaughlan and Eisenberg, 1975).

These ionophores are now important tools for the study of Ca^{2+} movements across the mitochondrial membrane and of Ca^{2+}-sensitive mitochondrial reactions that are influenced as a result of this transport (Reed and Lardy, 1972). Of relevance to the present discussion, however, is the recent report of Blondin (1974), in which an ionophore is claimed to have been isolated from beef heart mitochondria (see Table V).

This work follows the isolation of an Na^+,K^+ ionophore also from heart mitochondria (Blondin *et al.*, 1971). The divalent cation ionophore apparently has properties similar to those of the above-mentioned carboxylic ionophores; it is lipophilic, will induce a cation–proton exchange across an artificial membrane, and will induce the transfer (influx and efflux) of Mg^{2+} and Ca^{2+} across the mitochondrial membrane (Blondin, 1974). The isolation procedure used would imply a membrane origin of the ionophore in the mitochondria. If they can be upheld, the findings of Blondin are of obvious potential importance to the mechanism of Ca^{2+} transport in mitochondria.

L. Criteria for the Existence in Mitochondria of a Specific Carrier System for Calcium: Species and Tissue Specificity of Mitochondrial Calcium Transport

While a large proportion of studies on Ca^{2+} transport in mitochondria has been carried out with those isolated from rat liver, it is most probable that mitochondria from all mammalian tissues and the great majority of cell species are capable of transporting Ca^{2+}, as pointed out already by Carafoli and Lehninger (1971). The range of tissues shown in Table VI from which mitochondria have been isolated and for which there is evidence of a Ca^{2+} transport system is far from complete. However, the main purpose of presenting this information is to show the potentially ubiquitous occurrence of the Ca^{2+} transport system in various types of mitochondria. As well, and perhaps more important, it provides some insight into the nature of the evidence various authors cite as supporting the existence of the transport system in a particular species of mitochondria.

It should be clear from earlier considerations in this review that some aspects of this evidence are stronger and more unambiguous than others. For this reason, the nature of the evidence in the respective reports is categorized into what the author feels is "strong" and "weak" (see also

TABLE VI

Species of Mitochondria for Which There Is Evidence of a Specific Transport System for Calcium

Source of mitochondria	Nature of evidence*	Added feature*	Reference
Liver	a–g	i	Numerous (see Carafoli and Lehninger, 1971; Reed and Bygrave, 1975a; Dorman *et al.*, 1975)
Heart	d–f		Brierley *et al.* (1963, 1964, 1970), Scarpa and Grazziotti (1973), Jacobus *et al.* (1975)
Kidney	e–g		DeLuca and Engstrom (1961), Vasington and Murphy (1962), Carafoli and Lehninger (1971)
Spleen	f,g		Carafoli and Lehninger (1971)
Brain	f,g		Tjioe *et al.* (1970), Böhme *et al.* (1973), Lazarewicz *et al.* (1974)
Smooth muscle	d,f		Batra (1973), Vallieres *et al.* (1975), Wikström *et al.* (1975)
Adrenal cortex	e		Carafoli and Lehninger (1971), Simpson and Williams-Smith (1975)
Chondrocytes	f		Shapiro and Lee (1975)
Sperm	d,f	h	Storey and Keyhani (1974)
Hepatoma	f		R. F. W. Thorne and F. L. Bygrave (unpublished)
Ascites tumor	a–c,f	j	Thorne and Bygrave (1974a,b, 1975)
Insect flight muscle	a–d		Dawson *et al.* (1971), Hansford (1971), Wohlrab (1974)
		h	Bygrave *et al.* (1975), Wohlrab (1975)
Crab hepato-pancreas	e–g		Chen *et al.* (1974)
Plant	e–g		Hanson and Miller (1967), Chen and Lehninger (1973), Wilson and Minton (1974)

[a] Initial rate measurement of $^{45}Ca^{2+}$ transport at varying concentrations of Ca^{2+} indicating saturation, high affinity for "free" Ca^{2+}, and a sigmoidal relation between initial rate and Ca^{2+} concentration.

[b] Inhibition of Ca^{2+} transport by low concentrations of ruthenium red.

[c] Inhibition of Ca^{2+} transport by low concentrations of La^{3+} or other ions of the lanthanide series.

[d] Initial rate measurement of Ca^{2+} transport using murexide with data showing saturation and a sigmoidal relation between initial rate and Ca^{2+} concentration.

[e] Presence of high-affinity binding sites for Ca^{2+}.

[f] $^{45}Ca^{2+}$ measurements, but not of initial rate, and/or ability of Ca^{2+} to stimulate respiration.

[g] Lack of Ca^{2+} transport when "energy" is inhibited.

[h] Ability of mitochondria to transport Ca^{2+} changes according to the stage of mitochondrial development.

[i] Ability of mitochondria to transport Ca^{2+} changes according to the hormonal state of the animal.

[j] High concentrations of Ca^{2+} fail to uncouple oxidative phosphorylation.

* a–d, h are regarded as strong items of evidence; e is regarded as a weak argument; g can be weak or strong depending on the nature of the inhibitor as Ca^{2+} transport can occur when the energy of respiration or ATP hydrolysis is inhibited.

Stein, 1967). Thus the evidence supporting the existence of a Ca^{2+} transport system in mitochondria is regarded as being very strong when the following criteria are established: (1) initial rate measurements have been carried out with the elimination of nonspecific (external) binding; (2) the initial rate has been determined at various Ca^{2+} concentrations and shown to exhibit saturation, a high affinity for Ca^{2+} and a sigmoidal curve when initial rate of Ca^{2+} transport is expressed as a function of Ca^{2+} concentration; (3) with initial rate measurements, ruthenium red is found to inhibit (noncompetitively) with a very low K_i value; and/or (4) with initial rate measurements, La^{3+} is found to inhibit (competitively) also with a very low K_i value; (5) the initial rate of Ca^{2+} transport is inhibited after the energy of the electrochemical gradient has been dissipated by the appropriate ionophore (valinomycin plus K^+).

Evidence based on the presence of "energy-dependent, high-affinity binding sites" for Ca^{2+} (see Section III,H) and on the thermodynamic (i.e., nonkinetic) measurement of Ca^{2+} transport without regard for nonspecific binding is considered to be weak.

Moreover, when one examines a species of mitochondria for the purpose of establishing the existence of a Ca^{2+} transport system, it is important to bear in mind two further points. The first is that the "activity" can change according to the developmental and/or hormonal state of the tissue (see Section V). Thus Bygrave et al. (1975) and Wohlrab (1975) showed that a specific Ca^{2+} transport system exists in the flight-muscle mitochondria of the blow fly, but that it is most active at the time of adult emergence. Within about 24 hours the ability of the mitochondria to transport Ca^{2+} is about 20% of that at emergence. Changes in the activity of mitochondrial Ca^{2+} transport are seen also during the maturation of sperm cells (Storey and Keyhani, 1974), liver (Nakazawa et al., 1973; Pollack, 1975), and of heart (Mela et al., 1975).

The second point to bear in mind is the choice of the components that make up the incubation medium. Many potential components of reaction mixtures readily chelate Ca^{2+}. Among these are ATP and dicarboxylic acids, which often are used to provide the energy for Ca^{2+} transport, and inorganic phosphate, which is used to potentiate Ca^{2+} transport. As well, quite different rates of Ca^{2+} transport can occur depending on whether a sucrose medium or a salt (KCl) medium is used (see, for example, Reed and Bygrave, 1974a; Bygrave et al., 1975).

To summarize, then, a number of conditions need to be considered when setting out to establish the existence or otherwise of a specific Ca^{2+} transport system in a particular species of mitochondria. These include the choice of the incubation system, the precise nature of the experiments to be carried out, and, in developing systems, the possibility that the "activity" changes according to the stage of mitochondrial development.

M. SUMMARIZING FEATURES OF MITOCHONDRIAL CALCIUM TRANSPORT AND THE FORMULATION OF A MECHANISM FOR THE SYSTEM

The information in Table VII summarizes the known properties of the mitochondrial Ca^{2+} transport system that have been described in detail in this review. From this and other information it is possible to formulate at least the rudiments of a mechanism for the transport of Ca^{2+} across the inner mitochondrial membrane.

Transport is visualized as occurring in several stages (see Section III,H).

1. Interaction at the outer surface of the inner membrane: Ca^{2+} binds with high affinity to two interacting binding sites for Ca^{2+}; these contain carboxyl groups and are situated on the carrier.

2. Translocation through the inner membrane: The bound Ca^{2+} is rapidly transported from the outside of the membrane to the inside on the carrier in response to the membrane potential. The process most likely involves conformational changes in the carrier molecule.

3. Release of the Ca^{2+} into the matrix space: The release of the transported Ca^{2+} into the matrix space is the rate-limiting step in the

TABLE VII

SUMMARY OF THE PROPERTIES OF THE CALCIUM TRANSPORT SYSTEM IN MITOCHONDRIA[a]

Location	Inner membrane
Concentration[b]	Possibly only several pmoles/mg protein
Velocity (measured at 0°C)	0.4–0.7 nmoles/sec per mg protein; 1.0 nmole/ sec per mg protein in presence of 2 mM phosphate
Affinity for "free" Ca^{2+}	2–4 μM
Hill coefficient	1.7–1.8
Competitive inhibitor	La^{3+} ($K_i \simeq 2 \times 10^{-8}\ M$)
Noncompetitive inhibitor	Ruthenium red ($K_i \simeq 3 \times 10^{-8}\ M$)
Metal ion specificity	$Ca^{2+} > Sr^{2+} > Mn^{2+} > Ba^{2+} > Fe^{2+} > La^{3+}$
pK_a of binding groups	7.5
Minimal energy requirement	Membrane potential
Maximal capacity[c]	
In absence of phosphate	Less than 100 nmoles/mg protein
In presence of phosphate	Up to several μmoles/mg protein

[a] Although most of the data were obtained with mitochondria from rat liver, it is anticipated that the basic properties will be seen in all mitochondria capable of transporting Ca^{2+}.

[b] Deduced from La^{3+} and ruthenium red inhibition data.

[c] In general, this is the situation. However, it is now recognized that mitochondria from some tissues and species are able to accumulate even greater amounts of Ca^{2+} (e.g., chondrocytes, ascites tumor cells).

entire transport system. It is promoted by proton-yielding permeant anions, such as inorganic phosphate.

4. Presumably the carrier then reverts to its original state in order to transport further Ca^{2+} ions into the matrix space of the mitochondrion.

A schematic representation of this mechanism has been presented elsewhere (Reed and Bygrave, 1975a).

It is widely recognized that even a general model of metabolite transport across any biological membrane is currently difficult to construct (see Singer, 1974). At this stage, therefore, one can only ask questions of the molecular architecture of the mitochondrial Ca^{2+} transport system.

Does the Ca^{2+} carrier constitute an integral protein of the mitochondrial membrane spanning it from one side to the other? Does its molecular arrangement in the membrane comprise a "pore" or transmembrane channel (Singer, 1974) through which Ca^{2+} may be specifically transported? If so, is the same pore also the vehicle for Ca^{2+} exit from the mitochondria? If the glycoprotein isolated and studied by Carafoli and Sottocasa (1974) is a genuine component of the mitochondrial Ca^{2+} transport system, is it the transmembrane carrier or does the molecule represent a binding protein that attaches (peripherally) to the outer surface of the transmembrane channel, thereby conferring specificity and recognition sites for Ca^{2+}? The fact that the glycoprotein is very hydrophilic, makes it a most unlikely candidate for the transmembrane carrier.

It is anticipated that answers to most of these and numerous other fundamental questions will not be to hand for some time to come.

IV. The Control of Mitochondrial Calcium Transport

In attempting to identify both those factors that can influence mitochondrial Ca^{2+} transport and the rate-limiting steps in the mechanism, one is immediately confronted by the difficulty that the transport of the ion is itself obligatorily dependent on the existence of a membrane potential (see Section III,G). Thus in the present context it is important to discriminate between those factors that will influence Ca^{2+} transport *directly,* i.e., by direct interaction with the carrier molecule in the inner membrane, and those that will influence it *indirectly,* i.e., by interaction with, for example, the proton gradient or membrane potential.

Table VIII lists those factors reported in the literature that are able to influence the inward and outward movements of Ca^{2+} in mitochondria. What is immediately apparent is that information on this aspect of mitochondrial Ca^{2+} transport is scant. Yet, as will be seen (see Section

TABLE VIII

FACTORS REPORTEDLY CAPABLE OF INFLUENCING KINETIC AND THERMODYNAMIC
ASPECTS OF MITOCHONDRIAL CALCIUM TRANSPORT

Direction of transport	Nature of influence	Factor
Influx	Direct	External Ca^{2+} concentration
	Indirect	Magnitude of proton electrochemical gradient; permeant anions, adenine nucleotides, phosphoenolpyruvate
Efflux	Direct	?
	Indirect	Magnitude of proton electrochemical gradient, permeant anions, cAMP, Na^+, adenine nucleotides, phosphoenolpyruvate, cytoplasmic metabolic factor

V), such information is crucial for our full understanding of the role of mitochondrial Ca^{2+} transport in the regulation of cell metabolism.

The only factor apparent to the author that will directly influence the inward movement of the ion is the concentration of Ca^{2+} in the medium (see the cooperative phenomenon, Section III,C). Other factors may well do so but have not yet been identified. It is not known what factors are able directly to influence Ca^{2+} efflux from mitochondria.

On the other hand, several factors (reportedly) are capable of altering the rate and extent of Ca^{2+} influx and efflux indirectly. By artificially changing the magnitude of the proton electrochemical gradient, such as by limiting respiratory activities or by adding specific inhibitors or ionophores, it is possible to alter the rate and extent of Ca^{2+} transport. However, it is difficult to imagine that the magnitude of the gradient would change significantly *in situ* to be of physiological significance, although this has to be verified experimentally.

A number of physiological factors are reported to be able to influence Ca^{2+} movements in mitochondria. These include cyclic AMP (Borle, 1974; Matlib and O'Brien, 1974), phosphoenol pyruvate (Chudapongse and Haugaard, 1973; Peng *et al.*, 1974), inorganic phosphate (Drahota *et al.*, 1965; Harris, 1972), adenine nucleotides (Le Blanc *et al.*, 1970; Le Blanc and Clauser, 1974), Na^+ (Carafoli *et al.*, 1974), and also a cytoplasmic metabolic factor (CMF) isolated from the soluble fraction of mammalian cells (Kun *et al.*, 1969; Lee *et al.*, 1971; Binet and Volfin, 1974, 1975a).

Detailed discussion of the interactions that have been described are beyond the scope of the present review and will be considered elsewhere (Bygrave, 1977). What is evident is that the movements of Ca^{2+} into and out of mitochondria can be influenced by a range of metabolites which themselves are capable of movement into and out of the mitochondria. Moreover, many of them are known to have specific regulatory functions in cell metabolism. How their movements and those of Ca^{2+} are all coordinated and integrated into the cell metabolic network remains an intriguing question. One important feature emerging from the assembled data, however, is that the intramitochondrial Mg^{2+}, phosphate, and adenine nucleotide levels are important determinants in the "stability" of that Ca^{2+} transported into the mitochondria (see, for example, Binet and Volfin, 1975b; Siliprandi et al., 1975). The possible role of protons in the control of Ca^{2+} transport was considered earlier (Section III,G).

PERMEANT ANIONS AND THE RATE-LIMITING STEP

The ability of inorganic phosphate (Rossi and Lehninger, 1964; Chance and Yoshioka, 1966) and of acetate (Rasmussen et al., 1965; Mela and Chance, 1968) to stimulate both the rate and extent of Ca^{2+} transport by mitochondria is now well established. It is not the intention to discuss the details of these effects (see Lehninger et al., 1967; Harris, 1972; Harris et al., 1974; Lehninger, 1974) except as they apply directly to the mechanism of the Ca^{2+} carrier.

Little attempt has been made in the past to analyze the kinetics of Ca^{2+} transport in the absence and in the presence of these anions. However, recent kinetic analyses of mitochondrial Ca^{2+} transport (Reed and Bygrave, 1975a; Thorne and Bygrave, 1975) show that the addition of low concentrations of phosphate to the incubation medium increases the maximal velocity of Ca^{2+} transport but has little influence, if any, on the value of the K_m and the Hill coefficient (Fig. 4). Similar effects were found when acetate was present in place of the phosphate. Reed and Bygrave (1975a) further showed that the inclusion of thiocyanate, which penetrates as the dissociated species (Mitchell and Moyle, 1969b), had no effect on either the rate or extent of transport.

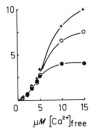

FIG. 4. Influence of inorganic phosphate (P_i) on the initial rate measurement of Ca^{2+} transport in ascites tumor mitochondria as a function of Ca^{2+} concentration. P_i: +, 200 μM; $\bigcirc$, 50 μM; $\bullet$, 0 μM. Ordinate: initial rate as nanomoles of calcium per milligram of protein in ten seconds at 10°C. From Thorne and Bygrave (1975).

This specificity pattern for anion stimulation of the initial rate of Ca^{2+} transport is consistent with that recently outlined by Lehninger (1974). Those anions belonging to that class which stimulate Ca^{2+} transport are characterized by an ability to yield protons once inside the mitochondrial matrix; those which do not stimulate are unable to yield a proton (Lehninger, 1974). The critical point however is that the maximal velocity of mitochondrial Ca^{2+} transport can be shown to be increased simply by including in the medium permeant anions, which themselves have no effect on energy generation or maintenance.

The constancy of the values for the K_m and the Hill coefficient in the absence and presence of permeant anions is consistent with a lack of direct interaction of these compounds with the Ca^{2+} carrier, a conclusion also reached by Case (1975).

This information then provides evidence that the energy source is not the rate-limiting step in Ca^{2+} transport. In addition we have shown that the initial rate of Ca^{2+} transport can change independently of energy maintenance (Bygrave et al., 1975; Dorman et al., 1975). The dissociation of the Ca^{2+} from the carrier in the internal phase of the mitochondria most probably is the rate-limiting step (Reed and Bygrave, 1975a). The stimulation of the maximal velocity by phosphate and acetate can be ascribed (Reed and Bygrave, 1975a) to their causing a decrease in pH of the internal phase (Rasmussen et al., 1965; Chance and Mela, 1966; Gear et al., 1967).

Presumably the carrier-mediated Ca^{2+} that is transported into the mitochondria in the absence of permeant anions, remains bound to anionic sites on the inside of the inner membrane. In the presence of these anions the matrix pH is lowered sufficiently to effectively dissociate the ion from the membrane. Indeed, Reed and Bygrave (1975a) were able to calculate from kinetic data that a fall in the internal pH of 0.3 pH unit at about pH 7.4, would be sufficient to double the rate constant release of the ion and consequently double the maximal velocity.

V. The Physiological Role of Mitochondrial Calcium Transport

As research into the mechanism of mitochondrial Ca^{2+} transport has intensified during the last several years, so has interest in the question of the physiological role of the process. In contemplating a physiological role for the transport of Ca^{2+} by mitochondria, several factors need to be considered. First, the physiological role may be expressed differently in different cells according to the particular specialized function they carry out. Second, the ability of mitochondria themselves to sequester and release Ca^{2+} should be related, as far as possible, to the ability of other vesicular components of the cell to perform the same task. Third, the possibility should be considered that within a given cell species the ability of the mitochondria to transport and retain Ca^{2+} can change (transiently) according, for instance, to developmental and/or hormone-induced cellular events.

The question of the physiological role of mitochondrial Ca^{2+} transport will be considered here from several viewpoints, but as the topic is the subject of a review to appear elsewhere (Bygrave, 1977), only the principal features of these viewpoints will be discussed.

That mitochondria might play a part in cell homeostasis and the control of the ionic environment was suggested some time ago (Bygrave, 1964, 1967; Lehninger, 1964; Carafoli, 1967) although few experiments were directed then toward this aspect of mitochondrial Ca^{2+} transport. Among a number of specific physiological functions that might involve the participation of Ca^{2+} transport by mitochondria are muscle contraction–relaxation (see Langer, 1973; Carafoli, 1975b) and bone formation (Lehninger, 1970; Becker et al., 1974).

In our view, there is a quite fundamental and general physiological role that can be assigned to mitochondrial Ca^{2+} transport in a range of species—that of modifying cell metabolism by control of the ionic environment. The arguments constituting this hypothesis can be considered in three broad categories; the sensitivity of a range of cell metabolic processes to Ca^{2+} ions, the properties of the mitochondrial transport system, and the elucidation of biosystems in which the "activity" of mitochondrial Ca^{2+} transport can be shown to change according to physiological circumstances (Bygrave, 1975).

One cannot fail to be impressed by the large number and variety of enzymes, metabolic pathways, and events in the cell that are sensitive to low concentrations of Ca^{2+} (Heilbrunn, 1952; Dixon and Webb, 1964; Bygrave, 1964, 1967, 1976a; Bianchi, 1968; Rasmussen, 1970). Particularly relevant is the finding that in many instances of Ca^{2+} inhibition the mechanism can be traced to an antagonistic action of the Ca^{2+} with the (usually) obligatory ion, Mg^{2+}. This is seen most clearly in the enzyme pyruvate kinase (Bygrave, 1966a,b; Meli and Bygrave, 1972) and as well in the pathways of phospholipid (Roberts and Bygrave, 1973) and protein biosynthesis (Rao et al., 1974). Thus, what logically develops from this is the need to consider not the Ca^{2+} concentration alone, but rather the Mg^{2+}/Ca^{2+} ratio, in a particular environment. This takes us to the next point.

A number of features of the mitochondrial Ca^{2+} transport system are such that they can be considered as being specifically geared for rapidly changing the Mg^{2+}/Ca^{2+} ratio outside the mitochondria where many of these ion-sensitive reactions are located. Particularly prominent are the high affinity for Ca^{2+}, the cooperative nature of the transport process, which is reminiscent of regulatory behavior (Monod et al., 1965), the rapid rates of transport, their capacity for transport (Borle, 1973) and equally important, the metal ion specificity. It will be recalled (see Section III,L) that most species of mitochondria, except those from heart, are unable to transport Mg^{2+}. Thus, in this way the mitochondria in principle are capable of rapidly changing the Mg^{2+}/Ca^{2+} ratio in the extramitochondrial medium.

These ideas have been put to test in an *in vitro* system wherein pyruvate kinase activity, which as mentioned above is sensitive to the Mg^{2+}/Ca^{2+} ratio in the environment (Bygrave, 1966b; Meli and Bygrave, 1972), was measured in the presence of mitochondria (see Scheme 4). The incubation conditions were such that initially Mg^{2+}, but not Ca^{2+} nor energy for Ca^{2+} transport (succinate), was present; under these circumstances the rate of pyruvate kinase activity was maximal. Upon addition of Ca^{2+}, containing radiocalcium, the rate was inhibited some 75%. Succinate was added and the mitochondria were able then to transport the Ca^{2+} away from the immediate environment of the enzyme, thus restoring the high Mg^{2+}/Ca^{2+} ratio and permitting again high rates of pyruvate kinase activity. Later the uncoupler, CCCP, was added to the system. This induced the (irreversible) release of the transported Ca^{2+}, which in turn led to a lowering of the Mg^{2+}/Ca^{2+} ratio with a concomitant drop in pyruvate kinase activity. This experiment leaves little doubt about the potential ability of mitochondria to modify enzyme activities by controlling the extramitochondrial ionic environment. Similar considerations can be applied to the enzymes located inside the mitochondria that are also sensitive to Mg^{2+} and Ca^{2+} (see, for example, Gevers and Krebs, 1966; Kimmich and Rasmussen, 1969; Lin et al., 1969; Denton et al., 1972, 1975; Schuster and Olson, 1974b; Randle et al., 1974).

It was with these ideas in mind that we undertook an examination of mitochondrial Ca^{2+} transport in mitochondria from developing flight muscle of the sheep blow fly (Bygrave et al., 1975), from insulin-challenged liver cells (Barritt et al., 1975; Dorman et al., 1975), and from the rapidly dividing Ehrlich ascites tumor cells (Thorne and Bygrave, 1973; 1974a,b; McIntyre and Bygrave, 1974; Bygrave, 1976b). We argued that, if Ca^{2+} transport by mitochondria does play a physiological role in cell metabolism, one might reasonably expect to find the "activity" of such transport to change (transiently) during cell development and following hormonal perturbation and perhaps to possess permanently altered characteristics in maximally deviated cells, such as those of the ascites tumor.

In fact we did discover that metabolically significant changes of the

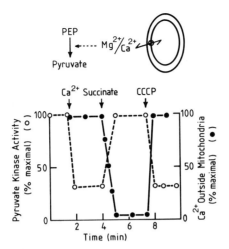

SCHEME 4. Modification by mitochondrial Ca^{2+} transport of the $Mg^{2+}:Ca^{2+}$ ratio and its influence on Ca^{2+}-sensitive enzyme activities. PEP, phosphoenol pyruvate; CCCP, carbonyl cyanide m-chlorophenyl hydrazone. From Meli and Bygrave (1972).

Ca^{2+} transport system in mitochondria do take place. In our view these findings constitute the most powerful evidence to date that mitochondrial Ca^{2+} transport does play a major role in controlling cell metabolism.

BIOSYSTEMS FOR THE STUDY OF MITOCHONDRIAL CALCIUM TRANSPORT

A major drawback to using mitochondria isolated from mammalian sources in the study of membrane structure, function, and biogenesis is the inability to induce the formation of membrane mutants. By contrast, this clearly is the major attribute to using for example yeast cells (Schatz, 1969) and is a most powerful tool in any study on mitochondrial membranes. Since mitochondria from the yeast *Saccharomyces* appear to lack the ability to transport Ca^{2+} (Carafoli *et al.*, 1970), they offer little in the study of this system. For this reason alone, the fact that Ca^{2+} transport in mitochondria can now be shown to *change* or undergo perturbations under a variety of physiological conditions provides a potentially significant and valuable tool for examining a number of aspects of mitochondrial Ca^{2+} transport, which otherwise would not be possible. These will now be outlined.

1. Changes in Calcium Transport during Development of Mitochondria

It is now established that mitochondria isolated from the flight muscle of the sheep blow fly, *Lucilia cuprina,* and perhaps from other species of fly (Wohlrab, 1974, 1975), possess a specific Ca^{2+} transport system with properties obtained from kinetic measurements (Bygrave *et al.*, 1975), very similar to those known to occur in mammalian mitochondria. However, the most exciting feature of the transport system is that its "activity" changes according to the stage of mitochondrial development. Using the rate of ADP-stimulated respiration as an index to follow the functional development of the mitochondria, Bygrave *et al.* (1975) showed that, at emergence, when the mitochondria begin a rapid phase of development, their ability to transport Ca^{2+} is maximal. Within about 4 hours, when the phase of rapid (functional) development is nearing completion, the ability to transport Ca^{2+} has already begun to decline. By the age of about 15 hours after emergence, the rate of mitochondrial Ca^{2+} transport has declined to values approaching 20% of that seen at emergence (see also Wohlrab, 1975).

This system offers much for the study of mitochondrial Ca^{2+} transport. First, it will be possible to correlate the change in Ca^{2+} transport activity with that of *other metabolite* transport systems in these mitochondria (see Doy *et al.*, 1975). This information could provide clues toward our understanding the way in which some of these—for example, the phosphate transport system—might be involved in the control of Ca^{2+} transport. Second, it will be possible to correlate the *development* of the proton electrochemical gradient across the inner membrane of the mitochondria with that of the Ca^{2+} gradients. This in turn will provide further insight into the role of energy for Ca^{2+} transport. Information on the *biogenesis* and possible turnover of the Ca^{2+} carrier can be obtained by administering specific *inhibitors* of protein synthesis into the fly at different stages of the life cycle (Campbell and Birt, 1975). It should be possible also to determine whether the concentration of the Ca^{2+} *carrier* in the membrane changes during development. Finally, the system allows a direct correlation to be made between the apparent decay in activity of mitochondrial Ca^{2+} transport and the *physiological factors* involved in preparing the insect for flight.

2. Transient Changes in Mitochondrial Calcium Transport Induced by Hormones

We have reported recently that the administration of insulin to rats induces changes in the Ca^{2+} transport system of the mitochondria subsequently isolated from the liver (Barritt *et al.*, 1975; Dorman *et al.*, 1975). From initial rate measurements we observed that the rate of Ca^{2+} transport is increased up to 60% depending on the concentration of insulin administered and the time at which the mitochondria are isolated after such administration. The second major change is that the mitochondria from livers of the insulin-treated rats are able to retain the accumulated Ca^{2+} for considerable periods of time. Significantly, and in contrast to the fly system, there is no alteration in ability of the mitochondria to carry out respiration in the absence or in the presence of ADP. The changes observed in mitochondrial Ca^{2+} transport are transient, and they are prevented if cycloheximide is coinjected with the insulin (Dorman et al., 1975).

In the insulin-induced system it is clear that the "activity" of mitochondrial Ca^{2+} transport changes independently of the magnitude of the proton electrochemical gradient across the inner membrane. By inference then, factors other than this gradient must have a controlling influence on Ca^{2+} transport. It will be possible to examine this question in these mitochondria. For example, it will be of interest to relate changes in other metabolite transport systems with those that are seen with Ca^{2+} transport. In this context there is no change in the ability of the mitochondria to translocate ADP and ATP (Dorman et al., 1975).

The data already obtained provide evidence for the existence of a specific (protein) carrier for Ca^{2+} whose activity can be modified by cycloheximide-sensitive, insulin-mediated cellular events. Aspects of the biogenesis of the carrier can be examined in this system, as well as the sequence of events that transpires between the interaction of hormone with the insulin-sensitive receptor at the cell membrane surface (Sica and Cuatrecasas, 1973) and the actual molecular changes that occur in the inner membrane of the mitochondria. This system then has provided new information on hitherto undetected effects of insulin on mammalian mitochondria. Finally, the insulin-induced system will provide new insights also into the mechanism of Ca^{2+} release by liver mitochondria.

3. Permanent Changes in Mitochondrial Calcium Transport in Tumor Cells

Mitochondria isolated from the maximally deviated Ehrlich ascites tumor cells have been shown to possess a Ca^{2+} transport system with properties virtually identical to those of normal mitochondria (see Thorne and Bygrave, 1975; reviewed by Bygrave, 1976). On the other hand, they are able to tolerate extremely high concentrations of Ca^{2+} even in the presence of very high concentrations of inorganic phosphate and for prolonged periods (McIntyre and Bygrave, 1974), and the ion fails to uncouple oxidative phosphorylation in these organelles (Thorne and Bygrave, 1974a,b; Bygrave, 1976b).

Since the uncoupling effect of the Ca^{2+} in normal mitochondria reflects interactions of the ion with the (inner) membrane (Bygrave and Reed, 1970), its absence in the tumor mitochondria presumably in turn reflects some permanent change to this membrane that confers Ca^{2+}-insensitivity and prevents release of the ion. Little is known of the mechanism by which Ca^{2+} induces uncoupling even in normal mitochondria and further examination of the tumor mitochondria in this context should provide some answer to this question (Bygrave, 1976b). Moreover, it may well be that the *transient* change in the Ca^{2+} release mechanism seen in the (normal) insulin-induced system and the *permanent* changes seen in the tumor mitochondria, are reflections of the same or similar molecular perturbations. That this permanent change in mitochondrial Ca^{2+} transport activity in the tumor is related to their altered metabolism is an interesting hypothesis amenable to experimentation.

VI. Concluding Remarks

It should be apparent that although considerable progress has been made in the most recent phase of activity in the field of mitochondrial Ca^{2+} transport, many aspects of the topic are only in their infancy. There is little doubt that mitochondria isolated from a range of tissues and species possess a specific carrier in their inner membrane whose function is to rapidly transport Ca^{2+} inwardly and outwardly against electrochemical and metabolite concentration gradients. Much has been gleaned especially from appropriate kinetic data, about the mechanism of the carrier, the involvement of "energy" and about the way in which specific inhibitors prevent the movements of Ca^{2+} across the inner membrane via this carrier.

Particular emphasis was placed on the potential hazards that confront the student of mitochondrial Ca^{2+} transport. Clearly defined precautions need to be and must be taken in order to extract the most unequivocal information from experiments involving the transport of Ca^{2+} by mitochondria.

Among the more evident and important immediate problems to be faced are, first, the question of the concentrations of "free" and "bound" Ca^{2+} in the interior (matrix) space of mitochondria and the nature of the intramitochondrial Ca^{2+}-binding sites. Little can be said of the quantitative relation between the membrane potential and Ca^{2+} gradient until the "activity" of the internal Ca^{2+} is known. It is to be hoped that answers to some of these problems may come from appropriate studies employing magnetic resonance techniques (see Gunter and Puskin, 1975). A second problem is how the energy of the electrical gradient is utilized at the molecular level to allow Ca^{2+} transport to proceed. Closely allied to this is the need to determine the physicochemical nature of the carrier molecule *in situ* and/or *in vitro*.

The review has drawn attention to the means by which some of these answers can be provided and how certain newly described biosystems will facilitate their assembly.

It was pointed out in the Introduction that the study of Ca^{2+} transport by mitochondria bears not only on the specific question of metabolite transport across the inner mitochondrial membrane, but also on the more general problem of the physiological role of the process. The hypothesis, advanced earlier elsewhere, that the major role of mitochondrial Ca^{2+} transport is to control cell metabolism by modification of the ionic environment, has been reinforced. The more recent evidence summarized here, includes that which clearly establishes an intimate metabolic link between fundamental cell physiological events, such as cell development and hormonal perturbation of metabolism, on the one hand, and an altered ability of mitochondria to transport Ca^{2+}, on the other.

This latter information has provided a new dimension to the problem of mitochondrial Ca^{2+} transport and announces a new era in its study. As well it firmly establishes the transport process as a key event in the cellular metabolic network. Perhaps the most valuable and exciting aspect of these findings is the potential wealth of new information that can now be gained relating to both the molecular mechanism and physiological role of Ca^{2+} transport in mitochondria from normal and from aberrant cells.

Appendix: Chemical Formulas of Specific Compounds Employed in the Study of Mitochondrial Calcium Transport

Compound	Chemical formula	Reference

EDTA (ethylenediaminetetraacetic acid)

$$^-OOCCH_2 \diagdown N-CH_2-CH_2-N \diagup CH_2COO^- $$
$$^-OOCCH_2 \diagup \qquad \qquad \diagdown CH_2COO^-$$

EGTA (ethyleneglycolbis(aminoethylether)-
   N, N'-tetraacetic acid

Schmid and
Reilley (1957)

$$^-OOCCH_2 \diagdown N-CH_2-CH_2-O-CH_2-CH_2-O-CH_2-CH_2-N \diagup CH_2COO^-$$
$$^-OOCCH_2 \diagup \qquad \qquad \qquad \qquad \qquad \qquad \diagdown CH_2COO^-$$

NTA (nitrilotriacetic acid or triglycolamic acid)

$$N(CH_2COO^-)_3$$

Ruthenium red

Fletcher *et al.*
(1961)

$$[(NH_3)_5Ru-O-Ru(NH_3)_4-O-Ru(NH_3)_5]^{6+} \ Cl_6^-$$

Murexide (ammonium purpurate; 5,5'-nitrilodibarbituric acid,
   ammonium derivative)

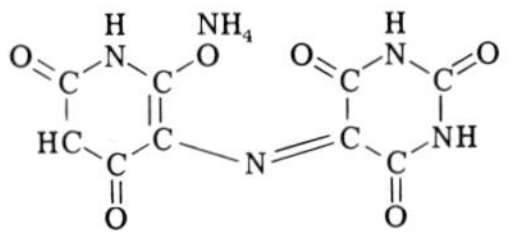

Geier (1967, 1968)

Chlortetracycline

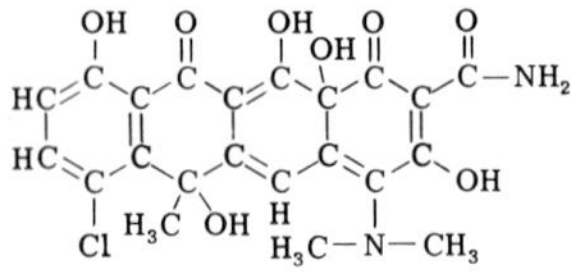

Caswell and
Hutchinson (1971)

A23187

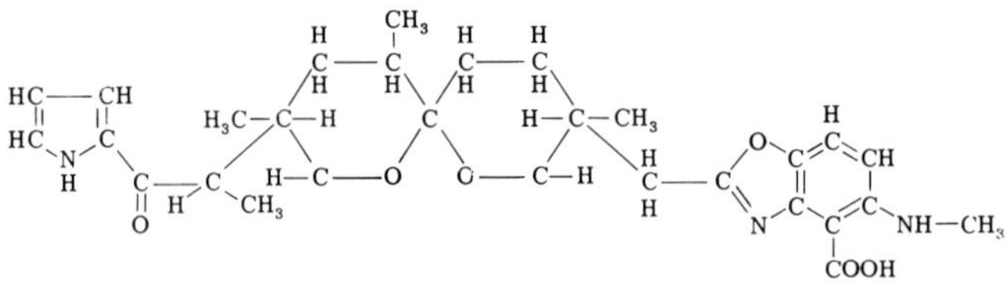

Chaney *et al.* (1974)

X587

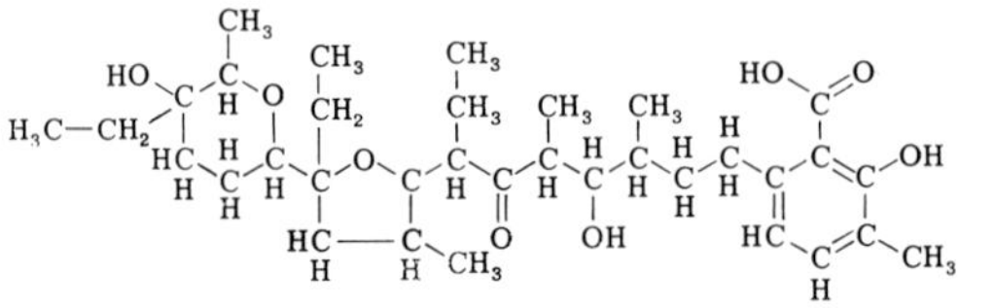

Johnson *et al.*
(1970)

ACKNOWLEDGMENTS

But for the contributions of the following, to whom I express deep appreciation, this review could not have been written: Drs. Ken Reed, Terry Spencer, and Rupert Thorne for collaboration in much of the work from the author's laboratory; Professor Gottfried Schatz for critical appraisal of the manuscript, for kind hospitality at the Biocenter, University of Basel, where much of the review was written, and for the generous provision of typing facilities; Mrs. Marie-Jeanne Wullschleger for typing the manuscript; and my wife, Patricia, for ever-present encouragement and forbearance. I am grateful to Drs. Thomas Gunter and Giovanni Sottocasa for providing me with preprints of some of their work.

REFERENCES

Åkerman, K. E., Saris, N.-E. L., and Jarvisalo, J. D. (1974). *Biochem. Biophys. Res. Commun.* **58,** 801–807.

Ashley, C. C., and Caldwell, P. C. (1974). *Biochem. Soc. Symp.* **39,** 29–50.

Azzone, G. F., and Massari, S. (1973). *Biochim. Biophys. Acta* **301,** 195–226.

Azzone, G. F., Massari, S., Rossi, E., and Scarpa, A. (1969). *Mitochondria: Struct. Funct., Fed. Eup. Biochem. Soc., Meet., 5th, 1968* FEBS Symp., Vol. 17, pp. 301–314.

Barritt, G. J., Dorman, D. D., and Bygrave, F. L. (1975). *Biochem. Soc. Trans.* **3,** 711–712.

Bartley, W., and Amoore, J. E. (1958). *Biochem. J.* **69,** 348–360.

Batra, S. C. (1973). *Biochem. Pharmacol.* **22,** 803–809.

Becker, G. L., Chen, C.-H., Greenawalt, J. W., and Lehninger, A. L. (1974). *J. Cell Biol.* **61,** 316–326.

Bianchi, C. P. (1968). "Cell Calcium," p. 12. Butterworth, London.

Bielawski, J., and Lehninger, A. L. (1966). *J. Biol. Chem.* **241,** 4316–4322.

Binet, A., and Volfin, P. (1974). *Arch. Biochem. Biophys.* **164,** 756–764.

Binet, A., and Volfin, P. (1975a). *Arch. Biochem. Biophys.* **170,** 576–586.

Binet, A., and Volfin, P. (1975b). *FEBS Lett.* **49,** 400–403.

Blondin, G. A. (1974). *Biochem. Biophys. Res. Commun.* **56,** 97–105.

Blondin, G. A., De Castro, A. F., and Senior, A. E. (1971). *Biochem. Biophys. Res. Commun.* **43,** 28–35.

Bogucka, K., and Wojtczak, L. (1971). *Biochem. Biophys. Res. Commun.* **44,** 1330–1337.

Böhme, G., Lutze, G., Pollak, K-H., Winter, O., Thews, J., and Kassebaum, I. (1973). *J. Neurochem.* **21,** 1509–1516.

Borle, A. B. (1973). *Fed. Proc., Fed. Am. Soc. Exp. Biol.* **32,** 1944–1950.

Borle, A. B. (1974). *J. Membr. Biol.* **16,** 221–236.

Boyer, P. D. (1965). *In* "Oxidases and Related Redox Systems" (T. E. King, H. S. Mason, and M. Morrison, eds.), Vol. 1, pp. 994–1008. Wiley, New York.

Boyer, P. D. (1975). *FEBS Lett.* **58,** 1–6.

Boyer, P. D., Stokes, B. O., Wolcott, R. G., and Degani, C. (1975). *Fed. Proc., Fed. Am. Soc. Exp. Biol.* **34,** 1711–1717.

Brand, M. D., and Lehninger, A. L. (1975). *J. Biol. Chem.* **250,** 7958–7960.

Brierley, G. P., Murer, E., Bachman, E., and Green, D. E. (1963). *J. Biol. Chem.* **238,** 3482–3489.

Brierley, G. P., Murer, E., and Bachman, E. (1964). *J. Biol. Chem.* **239,** 2706–2712.

Brierley, G. P., Jurkowitz, M., Scott, K. M., and Merola, A. J. (1970). *J. Biol. Chem.* **245**, 5404–5411.

Bygrave, F. L. (1964). Ph. D. Thesis, University of Queensland, Brisbane, Australia.

Bygrave, F. L. (1966a). *Biochem. J.* **101**, 480–487.

Bygrave, F. L. (1966b). *Biochem. J.* **101**, 488–491.

Bygrave, F. L. (1967). *Nature (London)* **214**, 667–671.

Bygrave, F. L. (1975). *Fed. Eur. Biochem. Soc., Meet, 10th, 1975* Abstract 1131.

Bygrave, F. L. (1976a). *In* "An Introduction to Bio-Organic Chemistry" (D. R. Williams, ed.), pp. 171–186. Thomas, Springfield, Illinois.

Bygrave, F. L. (1976b). *In* "Control Mechanisms in Cancer" (W. E. Criss, T. Ono, and J. R. Sabine, eds.), pp. 411–423. Raven, New York.

Bygrave, F. L. (1977). *Essays Biochem.* (to appear).

Bygrave, F. L., and Lehninger, A. L. (1967). *Proc. Natl. Acad. Sci. U.S.A.* **57**, 1409–1415.

Bygrave, F. L., and Reed, K. C. (1970). *FEBS Lett.* **7**, 339–342.

Bygrave, F. L., Reed, K. C., and Spencer, T. L. (1971a). *Nature (London), New Biol.* **230**, 89.

Bygrave, F. L., Reed, K. C., and Spencer, T. L. (1971b). *In* "Energy Transduction in Respiration and Photosynthesis" (E. Quagliariello, S. Papa, and C. S. Rossi, eds.), pp. 981–988. Adriatica Editrice, Bari.

Bygrave, F. L., Daday, A. A., and Doy, F. A. (1975). *Biochem. J.* **146**, 601–608.

Campbell, A. J., and Birt, L. M. (1975). *Biochem. J.* **150**, 227–234.

Carafoli, E. (1965a). *Biochim. Biophys. Acta* **97**, 99–106.

Carafoli, E. (1965b). *Biochim. Biophys. Acta* **97**, 107–117.

Carafoli, E. (1967). *J. Gen. Physiol.* **50**, 1849–1864.

Carafoli, E. (1973). *Biochimie* **55**, 755–762.

Carafoli, E. (1974). *Biochem. Soc. Symp.* **39**, 89–109.

Carafoli, E. (1975a). *Mol. Cell. Biochem.* **8**, 133–140.

Carafoli, E. (1975b). *Recent Adv. Stud. Card. Struct. Metab.* **5**, 151–163.

Carafoli, E., and Azzi, A. (1972). *Experientia* **28**, 906–908.

Carafoli, E., and Lehninger, A. L. (1971). *Biochem. J.* **122**, 681–690.

Carafoli, E., and Sottocasa, G. L. (1974). *In* "Dynamics of Energy-Transducing Membranes" (L. Ernster, R. W. Estabrook, and E. C. Slater, eds.), pp. 455–469. Elsevier, Amsterdam.

Carafoli, E., Rossi, C. S., and Lehninger, A. L. (1964). *J. Biol. Chem.* **239**, 3055–3061.

Carafoli, E., Balcavage, W. X., Lehninger, A. L., and Mattoon, J. R. (1970). *Biochim. Biophys. Acta* **205**, 18–26.

Carafoli, E., Hansford, R. G., Sacktor, B., and Lehninger, A. L. (1971). *J. Biol. Chem.* **246**, 964–972.

Carafoli, E., Tiozzo, R., Lugli, C., Crovetti, F., and Kratzing, C. C. (1974). *J. Mol. Cell. Cardiol.* **6**, 361–371.

Case, G. D. (1975). *Biochim. Biophys. Acta* **375**, 69–86.

Case, G. D., Vanderkooi, J. M., and Scarpa, A. (1974). *Arch. Biochem. Biophys.* **157**, 183–196.

Caswell, A. H. (1972). *J. Membr. Biol.* **7**, 345–364.

Caswell, A. H., and Hutchinson, J. D. (1971a). *Biochem. Biophys. Res. Commun.* **42**, 43–49.

Caswell, A. H., and Hutchinson, J. D. (1971b). *Biochem. Biophys. Res. Commun.* **43**, 625–630.

Cereijo-Santalo, R. (1970). *Membr. Ion Transp.* **2**, 229–258.

Chan, T. L., Greenawalt, J. W., and Pedersen, P. L. (1970). *J. Cell Biol.* **45**, 291–305.
Chance, B. (1956). *Proc. Int. Congr. Biochem., 3rd, 1955* p. 300.
Chance, B. (1959). *In* "Symposium on Metabolic Control" (E. Wolstenholme, ed.), p. 95. Churchill, London.
Chance, B. (1965). *J. Biol. Chem.* **240**, 2729–2748.
Chance, B. (1972). *In* "Methods in Enzymology" (A. San Pietro, ed.), Vol. 24, pp. 322–335. Academic Press, New York.
Chance, B., and Mela, L. (1966). *Biochemistry* **5**, 3220–3223.
Chance, B., and Montal, M. (1971). *Curr. Top. Membr. Transp.* **2**, 99–156.
Chance, B., and Yoshioka, T. (1966). *Biochemistry* **5**, 3224–3229.
Chaney, M. O., Demarco, P. V., Jones, N. D., and Occolowith, J. L. (1974). *J. Am. Chem. Soc.* **96**, 1932–1933.
Chapman, D. (1975). *Q. Rev. Biophys.* **8**, 185–235.
Chappell, J. B. (1968). *Br. Med. Bull.* **24**, 150–157.
Chappell, J. B., and Crofts, A. R. (1965). *Biochem. J.* **95**, 378–386.
Chappell, J. B., and Crofts, A. R. (1966). *In* "Regulation of Metabolic Processes in Mitochondria" (J. M. Tager *et al.,* eds.), pp. 293–314. Elsevier, Amsterdam.
Chappell, J. B., and Haarhoff, K. N. (1967). *In* "Biochemistry of Mitochondria" (E. C. Slater, Z. Kaniuga, and L. Wojtczak, eds.), pp. 75–91. Academic Press, New York.
Chappell, J. B., Greville, G. D., and Bicknell, K. E. (1962). *Biochem. J.* **84**, 61P.
Chappell, J. B., Cohn, M., and Greville, G. D. (1963). *In* "Energy-linked Functions of Mitochondria" (B. Chance, ed.), pp. 219–231. Academic Press, New York.
Chappell, J. B., McGivan, J. D., and Crompton, M. (1972). *In* "The Molecular Basis of Biological Transport" (J. F. Woessner, Jr. and F. Huijing, eds.), pp. 55–81. Academic Press, New York.
Chen, C.-H., and Lehninger, A. L. (1973). *Arch. Biochem. Biophys.* **157**, 183–196.
Chen, C.-H., Greenawalt, J. W., and Lehninger, A. L. (1974). *J. Cell Biol.* **61**, 301–305.
Christiansen, R. O., Loyter, A., Steensland, H., Saltzgaber, J., and Racker, E. (1969). *J. Biol. Chem.* **244**, 4428–4436.
Chudapongse, P., and Haugaard, N. (1973). *Biochim. Biophys. Acta* **307**, 599–606.
Cleland, W. W. (1970). *In* "The Enzymes" (P. D. Boyer, ed.), 3rd ed., Vol. 2, pp. 1–65. Academic Press, New York.
Coty, W. A., and Pedersen, P. L. (1974). *J. Biol. Chem.* **249**, 2593–2598.
Davies, R. E., and Ogston, A. G. (1950). *Biochem. J.* **46**, 324–333.
Dawson, A. P., Dunnett, S. J., and Selwyn, M. J. (1971). *Eur. J. Biochem.* **21**, 42–47.
DeLuca, H. F., and Engstrom, G. W. (1961). *Proc. Natl. Acad. Sci. U.S.A.* **47**, 1744–1750.
Denton, R. M., Randle, P. J., and Martin, B. R. (1972). *Biochem. J.* **128**, 161–163.
Denton, R. M., Randle, P. J., Bridges, B. J., Cooper, R. H., Kerbey, A. L., Pask, H. T., Severson, D. L., Stansbie, D., and Whitehouse, S. (1975). *Mol. Cell. Biochem.* **9**, 27–53.
Dixon, M., and Webb, E. C. (1964). "Enzymes," 2nd ed., p. 420. Academic Press, New York.
Docktor, M. E., and Magnuson, J. A. (1973). *Biochem. Biophys. Res. Commun.* **54**, 790–795.
Docktor, M. E., and Magnuson, J. A. (1974). *J. Supramol. Struct.* **2**, 32–44.
Dorman, D. D., Barritt, G. J., and Bygrave, F. L. (1975). *Biochem. J.* **150**, 389–395.
Doy, F. A., Daday, A. A., and Bygrave, F. L. (1975). *FEBS Lett.* **54**, 245–248.
Drahota, Z., Carafoli, E., Rossi, C. S., Gamble, R. L., and Lehninger, A. L. (1965). *J. Biol. Chem.* **240**, 2712–2720.

Ernster, L., and Nordenbrand, K. (1967). *Fed. Eur. Biochem. Soc., Meet., 4th, 1967* p. 108.

Fanburg, F., and Gergely, J. (1965). *J. Biol. Chem.* **240**, 2721–2728.

Flatmark, T., and Romslo, I. (1975). *J. Biol. Chem.* **250**, 6432–6438.

Fletcher, J. M., Greenfield, B. F., Hardy, C. J., Scargill, D., and Woodward, J. C. (1961). *J. Chem. Soc.* pp. 2000–2006.

Gear, A. R. L., Rossi, C. S., Reynafarje, B., and Lehninger, A. L. (1967). *J. Biol. Chem.* **242**, 3403–3413.

Geier, G. (1967). *Helv. Chim. Acta* **50**, 1879–1884.

Geier, G. (1968). *Helv. Chim. Acta* **51**, 94–105.

Gevers, W., and Krebs, H. A. (1966). *Biochem. J.* **98**, 720–735.

Gomez-Puyou, A., Tuena de Gomez-Puyou, M., Becker, G., and Lehninger, A. L. (1972). *Biochem. Biophys. Res. Commun.* **47**, 814–819.

Green, D. E., ed. (1974). "Symposium on the Mechanism of Energy Transduction in Biological Systems," Annals, Vol. 227. N. Y. Acad. Sci., New York.

Greenawalt, J. W., Vasington, F. D., and Caplan, A. I. (1965). *J. Cell Biol.* **27**, 38A.

Greville, G. D. (1969). *Curr. Top. Bioenerg.* **3**, 1–78.

Gunter, T. E., and Puskin, J. S. (1972). *Biophys. J.* **12**, 625–635.

Gunter, T. E., and Puskin, J. S. (1975). *Ann. N. Y. Acad. Sci.* **264**, 112–123.

Gunter, T. E., Puskin, J. S., and Russell, P. R. (1975). *Biophys. J.* **15**, 319–333.

Haljamae, H., and Wood, D. C. (1971). *Anal. Biochem.* **42**, 155–170.

Hansford, R. G. (1971). *Biochem. J.* **121**, 771–780.

Hanson, J. B., and Miller, R. J. (1967). *Proc. Natl. Acad. Sci. U.S.A.* **58**, 727–734.

Harris, E. J. (1972). *J. Membr. Biol.* **9**, 141–154.

Harris, E. J., and van Dam, K. (1968). *Biochem. J.* **106**, 759–766.

Harris, E. J., Judah, J. D., and Ahmed, K. (1966). *Curr. Top. Bioenerg.* **1**, 225–277.

Harris, E. J., Wimhurst, J. M., and Landeata, I. (1974). *Eur. J. Biochem.* **45**, 1520–1524.

Haugaard, N., Haugaard, E. S., and Lee, N. H. (1969). *Proc. K. Ned. Akad. Wet., Ser. C.* **72**, 1.

Heilbrunn, L. V. (1952). "An Outline of General Physiology," 3rd ed. Saunders, Philadelphia, Pennsylvania.

Henderson, P. J. F. (1971). *Annu. Rev. Microbiol.* **25**, 393–428.

Henderson, P. J. F. (1972). *Biochem. J.* **127**, 321–333.

Heppel, L. A. (1971). *In* "Structure and Function of Biological Membranes" (L. I. Rothfield, ed.), pp. 223–247. Academic Press, New York.

Hunt, G. A. R. (1975). *FEBS Lett.* **58**, 194–196.

Jacobson, K., and Papahadjopoulos, D. (1975). *Biochemistry* **14**, 152–166.

Jacobus, W. E., Tiozzo, R., Lugli, G., Lehninger, A. L., and Carafoli, E. (1975). *J. Biol. Chem.* **250**, 7863–7870.

Johnson, J. H., and Pressman, B. C. (1968). *Biochim. Biophys. Acta* **153**, 500–503.

Johnson, S. M., Herrin, J., Liu, S. J., and Paul, I. C. (1970). *J. Am. Chem. Soc.* **92**, 4428–4435.

Kimmich, G. A., and Rasmussen, H. (1969). *J. Biol. Chem.* **244**, 190–199.

Klingenberg, M. (1963). *In* "Energy-Linked Functions of Mitochondria" (B. Chance, ed.), p. 246. Academic Press, New York.

Klingenberg, M. (1970). *Essays Biochem.* **6**, 119–159.

Koshland, D. E. (1970). *In* "The Enzymes" (P. D. Boyer, ed.), 3rd ed., Vol. 1, pp. 341–396. Academic Press, New York.

Kun, E., Kearney, E. B., Weidemann, I., and Lee, N. B. (1969). *Biochemistry* **8**, 4443–4449.

Langer, G. A. (1973). *Annu. Rev. Physiol.* **35**, 55–86.

Lazarewicz, J. W., Haljamae, H., and Hamberger, A. (1974). *J. Neurochem.* **22,** 33–45.
Le Blanc, P., and Clauser, H. (1974). *Biochim. Biophys. Acta* **347,** 87–101.
Le Blanc, P., Bourdain, M., and Clauser, H. (1970). *Biochem. Biophys. Res. Commun.* **40,** 754–762.
Lee, N. B., Weidemann, I., and Kun, E. (1971). *Biochem. Biophys. Res. Commun.* **42,** 1030–1034.
Lehninger, A. L. (1949). *J. Biol. Chem.* **178,** 625–644.
Lehninger, A. L. (1964). "The Mitochondrion," pp. 175–178. Benjamin, New York.
Lehninger, A. L. (1969). *Ann. N. Y. Acad. Sci.* **147,** 816–823.
Lehninger, A. L. (1970). *Biochem. J.* **119,** 129–138.
Lehninger, A. L. (1971). *Biochem. Biophys. Res. Commun.* **42,** 312–318.
Lehninger, A. L. (1974). *Proc. Natl. Acad. Sci. U.S.A.* **71,** 1520–1524.
Lehninger, A. L., and Carafoli, E. (1967). *In* "Methods in Enzymology" (R. W. Estabrook and M. E. Pullman, eds.), Vol. 10, pp. 745–748. Academic Press, New York.
Lehninger, A. L., and Carafoli, E. (1970). *In* "Biochemistry of the Phagocytic Process" (J. Schultz, ed.), pp. 9–22. North-Holland Publ., Amsterdam.
Lehninger, A. L., and Carafoli, E. (1971). *Arch. Biochem. Biophys.* **143,** 506–515.
Lehninger, A. L., Carafoli, E., and Rossi, C. S. (1967). *Adv. Enzymol. Relat. Areas Mol. Biol.* **29,** 259–320.
Lehninger, A. L., Rossi, C. S., Carafoli, E., and Reynafarje, B. (1969). *Mitochondria: Struct. Funct., Fed. Eur. Biochem. Soc., Meet., 5th, 1968* FEBS Symp., Vol. 17, pp. 369–377.
Lin, T. C., Pettit, F. H., and Reed, L. J. (1969). *Proc. Natl. Acad. Sci. U.S.A.* **62,** 234–241.
Loyter, A., Christiansen, R. O., Steensland, H., Saltzgaber, J., and Racker, E. (1969). *J. Biol. Chem.* **244,** 4422–4427.
Luft, J. H. (1971). *Anat. Rec.* **171,** 347–368.
Lundegårdh, H. (1945). *Ark. Bot.* **32A,** 1–139.
McGivan, J. D., and Klingenberg, M. (1971). *Eur. J. Biochem.* **20,** 392–399.
McIntyre, H. S., and Bygrave, F. L. (1974). *Arch. Biochem. Biophys.* **165,** 744–748.
McLaughlin, S., and Eisenberg, M. (1975). *Annu. Rev. Biophys. Bioeng.* **4,** 335–366.
Madeira, V. M. C. (1975). *Biochem. Biophys. Res. Commun.* **64,** 870–876.
Matlib, A., and O'Brien, P. J. (1974). *Biochem. Soc. Trans.* **2,** 997–1000.
Mela, L. (1967). *Fed. Proc., Fed. Am. Soc. Exp. Biol.* **26,** 456.
Mela, L. (1968a). *Arch. Biochem. Biophys.* **123,** 286–293.
Mela, L. (1968b). *Fed. Proc., Fed. Am. Soc. Exp. Biol.* **27,** 828.
Mela, L. (1969a). *Biochemistry* **8,** 2481–2486.
Mela, L. (1969b). *Ann. N. Y. Acad. Sci.* **147,** 824–828.
Mela, L., and Chance, B. (1968). *Biochemistry* **7,** 4059–4063.
Mela, L., and Chance, B. (1969). *Biochem. Biophys. Res. Commun.* **35,** 556–559.
Mela, L., Goodwin, C. W., and Miller, L. D. (1975). *Biochem. Biophys. Res. Commun.* **64,** 384–390.
Meli, J., and Bygrave, F. L. (1972). *Biochem. J.* **128,** 415–420.
Mitchell, P. (1961). *Nature (London)* **191,** 144–148.
Mitchell, P. (1966). "Chemiosmotic Coupling in Oxidative and Photosynthetic Phosphorylation." Glynn Res., Bodmin, Cornwall, England.
Mitchell, P. (1967). *Adv. Enzymol. Relat. Areas Mol. Biol.* **29,** 33–87.
Mitchell, P. (1972). *Bioenergetics* **3,** 5–24.
Mitchell, P., and Moyle, J. (1969a). *Eur. J. Biochem.* **7,** 471–484.
Mitchell, P., and Moyle, J. (1969b). *Eur. J. Biochem.* **9,** 149–155.

Monod, J., Wyman, J., and Changeux, J.-P. (1965). *J. Mol. Biol.* **12**, 88–118.
Moore, C. L. (1971). *Biochem. Biophys. Res. Commun.* **42**, 298–305.
Moore, C. L. (1972). *Metab. Pathways, 3rd Ed.* **6**, 573–626.
Moore, E. W. (1969). *Natl. Bur. Stand. (U.S.), Spec. Publ.* **314**, 215–285.
Morrison, J. F. (1969). *Biochim. Biophys. Acta* **185**, 269–286.
Nakazawa, T., Asami, K., Suzuki, H., and Yukawa, O. (1973). *J. Biochem. (Tokyo)* **73**, 397–406.
Nicholls, D. G. (1974). *Eur. J. Biochem.* **50**, 305–315.
Padan, E., and Rottenberg, H. (1973). *Eur. J. Biochem.* **40**, 431–437.
Palmieri, F. Stipani, I., Quagliariello, E., and Klingenberg, M. (1972). *Eur. J. Biochem.* **26**, 587–594.
Pedersen, P. L., and Coty, W. A. (1972). *J. Biol. Chem.* **247**, 3107–3113.
Peng, C. F., Price, D. W., Bhuvaneswaren, C., and Wadkins, C. L. (1974). *Biochem. Biophys. Res. Commun.* **56**, 134–141.
Pfaff, E., Heldt, H. W., and Klingenberg, M. (1969). *Eur. J. Biochem.* **10**, 484–493.
Pfieffer, D. R., Reed, P. W., and Lardy, H. A. (1974). *Biochemistry* **13**, 4007–4014.
Pollak, J. K. (1975). *Biochem. J.* **150**, 477–488.
Potter, V. R. (1947). *J. Biol. Chem.* **169**, 17–37.
Potter, V. R., Siekevitz, P., and Simonson, H. C. (1953). *J. Biol. Chem.* **205**, 893–908.
Pressman, B. C. (1967). *In* "Methods in Enzymology" (R. W. Estabrook and M. E. Pullman, eds.), Vol. 10, pp. 714–726. Academic Press, New York.
Pressman, B. C. (1970). *In* "Membranes of Mitochondria and Chloroplasts" (E. Racker, ed.), pp. 213–250. Van Nostrand-Reinhold, Princeton, New Jersey.
Pressman, B. C. (1973). *Fed. Proc., Fed. Am. Soc. Exp. Biol.* **32**, 1698–1703.
Pressman, B. C., and Park, J. K. (1963). *Biochem. Biophys. Res. Commun.* **11**, 182–186.
Prestipino, C., Ceccarelli, D., Conti, F., and Carafoli, E. (1974). *FEBS Lett.* **45**, 99–103.
Puskin, J. S., and Gunter, T. E. (1973). *Biochem. Biophys. Res. Commun.* **51**, 797–803.
Puskin, J. S., and Gunter, R. E. (1972). *Biochim. Biophys. Acta* **275**, 302–307.
Pullman, M. E., and Schatz, G. (1967). *Annu. Rev. Biochem.* **36**, 539–610.
Quagliariello, E., and Palmieri, F. (1970). *FEBS Lett.* **8**, 105–108.
Racker, E. (1970). *In* "Membranes of Mitochondria and Chloroplasts" (E. Racker, ed.), pp. 127–171. Van Nostrand-Reinhold, Princeton, New Jersey.
Randle, P. J., Denton, R. M., Park, H. T., and Severson, D. C. (1974). *Biochem. Soc. Symp.* **39**, 75–88.
Rao, K. N., de Smet, M., Howells, A. J., and Bygrave, F. L. (1974). *FEBS Lett.* **41**, 185–188.
Rasmussen, H. (1970). *Science* **170**, 404–412.
Rasmussen, H., Chance, B., and Ogata, E. (1965). *Proc. Natl. Acad. Sci. U.S.A.* **53**, 1069–1076.
Reed, K. C. (1972). *Biochem. Biophys. Res. Commun.* **50**, 1136–1142.
Reed, K. C. (1974). Ph.D. Thesis, Australian National University.
Reed, K. C., and Bygrave, F. L. (1974a). *Biochem. J.* **138**, 239–252.
Reed, K. C., and Bygrave, F. L. (1974b). *Biochem. J.* **140**, 143–155.
Reed, K. C., and Bygrave, F. L. (1974c). *Biochem. J.* **142**, 535–566.
Reed, K. C., and Bygrave, F. L. (1974d). *FEBS Lett.* **46**, 109–114.
Reed, K. C., and Bygrave, F. L. (1975a). *Eur. J. Biochem.* **55**, 497–504.
Reed, K. C., and Bygrave, F. L. (1975b). *Anal. Biochem.* **67**, 44–54.
Reed, P. W., and Lardy, H. A. (1972). *J. Biol. Chem.* **247**, 6970–6977.
Reynafarje, B., and Lehninger, A. L. (1969). *J. Biol. Chem.* **244**, 584–593.
Roberts, J. B., and Bygrave, F. L. (1973). *Biochem. J.* **136**, 467–475.

Robertson, R. N. (1960). *Biol. Rev. Cambridge Philos. Soc.* **35**, 231–264.

Robertson, R. N. (1968). "Protons, Electrons, Phosphorylation and Active Transport." Cambridge Univ. Press, London and New York.

Romslo, I. (1975). *Biochim. Biophys. Acta* **387**, 69–79.

Romslo, I., and Flatmark, T. (1975). *Biochim. Biophys. Acta* **385**, 80–94.

Rossi, C. S., and Lehninger, A. L. (1964). *J. Biol. Chem.* **239**, 3971–3980.

Rossi, C. S., Azzi, A., and Azzone, G. F. (1967). *J. Biol. Chem.* **242**, 951–957.

Rossi, C. S., Vasington, F. D., and Carafoli, E. (1973). *Biochem. Biophys. Res. Commun.* **50**, 846–852.

Rottenberg, H. (1970). *Eur. J. Biochem.* **15**, 22–28.

Rottenberg, H. (1973). *J. Membr. Biol.* **11**, 117–137.

Rottenberg, H., and Scarpa, A. (1974). *Biochemistry* **13**, 4811–4817.

Sallis, J. D., DeLuca, H. F., and Rasmussen, H. (1963). *J. Biol. Chem.* **238**, 4098–4102.

Sandri, G., Panfili, E., and Sottocasa, G. L. (1976). *Biochem. Biophys. Res. Commun.* **68**, 1272–1279.

Saris, N. E.-L. (1963). *Commentat. Biol., Soc. Sci. Fenn.* **28**, 1–59.

Scarpa, A. (1972). *In* "Methods in Enzymology" (A. San Pietro, ed.), Vol. 24, pp. 343–351. Academic Press, New York.

Scarpa, A. (1974). *In* "Dynamics of Energy-Transducing Membranes" (L. Ernster, R. W. Estabrook, and E. C. Slater, eds.), pp. 471–482. Elsevier, Amsterdam.

Scarpa, A., and Azzi, A. (1968). *Biochim. Biophys. Acta* **150**, 473–481.

Scarpa, A., and Azzone, G. F. (1970). *Eur. J. Biochem.* **12**, 328–335.

Scarpa, A., and Graziotti, P. (1973). *J. Gen. Physiol.* **62**, 756–772.

Schatz, G. (1969). *In* "Membranes of Mitochondria and Chloroplasts" (E. Racker, ed.), pp. 251–314. Van Nostrand-Reinhold, Princeton, New Jersey.

Schmid, R. W., and Reilley, C. N. (1957). *Anal. Chem.* **29**, 264–268.

Schuster, S. M., and Olson, M. S. (1974a). *J. Biol. Chem.* **249**, 7151–7158.

Schuster, S. M., and Olson, M. S. (1974b). *J. Biol. Chem.* **249**, 7159–7165.

Selwyn, M. J., Dawson, A. P., and Dunnett, S. J. (1970). *FEBS Lett.* **10**, 1–5.

Settlemire, C. T., Hunter, G. R., and Brierley, G. P. (1968). *Biochim. Biophys. Acta* **162**, 487–499.

Shamoo, A. E., Thompson, T. R., Campbell, K. P., Scott, T. L., and Goldstein, D. A. (1975). *J. Biol. Chem.* **250**, 8289–8291.

Shapiro, I. M., and Lee, N. H. (1975). *Arch. Biochem. Biophys.* **170**, 627–633.

Sica, V., and Cuatrecasas, P. (1973). *Biochemistry* **12**, 2282–2291.

Siekevitz, P., and Potter, V. R. (1953). *J. Biol. Chem.* **200**, 187–196.

Siliprandi, D., Toninello, A., Zoccarato, F., Rugolo, M., and Siliprandi, N. (1975). *Biochem. Biophys. Res. Commun.* **66**, 956–961.

Sillen, L. G., and Martell, A. E. (1964). *Chem. Soc., Spec. Publ.* **17**.

Sillen, L. G., Hogfeldt, E., Martell, A. E., and Smith, R. M. (1971). *Chem. Soc., Spec. Publ.* **25**.

Simpson, E. R., and Williams-Smith, D. L. (1975). *Biochim. Biophys. Acta* **404**, 309–320.

Singer, S. J. (1974). *Annu. Rev. Biochem.* **43**, 805–833.

Skulachev, V. P. (1971). *Curr. Top. Bioenerg.* **4**, 127–190.

Skulachev, V. P. (1972). *In* "Biomembranes: Molecular Arrangements and Transport Mechanisms" (L. L. M. Van Deenen, J. C. Riemersma, and J. M. Tager, eds.), pp. 371–386. North-Holland Publ., Amsterdam.

Slater, E. C. (1953). *Nature (London)* **172**, 975–978.

Slater, E. C., and Cleland, K. W. (1953). *Biochem. J.* **55**, 566–580.

Sluse, F. E., Goffart, G., and Liebecq, C. (1973). *Eur. J. Biochem.* **32**, 283–291.

Sordahl, L. (1975). *Arch. Biochem. Biophys.* **167**, 104–115.

Sottocasa, G. L., Sandri, G., Panfili, E., and de Bernard, B. (1971). *FEBS Lett.* **17**, 100–105.

Sottocasa, G. L., Sandri, G., Panfili, E., de Bernard, B., Gazzotti, P., Vasington, F. D., and Carafoli, E. (1972). *Biochem. Biophys. Res. Commun.* **47**, 808–813.

Southard, J. H., and Green, D. E. (1974). *Biochem. Biophys. Res. Commun.* **59**, 30–37.

Spencer, T. L., and Bygrave, F. L. (1972). *Biochem. J.* **129**, 355–365.

Spencer, T. L., and Bygrave, F. L. (1973). *Bioenergetics* **4**, 347–362.

Spencer, T. L., See, J. C., and Bygrave, F. L. (1976). *Biochim. Biophys. Acta* **423**, 365–373.

Stein, W. D. (1967). "The Movement of Molecules across Cell Membranes," p. 127. Academic Press, New York.

Storey, B. T., and Keyhani, E. (1974). *Fertil. Steril.* **25**, 976–984.

Straus, O., and Goldstein, A. (1943). *J. Gen. Physiol.* **26**, 559–585.

Stucki, J. W., and Ineichen, E. A. (1974). *Eur. J. Biochem.* **48**, 365–375.

Tashmukhamedov, B. A., Gagelgaus, A. I., Mamatkulov, Kh., and Makhmudova, E. M. (1972). *FEBS Lett.* **28**, 239–242.

Thiers, R. E., and Vallee, B. L. (1957). *J. Biol. Chem.* **226**, 911–920.

Thorne, R. F. W., and Bygrave, F. L. (1973). *Cancer Res.* **33**, 2562–2567.

Thorne, R. F. W., and Bygrave, F. L. (1974a). *Nature (London)* **248**, 348–351.

Thorne, R. F. W., and Bygrave, F. L. (1974b). *Biochem. J.* **144**, 551–558.

Thorne, R. F. W., and Bygrave, F. L. (1975). *FEBS Lett.* **56**, 185–188.

Tjioe, S., Bianchi, C. P., and Haugaard, N. (1970). *Biochim. Biophys. Acta* **216**, 270–273.

Träuble, H., and Eibl, H. (1974). *Proc. Natl. Acad. Sci. U.S.A.* **71**, 214–219.

Truesdell, A. H., and Pommer, A. M. (1963). *Science* **142**, 1292–1293.

Vainio, H., Mela, L., and Chance, B. (1970). *Eur. J. Biochem.* **12**, 387–391.

Vallieres, J., Scarpa, A., and Somlyo, A. P. (1975). *Arch. Biochem. Biophys.* **170**, 659–669.

Vasington, F. D. (1963). *J. Biol. Chem.* **238**, 1841–1847.

Vasington, F. D., and Greenawalt, J. W. (1964). *Biochem. Biophys. Res. Commun.* **15**, 133–138.

Vasington, F. D., and Greenawalt, J. W. (1968). *J. Cell Biol.* **39**, 661–675.

Vasington, F. D., and Murphy, J. V. (1962). *J. Biol. Chem.* **237**, 2670–2677.

Vasington, F. D., Gazzotti, P., Tiozzo, R., and Carafoli, E. (1972). *Biochim. Biophys. Acta* **256**, 43–54.

Vinogradov, A., and Scarpa, A. (1973). *J. Biol. Chem.* **248**, 5527–5531.

Werner, S., and Neupert, W. (1972). *Eur. J. Biochem.* **25**, 379–396.

Wikström, M., Ahonen, P., and Luukkainen, T. (1975). *FEBS Lett.* **56**, 120–123.

Williams, R. J. P. (1970). *Q. Rev., Chem. Soc.* **24**, 331–365.

Williams, R. J. P. (1974). *Biochem. Soc. Symp.* **39**, 133–138.

Wilson, R. H., and Minton, G. A. (1974). *Biochim. Biophys. Acta* **333**, 22–27.

Wohlrab, H. (1974). *Biochemistry* **13**, 4014–4018.

Wohlrab, H. (1975). *Fed. Eur, Biochem. Soc., Meet., 10th, 1975* Abstract 1114.

Subject Index

A

A-23187
  as carboxylic ionophore, 224–225
  effects on cellular processes, 245
Active phosphate
  energy stores and, 3–5
  splitting of
    in muscle contraction, 25–30
    in muscle recovery, 30–33
Adenylate cyclase, possibility of, in brush
    border membranes, 50
Adenylate deaminase reaction, 4
Adenylate kinase reaction, 4
Alamethicin
  as channel former, 230
  uncoupling activity of, 238–239
Alanine, transport by membrane vesicles,
    67–68, 72
Alanine aminopeptidase, in brush border
    membranes, 46, 47
Alcaligenes faecalis, ATPase headpieces
    in, 101
Alkaline phosphatase, in brush border
    membranes, 46, 47
Amino acids
  transport of, by membrane vesicles, 66–
    73
    sodium role in, 66–70
    specificities, 71–73
    sugar-transport interaction with, 70–71
Aminopeptidases, in brush border
    membranes, 46, 47
Antamanides, as ionophores, 223
Anion penetration, in studies of
    mitochondrial calcium transport, 266

Anion translocation, in mitochondria, 239–
    241
Antibiotics
  carboxylic type, effects on cellular
    processes, 245
  as models of channels or carriers, 249–
    250
Arginine, transport by membrane vesicles,
    66, 68, 72
Athiorhodaceae, energy economy in, 89
ATP
  in active phosphate pool, 3
    size, 4
  complex formation by,
    conformational changes, 202–203
    proton translocation by, 185–191
  formation of, 3
    in bacteria, 124–126
    stoichiometry of, 160–162
  induction of synthesis of, ionophores
    and, 233–235
  proton uptake driven by, 187–188
  transport systems dependent on, 115–118
ATPase
  in bacterial energy transduction, 99–105
  in calcium transport, 3
  calcium-stimulated activity of, 267

B

Bacillus megaterium, energy transduction
    in, 94
Bacillus subtilis, energy transduction in, 94
Bacteria
  chemical work in, 120–129
  coupling and uncoupling in, 132–137
    growth yield and, 134–136

319